**TEXAS INSTRUMENTS**

TI-92 Plus Module

A Supplement to the TI-92 Guidebook

The TI-92 Symbolic Manipulation was jointly developed by TI and the authors of the DERIVE® program, who are with Soft Warehouse, Inc., Honolulu, HI.

The TI-92 Geometry was jointly developed by TI and the authors of Cabri Geometry II™, who are with the Université Joseph Fourier, Grenoble, France.

Special appreciation goes to:

Bill Bauldry, Franck Bellemain, John Berry, Doug Child, Frank Demana, Wade Ellis Jr., Benny Evans, Jean-Michel Ferrard, Joe Fiedler, Sally Fischbeck, Philippe Fortin, Larry Gilligan, David Hertling, Millie Johnson, Michael Keyton, Bernhard Kutzler, Carl Leinbach, Henri Lemberg, Dennis Mick, Stuart Moskowitz, Richard O'Farrell, Adrian Oldknow, Dennis Pence, Tom Read, Michael Schneider, David Stoutemyer, John Symms, Dave Voltmer, Bert Waits, Mark Yoder

Texas Instruments contributors:

Chris Alley, Bea Aton, Gosia Brothers, Jim Carlsen, Linda Ferrio, Bud Gerwig, Mike Hosea, Vonnie Howard, Jeff Janis, Darrell Johnson, Chris McLean, Michelle Miller, John Powers, Shawn Prestridge, Russ Rosenquist, David Stone, Joan Terrell, Glen Thornton

US FCC Information Concerning Radio Frequency Interference

This equipment has been tested and found to comply with the limits for a Class B digital device, pursuant to Part 15 of the FCC rules. These limits are designed to provide reasonable protection against harmful interference in a residential installation. This equipment generates, uses, and can radiate radio frequency energy and, if not installed and used in accordance with the instructions, may cause harmful interference with radio communications. However, there is no guarantee that interference will not occur in a particular installation.

If this equipment does cause harmful interference to radio or television reception, which can be determined by turning the equipment off and on, you can try to correct the interference by one or more of the following measures:

• Reorient or relocate the receiving antenna.

• Increase the separation between the equipment and receiver.

• Connect the equipment into an outlet on a circuit different from that to which the receiver is connected.

• Consult the dealer or an experienced radio/television technician for help.

Caution: Any changes or modifications to this equipment not expressly approved by Texas Instruments may void your authority to operate the equipment.

Table of Contents

In general, this book describes the new TI-92 Plus features only. Appendix A is an exception. It gives you one convenient location to find details about every available function and instruction, both original and new.

Table of Contents (Continued)

What's New with the TI-92 Plus

After you install the TI-92 Plus Module, the following features will be available. Use this book to learn about these new features. For information about the calculator's basic operations, refer to the separate *TI-92 Guidebook*.

Upgradability with Flash ROM

The TI-92 Plus Module uses Flash technology, which lets you upgrade to future software versions without buying a new calculator.

For details, refer to:
Chapter 1

Tip: You can see which version of product code is in your TI-92 Plus. From the Home screen, press [F1] and select A:About.

Future software versions include maintenance upgrades that will be released free of charge, as well as new applications and major software upgrades that will be available for purchase from the TI web site.

To download and install upgrades from the TI web site, you must have an Internet-connected computer and a TI-GRAPH LINK™ (available separately) with software for the TI-92 Plus. You can also transfer the product code from one TI-92 Plus to another, provided that the receiving unit is also licensed to run that software.

Note about TI-GRAPH LINK

If you have a TI-GRAPH LINK cable and software for the TI-92, be aware that the software is not compatible with the TI-92 Plus. After you install the TI-92 Plus Module, you cannot use your existing TI-92 GRAPH LINK software.

Tip: TI-GRAPH LINK software for the TI-92 Plus can load saved TI-92 data to the TI-92 Plus.

For information about upgrading to TI-GRAPH LINK software for the TI-92 Plus, check the TI web site at:

http://www.ti.com/calc/docs/link.htm

or contact Texas Instruments as described in Appendix B of this book.

3D Animation, Contours, and Implicit Plots

Animate 3D surfaces in real time, rotate the graph around your line of sight, and use the expanded view to examine the graph. In 3D mode, you can also:

For details, refer to:
Chapter 2

Note: You can also use the new DrwCtour instruction (Appendix A) to draw contours in 3D graphing mode.

- View the graph along the x, y, and z axes by typing the letter X, Y or Z, respectively. Type 0 (zero) to return to your original view.

- Use the new CONTOUR LEVELS and WIRE AND CONTOUR graph format styles to draw contour lines that connect adjacent points that have the same z value.

- Use the new IMPLICIT PLOT graph format style to graph 2D implicit forms that cannot be graphed in function graphing mode.

What's New with the TI-92 Plus (Continued)

Differential Equations

Solve ordinary differential equations either numerically or symbolically.

For details, refer to:
Chapter 3

- For numeric solutions, you can graph 1st-order equations. To graph higher-order equations, you must define them as a system of 1st-order equations. You can:

  - Select either Euler or Runge-Kutta solution methods.

  - Draw a slope or direction field where applicable.

  - Set initial conditions for a particular solution.

- For exact symbolic solutions, you can use **deSolve()** to solve many 1st- and 2nd-order equations.

Interactive Numeric Solver

Use the Numeric Solver to solve for any variable in an equation, provided that you specify a value for all of the other variables. You can also graph the solution.

For details, refer to:
Chapter 4

Constants and Units of Measure

Use constants and units in your calculations, and create your own user-defined units. You can:

For details, refer to:
Chapter 5

- Select constants and units from a menu (◆ P) or type them directly from the keyboard.

Note: Constant and unit names always begin with an underscore character _ (2nd P).

- Convert one unit to another by using the ▶ conversion operator (2nd Y). To convert a temperature value or a temperature range (the difference between two temperature values), use **tmpCnv()** and **ΔtmpCnv()**, respectively.

- Set the default units for displayed results.

Number Bases

Perform calculations by entering numbers in decimal, binary, or hexadecimal form. You can also:

For details, refer to:
Chapter 6

- Set the Base mode to specify the form for displaying integer results.

- Convert one base to another by using the ▶ conversion operator (2nd Y).

- Manipulate the bits in a binary number by using **and**, **not**, **or**, **xor**, **rotate()**, and **shift()**.

User Data Archive and More RAM

The TI-92 Plus module contains additional RAM and a separate user data archive.

For details, refer to: Chapter 7

You can archive data, programs, or any other user variables to a safe location where they cannot be edited or deleted inadvertently.

By archiving variables that do not need to be edited frequently, you can free up RAM for applications that may require additional memory. The MEMORY and VAR-LINK screens have been modified to help you manage archived variables.

New and Enhanced Matrix Operations

New functions and instructions are:

For details, refer to: Appendix A

- **eigVl()** and **eigVc()** — eigenvalues and eigenvectors

- **LU** — LU decomposition

- **QR** — QR matrix factorization

Enhancements include:

- You can now specify an optional numeric tolerance for **det()**, **ref()**, **rref()**, and **simult()**, as well as **LU** and **QR**.

- **simult()** now accepts a matrix argument. **NewData** can also accept a matrix argument to create a data variable.

- Trigonometric and logarithmic functions now let you use a numeric square matrix as an argument to calculate functions of matrices.

Systems of Equations and Expressions

The **solve()** and **cSolve()** functions can now solve many systems of linear and nonlinear equations.

For details, refer to: Appendix A

The **zeros()** and **cZeros()** functions can now calculate the zeros of a system of expressions.

Geometry Languages and New Tools

View Geometry menus and messages in five languages: English, Spanish, Italian, French, and German. Also in the Geometry application:

For details, refer to: Chapter 1

- Two new Check Property tools (**Member** and **Equidistant**) have been added.

- The **Redefine Point** tool has been enhanced and renamed to **Redefine Object**.

What's New with the TI-92 Plus (Continued)

Programs and User-Defined Functions

New functions and instructions are:

For details, refer to:

Appendix A

- **CustmOn** and **CustmOff** — activate and remove a custom toolbar.

- **DispHome** — displays the Home screen.

- **Exec** — executes a string of Motorola 68000 op-codes as a form of assembly-language program.

- **getConfg()** — returns a list of calculator characteristics.

- **getUnits()** and **setUnits()** — return and set the default units for displayed results.

- **part()** — lets a program identify and extract all of the sub-expressions in the simplified result of an expression.

The **Disp**, **Output**, and **Pause** instructions now let you use a conversion operation as an optional expression. **Pause** also lets you scroll if the displayed expression is too big for the screen.

When evaluating a user-defined function or running a program, you can now specify an argument that includes the same variable that was used to define the function or create the program. This eliminates many Circular definition errors you may have seen on the TI-92.

For details, refer to:

Appendix B (circular definitions and local variables)

– and –

Chapter 1 (assembly-language programs)

Other changes affect the way local variables are used in user-defined functions and programs.

You can also run assembly-language programs.

Expanded Statistics Features

Use the new **SinReg** and **Logistic** instructions to model data with sine or logistic regression models. You can also:

For details, refer to:

Appendix A

- Use **NewPlot** to show statistical data as a modified box plot.

- Select Mod Box Plot as the Plot Type when you define a plot in the Data/Matrix Editor.

A modified box plot excludes points outside the interval [Q1–X, Q3+X], where X is defined as 1.5 (Q3–Q1). These points, called outliers, are plotted individually beyond the box plot's whiskers, using the mark that you select. Refer to the *TI-92 Guidebook* for more information about stat plots.

Complex Numbers and Variables

Now you can enter complex numbers in (r∠θ) polar form, as well as $re^{i\theta}$ and a+bi forms. However, the $re^{i\theta}$ form is not valid in Degree angle mode and will cause a Domain error if used in that mode.

For details, refer to:
Chapter 1

You can also designate a symbolic variable so that it will be treated as complex. Type an underscore _ (2nd P) as the last character in the variable name. Without the underscore, the variable is treated as real.

Other Additions and Enhancements

- Start a new calculation from a known state by using the **NewProb** instruction. On the Home screen, F6 is now the Clean Up menu, where you can select Clear a-z or NewProb.

For details, refer to:
Chapter 1

- New keyboard shortcuts make it easier to move the cursor on various screens. You can also use keyboard shortcuts to run a program from the Home screen.

- The new **BldData** instruction lets you create a data variable based on the graph information entered in the Y= Editor, Window Editor, etc.

For details, refer to:
Appendix A

- The new **isPrime()** function tests to see if the argument is prime.

- The **factor()** function now allows larger integer arguments.

Introduction

To start using the new TI-92 Plus features, install the module as described at the beginning of this chapter. The remainder of the chapter introduces some of the general features. For information about other new TI-92 Plus features, refer to the applicable chapters later in this book.

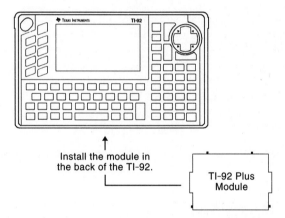

Install the module in the back of the TI-92.

TI-92 Plus Module

As a general rule, this book describes the new TI-92 Plus features only. For information about your TI-92's original features, refer to your separate *TI-92 Guidebook*.

Appendix A in this book is an exception. It gives you one convenient location to find details about every available function and instruction, both original and new. Many of the TI-92's original functions and instructions are updated for the TI-92 Plus.

Installing the TI-92 Plus Module

Before you can use the new TI-92 Plus features, you must first install the module into your TI-92. The TI-92 Plus features are available automatically when the module is installed.

Important: Before Installing the Module

Any data in your TI-92 will be erased when you install the new module. To retain this data, you can save the contents of your TI-92's memory:

Note: For information about using TI-92 data with the TI-92 Plus, refer to the compatibility information in Appendix B of this book.

- To another TI-92 as described on page 15.

  – or –

- To a PC or Macintosh computer by using an optional TI-GRAPH LINK™ (available separately). Refer to the manual that comes with your TI-GRAPH LINK.

  Note: Because the Backup option in TI-GRAPH LINK does not work between different software versions, you must use the Send and Receive options in TI-GRAPH LINK to save your data and variables.

Note about TI-GRAPH LINK

If you have a TI-GRAPH LINK cable and software for the TI-92, be aware that the software is not compatible with the TI-92 Plus. The cable works with both units. You can use your existing TI-GRAPH LINK software to save your TI-92 data, but you cannot use it to reload the data after the TI-92 Plus module is installed.

Tip: The TI-GRAPH LINK software for the TI-92 Plus can load saved TI-92 data to the TI-92 Plus.

For information about upgrading to TI-GRAPH LINK software for the TI-92 Plus, check the TI web site at:

http://www.ti.com/calc/docs/link.htm

or contact Texas Instruments as described in Appendix B of this book.

Installing/Replacing the Module

Begin by discharging any static electricity that may be built up on your body. Touch a grounded or anti-static surface or a metal fixture.

Depending on the manufacturing date of your TI-92, you will either be inserting the TI-92 Plus module into an empty compartment or replacing an older module that is similar to the TI-92 Plus module.

Note: If necessary, refer to the diagrams for installing AA batteries in Chapter 1: Getting Started in the TI-92 Guidebook.

1. Hold the TI-92 upright and slide the latch on the top of the unit to the right unlocked position. Then slide the rear cover down about 1/8 inch and remove it from the main unit.

2. With the unit ON, hold down the [ON] key and remove one of the four AA batteries. Release the [ON] key.

3. Loosen and remove the Phillips screw from the compartment cover and lift off the cover.

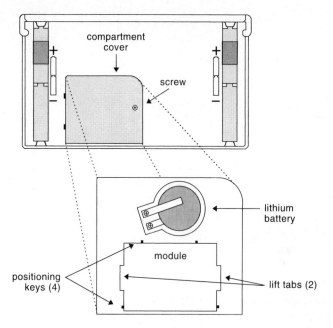

- compartment cover
- screw
- lithium battery
- module
- positioning keys (4)
- lift tabs (2)

4. If a module is already in your TI-92, remove it.

    a. Use the flat edge of a screwdriver to gently pry under and up on the module's lift tabs. Slightly pry up one lift tab and then the other.

    b. Continue until the module is loose enough to remove.

5. Orient the new module so that the four positioning keys are aligned, and then push down on the module with your thumb until the module is seated firmly.

6. Re-insert the battery that you removed earlier.

7. Replace the compartment cover, and then replace the rear cover. Slide the latch on the top of the unit to the locked position.

8. Adjust the display contrast by using ◆ − (lighten) and ◆ + (darken).

9. If you saved any previous data from your TI-92, reload it.

Under normal conditions, you should leave the module in place after installing it. Repeatedly removing and reinstalling a module may damage the connectors in the module or in the TI-92.

The TI-92 Plus

Throughout the rest of this book, TI-92 Plus is used to refer to the combination of your TI-92 and the installed TI-92 Plus module.

Finding the Software Version and Serial Number

In some situations, you may need to find out information about your TI-92 Plus, particularly the software version and the unit's serial number.

Displaying the "About" Screen

From the Home screen, press F1 and then select A:About.

Your screen will be different than the one shown to the right.

Press ENTER or ESC to close the screen.

When Do You Need this Information?

The information on the About screen is intended for situations such as:

• If you obtain new or upgraded software for your TI-92 Plus, you may need to provide your current software version and/or the serial number of your unit.

• If you have difficulties with your TI-92 Plus and need to contact technical support, knowing the software version may make it easier to diagnose the problem.

New Keyboard Shortcuts

With the TI-92 Plus, you can use new keyboard shortcuts to move the cursor or run up to nine user-defined or assembly-language programs.

Shortcuts to Move the Cursor

From:	Press:	To:
Home screen	◆ ⊙ or ◆ ⊙	If the cursor is in the history area, go to the oldest or to the newest history pair, respectively. If the cursor is in the entry line, go to the beginning or end of the entry line, respectively.
	⊛ ⊙ or ⊛ ⊙	Scroll "tall" objects in the history area.
Y= Editor	◆ ⊙ or ◆ ⊙	Go to function 1 or to the last defined function, respectively. If the cursor is on or past the last defined function, ◆ ⊙ goes to function 99.
Data/Matrix Editor	◆ ⊙ or ◆ ⊙	Go to row 1 in the current column or to the last row that contains data for any column on the screen, respectively. If the cursor is in or past that last row, ◆ ⊙ goes to row 999.
	◆ ⊙ or ◆ ⊙	Go to column 1 or to the last column that contains data, respectively. If the cursor is in or past that last column, ◆ ⊙ goes to column 99.
Program and Text Editors	◆ ⊙ or ◆ ⊙	Go to the beginning or end of the program or text, respectively.

Tip: In most applications and menu listings, you can press 2nd ⊙ and 2nd ⊙ to page one screen at a time.

Shortcuts to Run a Program

On the Home screen, you can use keyboard shortcuts to run up to nine user-defined or assembly-language programs. However, the programs must have the following names.

On Home screen, press:	To run a program, if any, named:
◆ 1	kbdprgm1()
⋮	⋮
◆ 9	kbdprgm9()

Note: The programs must be stored in the MAIN folder. Also, you cannot use a shortcut to run a program that requires an argument.

If you have a program with a different name and you would like to run it with a keyboard shortcut, copy or rename the existing program to kbdprgm1(), etc.

Using F6 Clean Up to Start a New Problem

Previously, the Home screen used F6 to clear (delete) all single-character variable names. Now, F6 displays a menu that lets you select from two "clean up" items.

F6 Clean Up Toolbar Menu

From the Home screen, press F6 to display the menu:

Menu Item	Description
Clear a–z	Clears (deletes) all single-character variable names in the current folder, unless the variables are locked or archived. You will be prompted to press ENTER to confirm the action.
	Single-character variable names are often used in symbolic calculations such as:
	$solve(a \cdot x^2 + b \cdot x + c = 0, x)$
	If any of the variables have already been assigned a value, your calculation may produce misleading results. To prevent this, you can select 1:Clear a–z before beginning the calculation.
NewProb	Places **NewProb** in the entry line. You must then press ENTER to execute the command.
	NewProb performs a variety of operations that let you begin a new problem from a cleared state without resetting the memory:
	• Clears all single-character variable names in the current folder (same as 1:Clear a–z), unless the variables are locked or archived.
	• Turns off all functions and stat plots (**FnOff** and **PlotsOff**) in the current graphing mode.
	• Performs **ClrDraw**, **ClrErr**, **ClrGraph**, **ClrHome**, **ClrIO**, and **ClrTable**.

Tip: When defining a variable that you want to retain, use more than one character in the name. This prevents it from being deleted inadvertently by 1:Clear a–z.

Note: For information about checking and resetting memory or other system defaults, refer to Chapter 18 in the TI-92 Guidebook.

Changing the Language Setting for Geometry

In the Geometry application only, you can display Geometry menus, labels, and warning and error messages in any of five languages. However, system messages and dialog boxes are displayed in English, regardless of the selected language.

From within the Geometry Application

To change the Language setting, you must first be in the Geometry application. Then:

1. Press F8 to display the File menu.

2. Select E:Language. Either:

Note: The language setting affects Geometry only. In other applications, English is always used, regardless of the language setting.

   • Move the cursor to highlight E:Language and press ENTER.

     – or –

   • Press E on the keyboard.

3. Select a particular language.

What Is Shown in the Selected Language?

All Geometry-specific menu items, dialog boxes, messages, and labels are shown in the selected language. However, the Geometry application also shows common dialog boxes and messages used by other applications, and these are always shown in English.

For example, after selecting a language:

   • If you press F8, the File menu items are shown in the selected language.

   • If you select the first item on the F8 menu, the OPEN dialog box is shown in English because all applications (not only Geometry) use the same OPEN dialog box.

Changes to the Geometry Tools

In the Geometry application, one tool has been enhanced and renamed, and two new tools have been added.

Redefine Point Is Changed to Redefine Object

On the F4 **Construction** toolbar menu:

You can now redefine objects other than points.

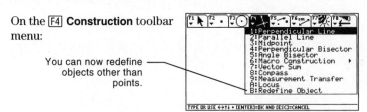

For information about how to use this tool, refer to Chapter 7 in the *TI-92 Guidebook*.

New Check Property Tools

On the F6 **Measurement** toolbar menu:

Check Property has two new tools: Member and Equidistant.

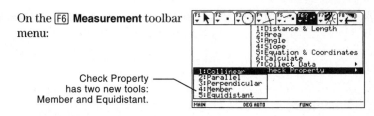

Determining if a Point Lies on an Object

The **Member** tool evaluates a point to determine whether or not it lies on an object.

1. Construct a point and a circle as shown to the right.

2. Press F6 and select 8:Check Property, and then select 4:Member.

3. Select the point (point to it and press ENTER).

4. Point to the circle and press ENTER.

5. If desired, move the empty text box to an easy-to-read location.

6. Press ENTER to display the property in the text box.

If you drag the point to lie on the circle, the displayed property automatically changes to Member. However, the point must be positioned so that it is "mathematically" on the circle. This may not be easy to do by simply dragging the point to the circle. To position the point mathematically, use **Redefine Object** in the F4 **Construction** toolbar menu.

Determining if Points Are Equidistant

The **Equidistant** tool evaluates any three points to determine whether or not the first point is equidistant from the two remaining points.

1. Construct a point and a segment as shown to the right.

2. Press F6 and select 8:Check Property, and then select 5:Equidistant.

3. Select the point (point to it and press ENTER).

    ↗ IS THIS POINT EQUIDISTANT

4. Point to each of the segment's endpoints, pressing ENTER each time.

5. If desired, move the empty text box to an easy-to-read location.

6. Press ENTER to display the property in the text box.

    Not equidistant

As with the **Member** tool, simply dragging the point so that it appears to be equidistant may not change the displayed property. To position the point so that it is equidistant mathematically, you can create a perpendicular bisector for the segment. Then use **Redefine Object** in the F4 **Construction** toolbar menu to position the point on the perpendicular bisector.

Entering Complex Numbers

Previously, you could enter complex numbers in rectangular form a+bi or polar form r$e^{i\theta}$. Now, you can also enter complex numbers in the polar form (r∠θ), where r is the magnitude and θ is the angle.

Overview of Complex Numbers

A complex number has real and imaginary components that identify a point in the complex plane. These components are measured along the real and imaginary axes, which are similar to the x and y axes in the real plane.

The point can be expressed in rectangular form or in either of two polar forms.

The i symbol represents the imaginary number $\sqrt{-1}$.

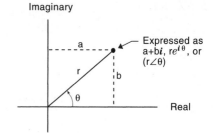

As shown below, the form that you can enter depends on the current Angle mode.

You can use the form:	When the Angle mode setting is:
a+bi	Radian or Degree
r$e^{i\theta}$	Radian only (In Degree angle mode, this form causes a Domain error.)
(r∠θ)	Radian or Degree

Use the following methods to enter a complex number.

To enter the:	Do this:
Rectangular form a+bi	Substitute the applicable values or variable names for a and b. a ⊞ b [2nd] [i] For example:

Note: *To get the i symbol, press* [2nd] [i] *(second function of* l*). Do not simply type an* l.

```
■2 + 3·i                                    2 + 3·i
2+3i
MAIN           RAD AUTO        FUNC 1/30
```

To enter the:	Do this:

Important: Do not use the $re^{i\theta}$ polar form in Degree angle mode. It will cause a Domain error.

Note: To get the e symbol, press [2nd] [eˣ]. Do not simply type an E.

Tip: To get the ∠ symbol, press [2nd] F.

Tip: To enter θ in degrees for (r∠θ), you can type a ° symbol (such as 45°). To get the ° symbol, press [2nd] D. You should not use degrees for $re^{i\theta}$.

Polar form $re^{i\theta}$ – or – (r∠θ) ⎯ Parentheses are required for the (r∠θ) form.	Substitute the applicable values or variable names for r and θ, where θ is interpreted according to the Angle mode setting. r [2nd] [eˣ] [2nd] [i] θ [ )] – or – [( ] r [2nd] F θ [ )] For example:

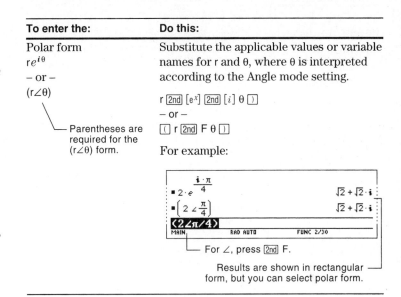

For ∠, press [2nd] F.

Results are shown in rectangular form, but you can select polar form.

Complex Format Mode for Displaying Results

Use [MODE] to set the Complex Format mode to one of three settings.

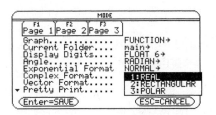

You can enter a complex number at any time, regardless of the Complex Format mode setting. However, the mode setting determines how results are displayed.

If Complex Format is:	The TI-92 Plus:

Note: You can enter complex numbers in any form (or a mixture of all forms) depending on the Angle *mode.*

REAL	Will not display complex results unless you: • Enter a complex number. – or – • Use a complex function such as **cFactor()**, **cSolve()**, or **cZeros()**. If complex results are displayed, they will be shown in either a+bi or $re^{i\theta}$ form.
RECTANGULAR	Displays complex results as a+bi.
POLAR	Displays complex results as: • $re^{i\theta}$ if the Angle mode = Radian – or – • (r∠θ) if the Angle mode = Degree

Entering Complex Numbers (Continued)

Using Complex Variables in Symbolic Calculations

Regardless of the Complex Format mode setting, undefined variables are treated as real numbers. To perform complex symbolic analysis, you can use either of the following methods to set up a complex variable.

Method 1: Use an underscore _ ([2nd] P) as the last character in the variable name to designate a complex variable. For example:

Note: *For best results in calculations such as* **cSolve()** *and* **cZeros()**, *use Method 1.*

z_ is treated as a complex variable (unless z already exists, in which case it retains its existing data type).

Method 2: Define a complex variable. For example:

x+y*i*→z

Then z is treated as a complex variable.

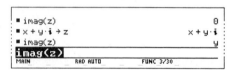

Complex Numbers and Degree Mode

Radian angle mode is recommended for complex number calculations. Internally, the TI-92 Plus converts all entered trig values to radians, but it does not convert values for exponential, logarithmic, or hyperbolic functions.

Note: *If you use* Degree *angle mode, you must make polar entries in the form* ($r\angle\theta$). *In* Degree *angle mode, an* $re^{i\theta}$ *entry causes an error.*

In Degree angle mode, complex identities such as $e^{\wedge}(i\theta) = \cos(\theta) + i \sin(\theta)$ are not generally true because the values for cos and sin are converted to radians, while those for $e^{\wedge}(\,)$ are not. For example, $e^{\wedge}(i45) = \cos(45) + i \sin(45)$ is treated internally as $e^{\wedge}(i45) = \cos(\pi/4) + i \sin(\pi/4)$. Complex identities are always true in Radian angle mode.

Assembly-Language Programs

You can run programs written for the TI-92 Plus in assembly language. Typically, assembly-language programs run much faster and provide greater control than the keystroke programs that you write with the built-in Program Editor.

Where to Get Assembly-Language Programs

Assembly-language programs, as well as keystroke programs, are available on the TI web site at:

http://www.ti.com/calc

The programs available from this site provide additional functions or features that are not built into the TI-92 Plus. Check the TI web site for up-to-date information.

After downloading a program from the web to your computer, use a TI-GRAPH LINK™ (available separately) to send the program to your TI-92 Plus. Refer to the manual that comes with the TI-GRAPH LINK.

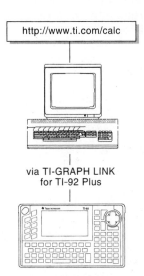

http://www.ti.com/calc

via TI-GRAPH LINK
for TI-92 Plus

Note about TI-GRAPH LINK

If you have a TI-GRAPH LINK cable and software for the TI-92, be aware that the software is not compatible with the TI-92 Plus. The cable works with both units. For information about upgrading to TI-GRAPH LINK software for the TI-92 Plus, check the TI web site at:

http://www.ti.com/calc/docs/link.htm

or contact Texas Instruments as described in Appendix B of this book.

Tip: The TI-GRAPH LINK software for the TI-92 Plus can load saved TI-92 data to the TI-92 Plus.

Running an Assembly-Language Program

After a TI-92 Plus assembly-language program is stored on your unit, you can run the program from the Home screen just as you would any other program.

Tip: If the program is not in the current folder, be sure to specify the pathname.

If the program requires one or more arguments, type them within the ( ). Refer to the program's documentation to find out about required arguments.

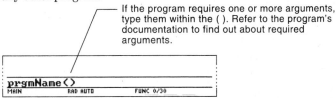

You can call an assembly-language program from another program as a subroutine, delete it, or use it the same as any other program.

Assembly-Language Programs (Continued)

You Cannot Edit an Assembly-Language Program

You cannot use your TI-92 Plus to edit an assembly-language program. The built-in Program Editor will not open assembly-language programs.

Displaying a List of Assembly-Language Programs

To list the assembly-language programs stored in memory:

1. Display the VAR-LINK screen ([2nd] [VAR-LINK]).

2. Press [F2] View.

3. Select the applicable folder (or All folders) and set Var Type = Assembly.

Note: *Assembly-language programs have an ASM data type.*

4. Press [ENTER] to display the list of assembly-language programs.

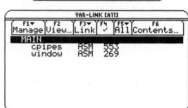

For Information about Writing an Assembly-Language Program

The information required to teach a novice programmer how to write an assembly-language program is beyond the scope of this book. However, if you have a working knowledge of assembly language, please check the TI web site (listed previously in this section) for specific information about how to access TI-92 Plus features.

The TI-92 Plus also includes an **Exec** command that executes a string consisting of a series of Motorola 68000 op-codes. These codes act as another form of an assembly-language program. Check the TI web site for available information.

Transmitting Variables between Units

You can transmit variables and folders between two TI-92 Plus units or between a TI-92 Plus and a TI-92. Except for having to specify the type of receiving unit, the procedure is the same as described in Chapter 18 in the *TI-92 Guidebook*.

Linking Two Units

Your TI-92 comes with a cable that lets you link two units. Using firm pressure, insert one end of the cable into the I/O port of each unit.

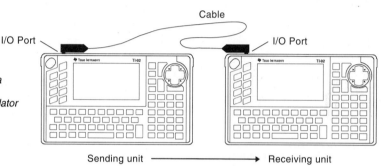

Note: *You cannot link a TI-92 Plus or TI-92 to another graphing calculator such as a TI-81, TI-82, TI-85, or TI-86.*

Either unit can send or receive, depending on how you set them up from the VAR-LINK screen.

Transmitting Variables

Note: *Set up the receiving unit first. If you set up the sending unit first, it may display an error message or remain BUSY until you cancel the transmission.*

Step:	On the:	Do this:
1.	Receiving unit	a. Display the VAR-LINK screen ([2nd] [VAR-LINK]).
		b. Press [F3] Link and select 2:Receive. The message VAR-LINK: WAITING TO RECEIVE and the BUSY indicator are displayed in the status line.
2.	Sending unit	a. Display the VAR-LINK screen ([2nd] [VAR-LINK]).
		b. Select the variables to send, as described in Chapter 18 in the *TI-92 Guidebook*.
		c. Press [F3] Link and select the type of receiving unit, either: • 1:Send to TI-92 Plus/TI-89 – or – • 3:Send to TI-92 This starts the transmission.

Transmitting Variables between Units (Continued)

Note: Depending on transmission speed and variable sizes, messages in the status line may be displayed only briefly.

- During transmission, messages are displayed in the status line of both units to show the name of each transmitted item.

- When transmission is complete, the VAR-LINK screen is updated on the receiving unit.

Rules for Transmitting Variables or Folders

If you select a:	What happens:
Variable (but not the folder it is in)	The variable is transmitted to the current folder on the receiving unit.
Locked variable	The variable is transmitted but it is unlocked on the receiving unit.
Archived variable	The variable is stored in RAM (not the user data archive) on the receiving unit. The transmitted variable is unlocked. **Note:** You cannot send an archived variable from a TI-92 Plus to a TI-92. If you need to send the variable, unarchive it first.
Folder	The folder and its contents are transmitted to the receiving unit. **Note:** If you use [F4] to select a folder, all variables in that folder are selected automatically. Use [F4] to deselect any variables that you do not want to transmit.

Canceling a Transmission

From either the sending or receiving unit:

1. Press [ON].

   An error message is displayed.

2. Press [ESC] or [ENTER].

```
          ERROR

 Link transmission

  ESC=CANCEL
```

For More Information

For compatibility information about using TI-92 variables (including functions and programs) on a TI-92 Plus and vice versa, refer to Appendix B in this book.

For information about common error and notification messages, refer to "Transmitting Variables between Two TI-92s" in Chapter 18 in the *TI-92 Guidebook*. Chapter 18 also includes information about using **GetCalc** and **SendCalc** to transmit variables under program control.

Upgrading Your TI-92 Plus Product Code

You can upgrade the software, or product code, on your TI-92 Plus. You can also transfer product code from one unit to another, provided that the receiving unit has the appropriate certificate that allows it to run that software.

Product Code Upgrades

For each TI-92 Plus, the product code is the combination of the base software that came with the unit and any upgrades that you have installed. (Typically, these applications are available via the [APPS] key. They are not simply programs that you run from the Home screen.)

Product code upgrades can include:

• Maintenance upgrades to your current product code (which will be released free of charge).

• Major software feature upgrades and new applications (which will be available for purchase).

To download product code upgrades from the TI web site, you must provide information that identifies your TI-92 Plus. (Instructions are given on the web.) This information is used to create a customized electronic *software certificate* that specifies which product code your unit is licensed to run.

Where to Get Upgrades

For up-to-date information about available upgrades and how to install them, check the TI web site at:

http://www.ti.com/calc

or contact Texas Instruments as described in Appendix B.

Note: *To upgrade multiple units, you can use the process on page 18.*

You can download a new software certificate and/or the new product code from the TI web site to a computer, and then use a TI-GRAPH LINK™ (available separately) to install them on your TI-92 Plus.

For more information, refer to the instructions on the web and in the manual that comes with the TI-GRAPH LINK.

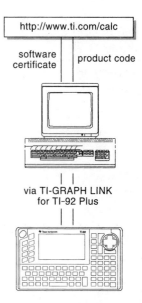

http://www.ti.com/calc

software certificate · product code

via TI-GRAPH LINK for TI-92 Plus

Upgrading Your TI-92 Plus Product Code (Continued)

**Note about
TI-GRAPH LINK**

If you have a TI-GRAPH LINK cable and software for the TI-92, be aware that the software is not compatible with the TI-92 Plus. The cable works with both units. For information about purchasing a TI-GRAPH LINK for the TI-92 Plus or upgrading your existing TI-GRAPH LINK software, check the TI web site at:

http://www.ti.com/calc/docs/link.htm

or contact Texas Instruments as described in Appendix B.

**Backing Up Your
Unit Before an
Installation**

When you install new product code, the installation process:

• Deletes all user-defined variables (in both RAM and the user data archive), functions, programs, and folders.

• Resets all system variables and modes to their original factory settings. This is equivalent to using the MEMORY screen to reset all memory.

To retain any existing variables, do the following *before installing the upgrade*:

• Transmit the variables to another TI-92 Plus as described on page 15.

– or –

• Use a TI-GRAPH LINK to send the variables to a computer.

**If You're Upgrading
Multiple TI-92 Plus
Units**

Each TI-92 Plus that you want to upgrade must have its own unique certificate. During download and installation, however, you can choose both the certificate and product code or only the certificate. To upgrade multiple units, you can transfer product code from one unit to another instead of installing the product code on each unit from a computer.

Tip: Generally, transmitting product code from unit to unit is much quicker than installing the product code from a computer.

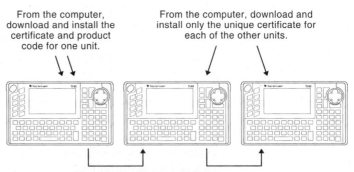

From the computer, download and install the certificate and product code for one unit.

From the computer, download and install only the unique certificate for each of the other units.

Starting with the first unit, transfer the product code from one unit to another as described on page 19.

Transferring Product Code from One TI-92 Plus to Another

Tip: You can see which version of product code is in your TI-92 Plus. From the Home screen, press F1 and select **A:About**.

If the sending unit has:	Then:
Original TI-92 Plus product code or a free maintenance upgrade for that code	The receiving unit does not need a new certificate. Its current certificate is valid, and the product code can be transferred.
Any other type of product code	The product code must first be purchased from TI for the receiving unit. The software certificate can then be downloaded and installed on the receiving unit, and the product code can be transferred.

To transfer product code, connect the sending and receiving units by using the cable that came with the TI-92. Refer to the illustration on page 15.

Step:	On the:	Do this:
1.	Receiving unit	a. Display the VAR-LINK screen ([2nd] [VAR-LINK]).
		b. Press [F3] Link and select 5:Receive Product Code.
		A warning message states that all memory (RAM and archive) will be cleared on the receiving unit. If you need to quit and back up any variables, press [ESC].
		c. Press [ENTER].
		The message WAITING TO RECEIVE is shown in the status line.
2.	Sending unit	a. Display the VAR-LINK screen ([2nd] [VAR-LINK]).
		b. Press [F3] Link and select 4:Send Product Code.
		A warning message is displayed similar to the one on the sending unit.
		c. Press [ENTER].

During the transfer, the receiving unit shows how the transfer is progressing. When the transfer is complete:

- The sending unit returns to the VAR-LINK screen.

- The receiving unit returns to the Home screen. The display contrast is reset to its factory setting, so you may need to use ♦ ⊟ (lighten) or ♦ ⊞ (darken) to adjust the contrast.

Upgrading Your TI-92 Plus Product Code (Continued)

Do Not Attempt to Cancel the Transfer

After the transfer starts, the receiving unit's existing product code is effectively deleted. If you interrupt the transfer before it is complete, the receiving unit will not operate properly. You will then need to reinstall the product code from a computer.

Error Messages

Most error messages are displayed on the sending unit. Depending on when the error occurs during the transfer process, you may see an error message on the receiving unit.

Error Message	Description
ERROR Link transmission ESC=CANCEL	The sending and receiving units are not connected properly, or the receiving unit is not set up to receive.
ERROR Unlicensed product code ESC=CANCEL	The certificate on the receiving unit is not valid for the product code on the sending unit. You must obtain and install a valid certificate as described earlier in this section.
ERROR Signature error ESC=CANCEL	An error occurred during the transfer. The current product code in the receiving unit is corrupted. You must reinstall the product code from a computer.
ERROR Batteries too low for sending/receiving product code ESC=CANCEL	Replace the batteries on the unit displaying this message.

New 3D Graphing Features

This chapter describes the new 3D graphing features included in the TI-92 Plus. If you are not already familiar with 3D graphing, refer to Chapter 14 in the *TI-92 Guidebook*.

The expanded view is a new feature that is useful for all types of 3D graphs. By using the expanded view, you can examine any 3D graph in more detail. For example:

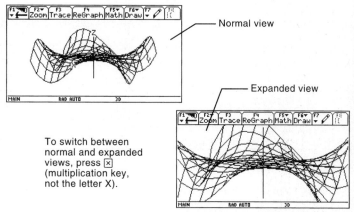

Normal view

Expanded view

Tip: *To view the graph along the x, y or z axis, you can type the letter* X, Y, *or* Z, *respectively.*

To switch between normal and expanded views, press ⨯ (multiplication key, not the letter X).

When you display a 3D graph, the expanded view is used automatically if:

Tip: *To switch from one format style to the next (skipping* IMPLICIT PLOT*), type the letter* F.

- You set or change the graph format style (◆ F) to CONTOUR LEVELS or IMPLICIT PLOT.

- The previous graph used the expanded view.

Note: *Typing the letter* F, *unlike using* ◆ F, *always retains the current view, either expanded or normal.*

If you press a cursor key to animate the graph as described in this chapter, the screen switches to the normal view automatically. You cannot animate a graph in the expanded view.

Preview of New 3D Graphing Features

Graph the 3D equation z(x,y) = (x³y − y³x) / 390. Animate the graph by using the cursor to interactively change the eye Window variable values that control your viewing angle. Then view the graph in different graph format styles.

Steps	Keystrokes	Display
1. Display the MODE dialog box. For Graph mode, select 3D.	[MODE] ⊙ 5 [ENTER]	
2. Display and clear the Y= Editor. Then define the 3D equation z1(x,y) = (x³y − y³x) / 390. *Notice that implied multiplication is used in the keystrokes.*	[♦][Y=] [F1] 8 [ENTER] [ENTER] ([) X [^] 3 Y [−] Y [^] 3 X [)] [÷] 3 9 0 [ENTER]	
3. Change the graph format to display and label the axes. Also set Style = WIRE FRAME. *You can animate any graph format style, but WIRE FRAME is fastest.*	[♦] F ⊙ ⊙ 2 ⊙ ⊙ 2 ⊙ ⊙ 1 [ENTER]	
4. Select the ZoomStd viewing cube, which automatically graphs the equation. *As the equation is evaluated (before it is graphed), "evaluation percentages" are shown in the upper-left part of the screen.*	[F2] 6	
Note: *If you have already used 3D graphing, the graph may be shown in expanded view. When you animate the graph, the screen returns to normal view automatically. (Except for animation, you can do the same things in normal and expanded view.)*	[×] (press [×] to switch between expanded and normal view)	
5. Animate the graph by decreasing the eyeφ Window variable value. ⊙ *or* ⊙ *may affect* eyeθ *and* eyeψ, *but to a lesser extent than* eyeφ. *To animate the graph continuously, press and hold the cursor for about 1 second and then release it. To stop, press [ENTER].*	⊙ ⊙ ⊙ ⊙ ⊙ ⊙ ⊙ ⊙	

Steps	Keystrokes	Display
6. Return the graph to its initial orientation. Then move the viewing angle along the "viewing orbit" around the graph. *For information about the viewing orbit, refer to page 25.*	0 (zero, not the letter O) ⊙ ⊙ ⊙	
7. View the graph along the x axis, the y axis, and then the z axis.	X	
This graph has the same shape along the y axis and x axis.	Y	
	Z	
8. Return to the initial orientation.	0	
9. Display the graph in different graph format styles.	F (press F to switch from each style to the next)	
HIDDEN SURFACE		
CONTOUR LEVELS (may require extra time to calculate contours)		
WIRE AND CONTOUR		
WIRE FRAME		

Note: You can also display the graph as an implicit plot by using the GRAPH FORMATS dialog box (◆ F). If you press F to switch between styles, the implicit plot is not displayed.

Rotating a 3D Graph by Using eyeψ

In 3D graphing mode, the eyeθ and eyeφ Window variables let you set viewing angles that determine your line of sight. A new Window variable, eyeψ, lets you rotate the graph around that line of sight.

How the Viewing Angle Is Measured

The viewing angle has three components:

- eyeθ — angle in degrees from the positive x axis.

- eyeφ — angle in degrees from the positive z axis.

- eyeψ — angle in degrees by which the graph is rotated counterclockwise around the line of sight set by eyeθ and eyeφ.

Note: *When eyeψ=0, the z axis is vertical on the screen. When eyeψ=90, the z axis is rotated 90° counterclockwise and is horizontal.*

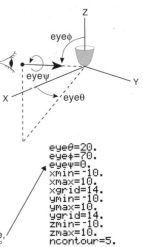

```
eyeθ=20.
eyeφ=70.
eyeψ=0.
xmin=-10.
xmax=10.
xgrid=14.
ymin=-10.
ymax=10.
ygrid=14.
zmin=-10.
zmax=10.
ncontour=5.
```

In the Window Editor (◆ [WINDOW]), always enter eyeθ, eyeφ, and eyeψ in degrees, regardless of the current angle mode.

Do not enter a ° symbol. For example, type 20, 70, and 0, not 20°, 70°, and 0°.

Effect of Changing eyeψ

The view on the Graph screen is always oriented along the viewing angles set by eyeθ and eyeφ. You can change eyeψ to rotate the graph around that line of sight.

Note: *During rotation, the axes expand or contract to fit the screen's width and height. This causes some distortion as shown in the example.*

When eyeψ=0, the z axis runs the height of the screen.

```
↑ z=10


↓ z=-10
```

When eyeψ=90, the z axis runs the width of the screen.

```
←+——————————+→
z=10        z=-10
```

As the z axis rotates 90°, its range (⁻10 to 10 in this example) expands to almost twice its original length. Likewise, the x and y axes expand or contract.

z1(x,y)=(x³y−y³x) / 390		In this example, eyeθ=20 and eyeφ=70

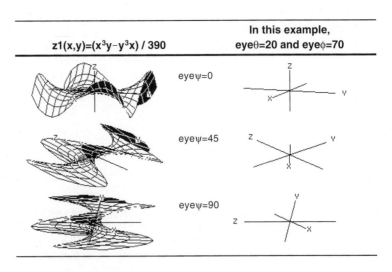

Animating a 3D Graph Interactively

After plotting any 3D graph, you can change the viewing angle interactively by using the cursor. Refer to the preview example on page 22.

The Viewing Orbit

Note: *The viewing orbit affects the* eye *Window variables in differing amounts.*

When using $\odot$ and $\odot$ to animate a graph, think of it as moving the viewing angle along its "viewing orbit" around the graph.

Moving along this orbit can cause the z axis to wobble slightly during the animation (as you can see in the preview example on page 22).

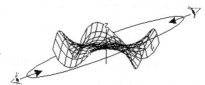

Animating the Graph

Note: *If the graph is shown in expanded view, it returns to normal view automatically when you press a cursor key.*

Tip: *After animating the graph, use* ENTER *or the space bar to stop and then re-start the animation in the same direction.*

Tip: *During an animation, you can press* F *to switch to the next graph format style.*

Tip: *To see a graphic that shows the* eye *angles, refer to page 24.*

To:	Do this:
Animate the graph incrementally	Press and release the cursor quickly.
Move along the viewing orbit:	$\odot$ or $\odot$
Change the viewing orbit's elevation: (primarily increases or decreases eyeϕ)	$\odot$ or $\odot$
Animate the graph continuously	Press and hold the cursor for about 1 second, and then release it. To stop, press ESC, ENTER, ON, or the space bar.
Change between 4 animation speeds (increase or decrease the incremental changes in the eye Window variables)	Press $+$ or $-$.
Change the viewing angle of a non-animated graph to look along the x, y, or z axis	Press X, Y or Z, respectively.
Return to the initial eye angle values	Press 0 (zero, not the letter O).

Animating a Series of Graph Pictures

You can also animate a graph by saving a series of graph pictures and then flipping (or cycling) through those pictures. Refer to "Animating a Series of Graph Pictures" in Chapter 15: Additional Graphing Topics in the *TI-92 Guidebook*. This method gives you more control over the Window variable values, particularly eyeψ (page 24), which rotates the graph.

Contour Plots

In a contour plot, a line is drawn to connect adjacent points on the 3D graph that have the same z value. This section discusses the CONTOUR LEVELS and WIRE AND CONTOUR graph format styles.

Selecting the Graph Format Style

In 3D graphing mode, define an equation and graph it as you would any 3D equation, with the following exception. Display the GRAPH FORMATS dialog box by pressing ◆ F from the Y= Editor, Window editor, or Graph screen. Then set:

Tip: From the Graph screen, you can press F to switch from one graph format style to the next (skipping IMPLICIT PLOT).

Style = CONTOUR LEVELS

– or –

Style = WIRE AND CONTOUR

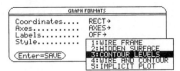

Note: Pressing F to select CONTOUR LEVELS does not affect the viewing angle, view, or Labels format as it does if you use ◆ F.

- For CONTOUR LEVELS, only the contours are shown.

  - The viewing angle is set initially so that you are viewing the contours by looking down the z axis. You can change the viewing angle as necessary.

  - The graph is shown in expanded view. To switch between expanded and normal view, press ⊠.

  - The Labels format is set to OFF automatically.

- For WIRE AND CONTOUR, the contours are drawn on a wire frame view. The viewing angle, view (expanded or normal), and Labels format retain their previous settings.

Style	z1(x,y)=(x³y−y³x) / 390	z1(x,y)=x²+.5y²−5

Looking down z axis

Note: These examples use the same x, y, and z Window variable values as a ZoomStd viewing cube. If you use ZoomStd, press Z to look down the z axis.

CONTOUR LEVELS

Using eyeθ=20, eyeφ=70, eyeψ=0

CONTOUR LEVELS

Note: Do not confuse the contours with the grid lines. The contours are darker.

WIRE AND CONTOUR

How Are Z Values Determined?

You can set the ncontour Window variable ($\bullet$ [WINDOW]) to specify the number of contours that will be evenly distributed along the displayed range of z values, where:

$$\text{increment} = \frac{\text{zmax} - \text{zmin}}{\text{ncontour} + 1}$$

The z values for the contours are:

zmin + increment
zmin + 2(increment)
zmin + 3(increment)
$\vdots$
zmin + ncontour(increment)

```
eyeθ=20.
eyeφ=70.
eyeψ=0.
xmin=-10.
xmax=10.
xgrid=14.
ymin=-10.
ymax=10.
ygrid=14.
zmin=-10.
zmax=10.
ncontour=5.
```

The default is 5. You can set this to 0 through 20.

If ncontour=5 and you use the standard viewing window (zmin=⁻10 and zmax=10) , the increment is 3.333. Five contours are drawn for z= ⁻6.666, ⁻3.333, 0, 3.333, and 6.666.

Note, however, that a contour is not drawn for a z value if the 3D graph is not defined at that z value.

Drawing a Contour for the Z Value of a Selected Point Interactively

If a contour graph is currently displayed, you can specify a point on the graph and draw a contour for the corresponding z value.

1. Press [F6] to display the Draw menu.

2. Select 7:Draw Contour.

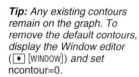

3. Either:

  • Type the point's x value and press [ENTER], and then type the y value and press [ENTER].

   – or –

  • Move the cursor to the applicable point. (The cursor moves along the grid lines.) Then press [ENTER].

Tip: Any existing contours remain on the graph. To remove the default contours, display the Window editor ($\bullet$ [WINDOW]) and set ncontour=0.

For example, suppose the current graph is z1(x,y)=x^2+.5y^2−5. If you specify x=2 and y=3, a contour is drawn for z=3.5.

Contour Plots (Continued)

Drawing Contours for Specified Z Values

From the Graph screen, press [F6] Draw and then select 8:DrwCtour. The Home screen is displayed automatically with DrwCtour in the entry line. You can then specify one or more z values individually or generate a sequence of z values.

Some examples are:

Tip: To remove the default contours, use [♦] [WINDOW] and set ncontour=0.

DrwCtour 5 ─────────────── Draws a contour for z=5.

DrwCtour {1,2,3} ─────────── Draws contours for z=1, 2, and 3.

DrwCtour seq(n,n,⁻10,10,2) ──── Draws contours for a sequence of z values from ⁻10 through 10 in steps of 2 (⁻10, ⁻8, ⁻6, etc.).

The specified contours are drawn on the current 3D graph. (A contour is not drawn if the specified z value is outside the viewing cube or if the 3D graph is not defined at that z value.)

Notes about Contour Plots

For a contour plot:

- You can use the cursor keys (page 25) to animate the contour plot.

- You cannot trace ([F3]) the contours themselves. However, you can trace the wire frame as seen when Style=WIRE AND CONTOUR.

- It may take awhile to evaluate the equation initially.

- Because of possible long evaluation times, you first may want to experiment with your 3D equation by using Style=WIRE FRAME. The evaluation time is much shorter. Then, after you're sure you have the correct Window variable values, use [♦] F to set Style=CONTOUR LEVELS or WIRE AND CONTOUR.

Example: Contours of a Complex Modulus Surface

The complex modulus surface given by z(a,b) = abs(f(a+b*i*)) shows all the complex zeros of any polynomial y=f(x). This theorem is well known in complex analysis theory but could not be visualized before.

Example

In this example, let f(x)=x^3+1. By substituting the general complex form x+y*i* for x, you can express the complex surface equation as z(x,y)=abs((x+y*i*)^3+1).

1. Use [MODE] to set Graph=3D.

2. Press [♦] [Y=], and define the equation:

   z1(x,y)=abs((x+y**i*)^3+1)

3. Press [♦] [WINDOW], and set the Window variables as shown.

4. Press [♦] F, turn on the axes, set Style = CONTOUR LEVELS, and return to the Window editor.

5. Press [♦] [GRAPH] to graph the equation.

   It will take awhile to evaluate the graph; so be patient. When the graph is displayed, the complex modulus surface touches the xy plane at exactly the complex zeros of the polynomial:

   $$-1, \frac{1}{2} + \frac{\sqrt{3}}{2} i, \text{ and } \frac{1}{2} - \frac{\sqrt{3}}{2} i$$

Note: For more accurate estimates, increase the xgrid and ygrid Window variables. However, this increases the graph evaluation time.

6. Press [F3], and move the trace cursor to the zero in the fourth quadrant.

   The coordinates let you estimate .428−.857*i* as the zero.

Tip: When you animate the graph, the screen changes to normal view. Use [×] to toggle between normal and expanded views.

7. Press [ESC]. Then use the cursor keys to animate the graph and view it from different eye angles.

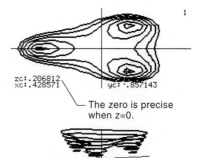

This example shows eyeθ=70, eyeφ=70, and eyeψ=0.

Implicit Plots

An implicit plot is used primarily as a way to graph 2D implicit forms that cannot be graphed in function graphing mode. Technically, an implicit plot is a 3D contour plot with a single contour drawn for z=0 only.

Explicit and Implicit Forms

In 2D function graphing mode, equations have an explicit form y=f(x), where y is unique for each value of x.

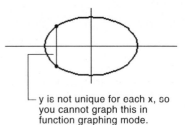

Many equations, however, have an implicit form f(x,y)=g(x,y), where you cannot explicitly solve for y in terms of x or for x in terms of y.

y is not unique for each x, so you cannot graph this in function graphing mode.

Tip: You can also graph many implicit forms if you either:

- *Express them as parametric equations. Refer to Chapter 11 in the TI-92 Guidebook.*

- *Break them into separate, explicit functions. Refer to the preview example in Chapter 3 in the TI-92 Guidebook.*

By using implicit plots in 3D graphing mode, you can graph these implicit forms without solving for y or x.

Rearrange the implicit form as an equation set to zero.

$$f(x,y)-g(x,y)=0$$

In the Y= Editor, enter the non-zero side of the equation. This is valid because an implicit plot automatically sets the equation equal to zero.

$$z1(x,y)=f(x,y)-g(x,y)$$

For example, given the ellipse equation shown to the right, enter the implicit form in the Y= Editor.

If $x^2+.5y^2=30$,
then $z1(x,y)=x^2+.5y^2-30$.

Selecting the Graph Format Style

In 3D graphing mode, define an appropriate equation and graph it as you would any 3D equation, with the following exception. Display the GRAPH FORMATS dialog box by pressing ◆ F from the Y= Editor, Window editor, or Graph screen.

Note: From the Graph screen, you can press F to switch to the other graph format styles. However, you must use ◆ F to return to IMPLICIT PLOT.

Then set:

Style = IMPLICIT PLOT

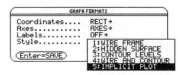

- The viewing angle is set initially so that you are viewing the plot by looking down the z axis. You can change the viewing angle as necessary.

- The plot is shown in expanded view. To switch between expanded and normal view, press ⊠.

- The Labels format is set to OFF automatically.

Note: These examples use the same x, y, and z Window variable values as a ZoomStd viewing cube. If you use ZoomStd, press Z to look down the z axis.

Style	$x^2-y^2=4$ z1(x,y)=x^2-y^2-4	sin(x)+cos(y)=$e^{(x \cdot y)}$ z1(x,y)=sin(x)+cos(y)$-e^{(x \cdot y)}$
IMPLICIT PLOT	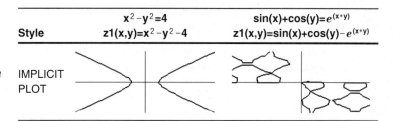	

Notes About Implicit Plots

For an implicit plot:

- The ncontour Window variable (page 27) has no affect. Only the z=0 contour is drawn, regardless of the value of ncontour. The displayed plot shows where the implicit form intersects the xy plane.

- You can use the cursor keys (page 25) to animate the plot.

- You cannot trace ([F3]) the implicit plot itself. However, you can trace the unseen wire frame graph of the 3D equation.

- It may take awhile to evaluate the equation initially.

- Because of possible long evaluation times, you first may want to experiment with your 3D equation by using Style=WIRE FRAME. The evaluation time is much shorter. Then, after you're sure you have the correct Window variable values, use ◆ F to set Style=IMPLICIT PLOT.

Example: Implicit Plot of a More Complicated Equation

You can use the IMPLICIT PLOT graph format style to plot and animate a complicated equation that cannot be graphed otherwise. Although it may take a long time to evaluate such a graph, the visual results can justify the time required.

Example

Graph the equation $\sin(x^4+y-x^3y) = .1$.

1. Use MODE to set Graph=3D.

2. Press ◆ [Y=], and define the equation:

   z1(x,y)=sin(x^4+y-x^3y)-.1

3. Press ◆ [WINDOW], and set the Window variables as shown.

4. Press ◆ F, turn on the axes, set Style = IMPLICIT PLOT, and return to the Window editor.

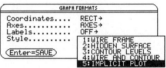

Note: For more detail, increase the xgrid and ygrid Window variables. However, this increases the graph evaluation time.

5. Press ◆ [GRAPH] to graph the equation.

   It will take awhile to evaluate the graph; so be patient.

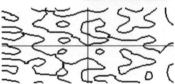

The graph shows where $\sin(x^4+y-x^3y) = .1$

Tip: When you animate the graph, the screen changes to normal view. Press ⨯ to switch between normal and expanded views.

6. Use the cursor keys to animate the graph and view it from different eye angles.

This example shows eyeθ= ⁻127.85, eyeφ=52.86, and eyeψ= ⁻18.26.

Differential Equation Graphing

Note: A differential equation is:

- *1st-order* when only 1st-order derivatives appear.
- *Ordinary* when all the derivatives are with respect to the same independent variable.

This chapter describes how to solve differential equations graphically on the TI-92 Plus. Before using this chapter, you should be familiar with Chapter 3: Basic Function Graphing in the *TI-92 Guidebook*.

The TI-92 Plus solves 1st-order systems of ordinary differential equations. For example:

y' = .001 y * (100 − y)

or coupled 1st-order differential equations such as:

y1' = ⁻y1 + 0.1 * y1 * y2
y2' = 3 * y2 − y1 * y2

You can solve higher-order equations by defining them as a system of 1st-order equations. For example:

y" + y = sin(t)　　can be defined as　　y1' = y2
　　　　　　　　　　　　　　　　　　　y2' = ⁻y1 + sin(t)

By setting appropriate initial conditions, you can graph a particular solution curve of a differential equation.

You can also graph a slope or direction field that helps you visualize the behavior of the entire family of solution curves.

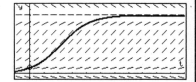

For graphing, the TI-92 Plus uses numerical methods that approximate the true solutions. The new **deSolve()** function lets you solve some differential equations symbolically. This chapter introduces **deSolve()**. Refer to Appendix A for more details.

Preview of Differential Equation Graphing

Graph the solution to the logistic 1st-order differential equation y' = .001y*(100–y). Start by drawing only the slope field. Then enter initial conditions in the Y= Editor and interactively from the Graph screen.

Steps	Keystrokes	Display
1. Display the MODE dialog box. For Graph mode, select DIFF EQUATIONS.	[MODE] ⊙ 6 [ENTER]	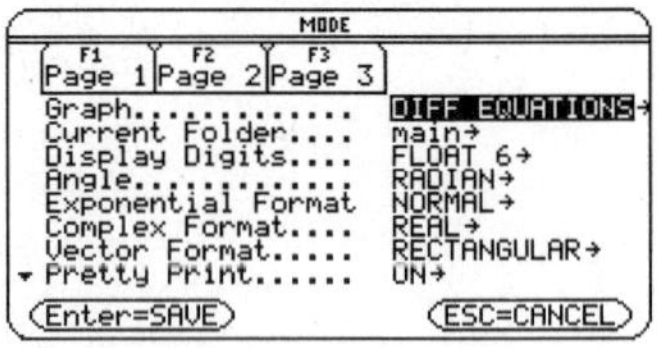
2. Display and clear the Y= Editor. Then define the 1st-order differential equation: y1'(t)=.001y1*(100–y1) *Press ⊠ to enter the ∗ shown above. Do not use implied multiplication between the variable and parentheses. If you do, it is treated as a function call.* *Leave the initial condition yi1 blank.*	♦ [Y=] [F1] 8 [ENTER] [ENTER] . 0 0 1 Y 1 ⊠ (1 0 0 [–] Y 1) [ENTER]	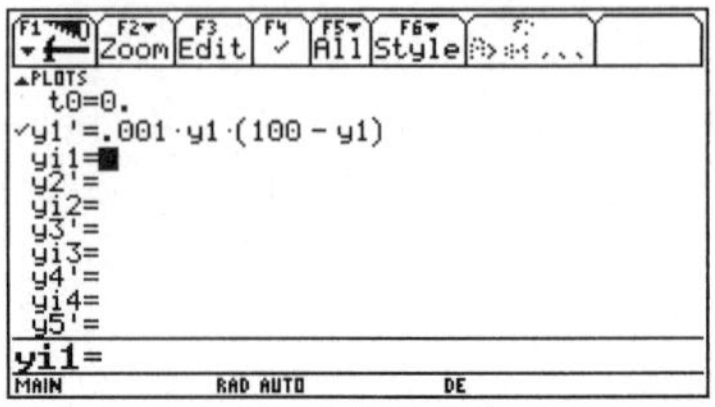 **Important:** With y1' selected, the TI-92 Plus will graph the y1 solution curve, not the derivative y1'.
3. Display the GRAPH FORMATS dialog box. Then set Axes = ON, Labels = ON, Solution Method = RK, and Fields = SLPFLD. **Important:** *To graph one differential equation, Fields must be set to SLPFLD or FLDOFF. If Fields=DIRFLD, an error occurs when you graph.*	♦ F ⊙ ⊙ ⊙ 2 ⊙ ⊙ ⊙ 2 ⊙ ⊙ 1 ⊙ ⊙ 1 [ENTER]	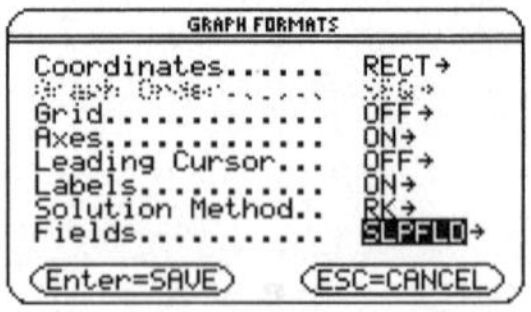
4. Display the Window Editor, and set the Window variables as shown to the right.	♦ [WINDOW] 0 ⊙ 10 ⊙ . 1 ⊙ 0 ⊙ [–] 10 ⊙ 110 ⊙ 10 ⊙ [–] 10 ⊙ 120 ⊙ 10 ⊙ 0 ⊙ . 001 ⊙ 2 0	t0=0. tmax=10. tstep=.1 tplot=0. xmin=-10. xmax=110. xscl=10. ymin=-10. ymax=120. yscl=10. ncurves=0. diftol=.001 fldres=20.
5. Display the Graph screen. *Because you did not specify an initial condition, only the slope field is drawn (as specified by Fields=SLPFLD in the GRAPH FORMATS dialog box).*	♦ [GRAPH]	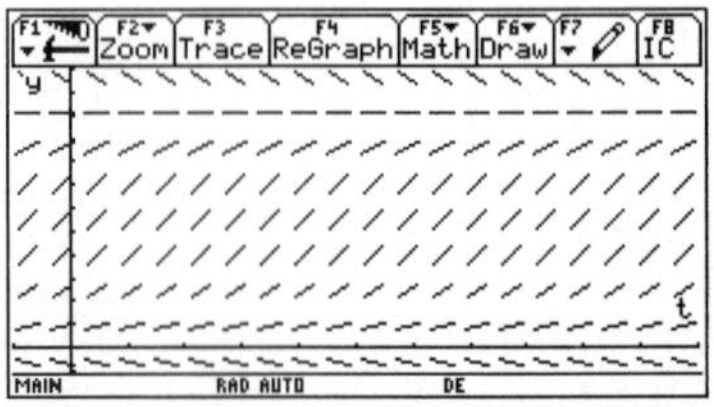

Steps	Keystrokes	Display

6. Return to the Y= Editor and enter an initial condition:

   yi1=10

   Keystrokes: ◆ [Y=]
   ENTER 1 0
   ENTER

   Display:
   ```
   F1▼▼ F2▼ F3 F4 F5▼ F6▼
   ▼ Zoom Edit ✓ All Style ▷ ...
   ▲PLOTS
     t0=0.
   ✓y1'=.001·y1·(100 – y1)
     yi1=10
   ```

7. Return to the Graph screen.

   Initial conditions entered in the Y= Editor always occur at t0. The graph begins at the initial condition and plots to the right. Then it plots to the left.

   Keystrokes: ◆ [GRAPH]

   The initial condition is marked with a circle.

8. Return to the Y= Editor and change yi1 to enter two initial conditions as a list:

   yi1={10,20}

   Keystrokes: ◆ [Y=] ⊙
   ENTER 2nd [{]
   1 0 , 2 0 2nd [}]
   ENTER

   Display:
   ```
   F1▼▼ F2▼ F3 F4 F5▼ F6▼
   ▼ Zoom Edit ✓ All Style ▷ ...
   ▲PLOTS
     t0=0.
   ✓y1'=.001·y1·(100 – y1)
     yi1={10  20}
   ```

9. Return to the Graph screen.

   Keystrokes: ◆ [GRAPH]

10. Use F8 IC to select an initial condition interactively. When prompted, enter t=40 and y1=45.

    When selecting an initial condition interactively, you can specify a value for t other than the t0 value entered in the Y= Editor or Window Editor.

    Instead of entering t and y1 after pressing F8, you can move the cursor to a point on the screen and then press ENTER.

    You can use F3 to trace curves for initial conditions specified in the Y= Editor. However, you cannot trace the curve for an initial condition selected interactively.

    Keystrokes: F8
    4 0 ENTER
    4 5 ENTER

    Initial Conditions=?
    t=40   y1=45

Overview of Steps in Graphing Differential Equations

To graph differential equations, use the same general steps used for y(x) functions as described in Chapter 3: Basic Function Graphing in the *TI-92 Guidebook*. Any differences are described on the following pages.

Graphing Differential Equations

Set Graph mode ([MODE]) to DIFF EQUATIONS. Also set Angle mode, if necessary.

Define equations and, optionally, initial conditions on Y= Editor ([♦] [Y=]).

Tip: *To turn off any stat data plots, press [F5] 5 or use [F4] to deselect them. Refer to Chapter 9 in the TI-92 Guidebook.*

Select ([F4]) which defined equations to graph.

Set the display style ([F6]) for an equation, if necessary.

Note: *The Fields format is critical, depending on the order of the equation (page 55).*

Set the graph format ([♦] F or [F1] 9). Solution Method and Fields are unique to differential equations.

Note: *Valid Axes settings depend on the Fields format (pages 48 and 55).*

Set the axes ([F7]), as applicable, depending on the Fields format.

Note: *Depending on the Solution Method and Fields formats, different Window variables are displayed.*

Tip: *[F2] Zoom also changes the viewing window.*

Define the viewing window ([♦] [WINDOW]).

Graph the equations ([♦] [GRAPH]).

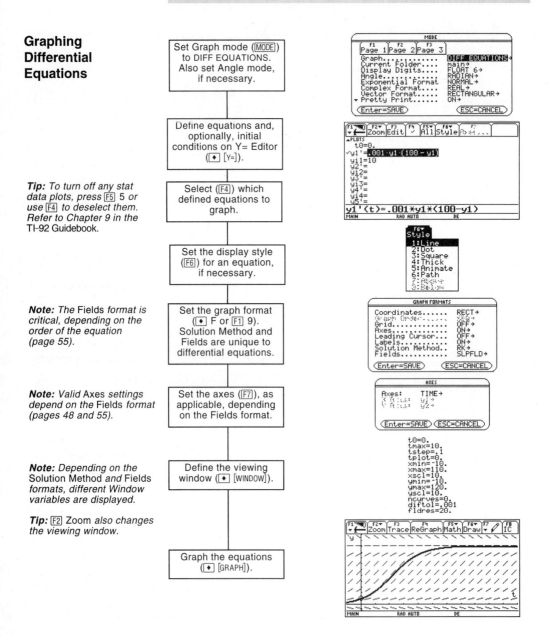

Differences in Diff Equations and Function Graphing

> This chapter assumes that you already know how to graph y(x) functions as described in Chapter 3: Basic Function Graphing in the *TI-92 Guidebook*. This section describes the differences.

Setting the Graph Mode

Use [MODE] to set Graph = DIFF EQUATIONS before you define differential equations or set Window variables. The Y= Editor and the Window Editor let you enter information for the *current* Graph mode setting only.

Defining Differential Equations on the Y= Editor

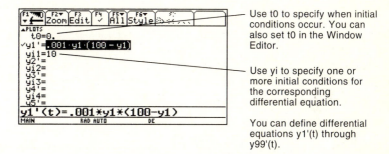

Use t0 to specify when initial conditions occur. You can also set t0 in the Window Editor.

Use yi to specify one or more initial conditions for the corresponding differential equation.

You can define differential equations y1'(t) through y99'(t).

*Tip: You can use the **Define** command from the Home screen to define functions and equations.*

When entering equations in the Y= Editor, do not use y(t) formats to refer to results. For example:

Enter: y1' = .001y1*(100−y1)
Not: y1' = .001y1(t)*(100−y1(t))

Do not use implied multiplication between a variable and parenthetical expression. If you do, it is treated as a function call.

Only 1st-order equations can be entered in the Y= Editor. To graph 2nd- or higher-order equations, you must enter them as a system of 1st-order equations. For information, refer to page 44.

For detailed information about setting initial conditions, refer to page 42.

Selecting Differential Equations

You can use [F4] to select a differential equation, but not its initial condition.

Important: Selecting y1' will graph the y1 solution curve, not the derivative y1'.

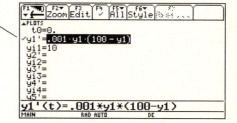

Selecting the Display Style

With [F6] Style, only the Line, Dot, Square, Thick, Animate, and Path styles are available. Dot and Square mark only those discrete values (in tstep increments) at which a differential equation is plotted.

**Setting Graph
Formats**

From the Y= Editor, Window
Editor, or Graph screen, press
◆ F.

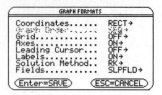

The formats affected by differential equations are:

Graph format	Description
Graph Order	Not available.
Solution Method	Specifies the method used to solve the differential equations.

- RK — Runge-Kutta method. For information about the algorithm used for this method, refer to Appendix B.

- EULER — Euler method.

The method lets you choose either greater accuracy or speed. Typically, RK is more accurate than EULER but takes longer to find the solution.

Important: *The* Fields *graph format is critical in successfully graphing differential equations. Refer to "Troubleshooting with the Fields Graph Format" on page 55.*

Tip: *If you press* ENTER *while a slope or direction field is being drawn, the graph pauses after the field is drawn but before the solutions are plotted. Press* ENTER *again to continue.*

Tip: *To cancel graphing, press* ON *.*

Fields	Specifies whether to draw a field for the differential equation.

- SLPFLD — Draws a slope field for only one 1st-order equation, with t on the x axis and the solution on the y axis. To see how a slope field is used, refer to the example starting on page 34.

- DIRFLD — Draws a direction field for only one 2nd-order equation (or system of two 1st-order equations), with axes determined by the custom axes settings. To see how a direction field is used, refer to the example starting on page 45.

- FLDOFF — Does not display a field. This is valid for equations of any order, but you must use it for 3rd- or higher-order. You must enter the same number of initial conditions for all equations in the Y= Editor (page 42). For an example, refer to page 47.

Setting Axes

In the Y= Editor, F7 Axes may or may not be available, depending on the current graph format.

If F7 is available, you can select the axes that are used to graph the differential equations. For more information, refer to page 48.

Axes	Description
TIME	Plots t on the x axis and y (the solutions to the selected differential equations) on the y axis.
CUSTOM	Lets you select the x and y axes.

Window Variables

Differential equation graphs use the following Window variables. Depending on the Solution Method and Fields graph formats, not all of these variables are listed in the Window Editor (◆ [WINDOW]) at the same time.

Variable	Description
t0	Time at which the initial conditions entered in the Y= Editor occur. You can set t0 in the Window Editor and Y= Editor. (If you set t0 in the Y= Editor, tplot is set to the same value automatically.)
tmax, tstep	Used to determine the t values where the equations are plotted: y'(t0) y'(t0+tstep) y'(t0+2∗tstep) ... not to exceed ... y'(tmax) If Fields = SLPFLD, tmax is ignored. Equations are plotted from t0 to both edges of the screen in tstep increments.
tplot	First t value plotted. If this is not a tstep increment, plotting begins at the next tstep increment. In some situations, the first points evaluated and plotted starting at t0 may not be interesting visually. By setting tplot greater than t0, you can start the plot at the interesting area, which speeds up the graphing time and avoids unnecessary clutter on the Graph screen.

Note: If tmax < t0, tstep *must be negative.*

Note: If Fields=SLPFLD, tplot *is ignored and is assumed to be the same as* t0.

Window Variables (Continued)

xmin, xmax, ymin, ymax	Boundaries of the viewing window.
xscl, yscl	Distance between tick marks on the x and y axes.
ncurves	Number of solution curves (0 through 10) that will be drawn automatically if you do not specify an initial condition. By default, ncurves = 0.

Note: *For information about how the Fields graph format affects whether ncurves is used, refer to page 42.*

When ncurves is used, t0 is set temporarily at the middle of the screen and initial conditions are distributed evenly along the y axis, where:

$$\text{increment} = \frac{\text{ymax} - \text{ymin}}{\text{ncurves} + 1}$$

The y values for the initial conditions are:

ymin + increment
ymin + 2∗(increment)
$\vdots$
ymin + ncurves∗(increment)

diftol	(Solution Method = RK only) Tolerance used by the RK method to help select a step size for solving the equation; must be $\geq 1\text{E}^-14$.
fldres	(Fields = SLPFLD or DIRFLD only) Number of columns (1 through 80) used to draw a slope or direction field across the full width of the screen.
Estep	(Solution Method = EULER only) Euler iterations between tstep values; must be an integer >0. For more accuracy, you can increase Estep without plotting additional points.
dtime	(Fields = DIRFLD only) Point in time at which a direction field is drawn.

Standard values (set when you select 6:ZoomStd from the [F2] Zoom toolbar menu) are:

t0 = 0.	xmin = ⁻1.	ymin = ⁻10.	ncurves = 0.
tmax = 10.	xmax = 10.	ymax = 10.	diftol = .001
tstep = .1	xscl = 1.	yscl = 1.	Estep = 1.
tplot = 0.			fldres = 20.
			dtime = 0.

You may need to change the standard values for the t variables to ensure that sufficient points are plotted.

The fldpic System Variable

When a slope or direction field is drawn, a picture of the field is stored automatically to a system variable named fldpic. If you perform an operation that regraphs the plotted equations but does not affect the field, the TI–92 Plus reuses the picture in fldpic instead of having to redraw the field. This can speed up the regraphing time significantly.

fldpic is deleted automatically when you exit the differential equation graphing mode or when you display a graph with Fields = FLDOFF.

Exploring a Graph

As in function graphing, you can explore a graph by using the following tools. Any displayed coordinates are shown in rectangular or polar form as set in the graph format.

Tool	For Differential Equation Graphs:
Free-Moving Cursor	Works just as it does for function graphs.
F2 Zoom	Works just as it does for function graphs.
	• Only x (xmin, xmax, xscl) and y (ymin, ymax, yscl) Window variables are affected.
	• The t Window variables (t0, tmax, tstep, tplot) are not affected unless you select 6:ZoomStd (which sets all Window variables to their standard values).
F3 Trace	Lets you move the cursor along the curve one tstep at a time. To move approximately ten plotted points at a time, press 2nd ⊙ or 2nd ⊙.
	If you enter initial conditions in the Y= Editor or let the ncurves Window variable plot curves automatically, you can trace the curves. If you use F8 IC from the Graph screen to select initial conditions interactively, you cannot trace the curves.
	QuickCenter applies to all directions. If you move the cursor off the screen (top or bottom, left or right), press ENTER to center the viewing window on the cursor location.
F5 Math	Only 1:Value is available.
	• With TIME axes, the y(t) solution value (represented by yc) is displayed for a specified t value.
	• With CUSTOM axes, the values that correspond to x and y depend on the axes you choose.

Tip: During a trace, you can move the cursor to a particular point by typing a value for t and pressing ENTER.

Tip: You can use QuickCenter at any time during a trace, even if the cursor is still on the screen.

Setting the Initial Conditions

You can enter initial conditions in the Y= Editor, let the TI-92 Plus calculate initial conditions automatically, or select them interactively from the Graph screen.

Entering Initial Conditions in the Y= Editor

You can specify one or more initial conditions in the Y= Editor. To specify more than one, enter them as a list enclosed in braces { } and separated by commas.

To enter initial conditions for the y1' equation, use the yi1 line; etc.

```
F1 ▾▾⎓  F2▾ Zoom  F3 Edit  F4 ✓  F5▾ All  F6▾ Style  F7 ⁞▷⁞⁝⁝⁌
  ▴PLOTS
    t0=0.
  ✓y1'=.001·y1·(100−y1)
    yi1=10
```

To specify when the initial conditions occur, use t0. This is also the first t evaluated for the graph.

To graph a family of solutions, enter a list of initial conditions.

```
F1 ▾▾⎓  F2▾ Zoom  F3 Edit  F4 ✓  F5▾ All  F6▾ Style  F7 ⁞▷⁞⁝⁝⁌
  ▴PLOTS
    t0=0.
  ✓y1'=.001·y1·(100−y1)
    yi1={10  20}
```

Enter {10,20} even though {10 20} is displayed.

Note: For information about defining a system for higher-order equations, refer to page 44.

For a 2nd- or higher-order differential equation, you must define a system of 1st-order equations in the Y= Editor.

If you enter initial conditions, you must enter the same number of initial conditions for each equation in the system. Otherwise, a Dimension error occurs.

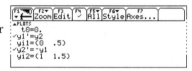

```
F1 ▾▾⎓  F2▾ Zoom  F3 Edit  F4 ✓  F5▾ All  F6▾ Style  F7 Axes...
  ▴PLOTS
    t0=0.
  ✓y1'=y2
    yi1={0   .5}
  ✓y2'=-y1
    yi2={1   1.5}
```

If You Do Not Enter an Initial Condition in the Y= Editor

If you do not enter initial conditions, the ncurves Window variable (◆ [WINDOW]) specifies the number of solution curves graphed automatically. By default, ncurves = 0. You can enter a value from 0 through 10. However, the Fields graph format (◆ F) and the Axes setting determine whether ncurves is used.

Tip: Without entering initial conditions, use SLPFLD (with ncurves=0) or DIRFLD to display a slope or direction field only.

Note: SLPFLD is for a single 1st-order equation only. DIRFLD is for a 2nd-order equation (or system of two 1st-order equations) only.

If Fields =	Then:
SLPFLD	Uses ncurves, if not set to 0, to graph curves.
DIRFLD	Ignores ncurves. Does not graph any curves.
FLDOFF	Uses ncurves if Axes = TIME (or if Axes = Custom and the x axis is t). Otherwise, a Diff Eq setup error occurs.

When ncurves is used, t0 is set temporarily at the middle of the Graph screen. However, the value of t0 as set in the Y= Editor or Window Editor is not changed.

Selecting an Initial Condition Interactively from the Graph Screen

When a differential equation is graphed (regardless of whether a solution curve is displayed), you can select a point on the Graph screen and use it as an initial condition.

Note: With SLPFLD or DIRFLD, you can select initial conditions interactively regardless of whether you enter initial conditions in the Y= Editor.

If Fields =	Do this:

SLPFLD
– or –
DIRFLD
	1. Press F8.
	
	2. Specify an initial condition. Either:
	
	• Move the cursor to the applicable point and press ENTER.
	
	– or –
	
	• For each of the two coordinates, type a value and press ENTER.
	
	   – For SLPFLD (1st-order only), enter values for t0 and y(t0).
	
	   – For DIRFLD (2nd-order or system of two 1st-order equations only), enter values for both y(t0) initial conditions, where t0 is the value set in the Y= Editor or Window Editor.
	
	A circle marks the initial condition and the solution curve is drawn.

Note: With FLDOFF, you can select initial conditions interactively. However, if three or more equations are entered, you must enter a single value (not a list) as the initial condition for each equation in the Y= Editor. Otherwise, a Dimension error occurs when graphing.

If Fields =	Do this:
FLDOFF	1. Press F8. You are prompted to select the axes for which you want to enter initial conditions. INTERACTIVE INITIAL CONDITIONS X Axis: t→ — t is a valid selection. It Y Axis: y1→ will let you specify a (Enter=SAVE) (ESC=CANCEL) value for t0. Your selections will be used as the axes for the graph. 2. You can accept the defaults or change them. Then press ENTER. 3. Specify an initial condition as described for SLPFLD or DIRFLD.

Note about Tracing a Solution Curve

When you enter initial conditions in the Y= Editor or let ncurves graph solution curves automatically, you can use F3 to trace the curves.

However, you cannot trace a curve drawn by selecting an initial condition interactively. These curves are drawn, not plotted.

Defining a System for Higher-Order Equations

> In the Y= Editor, you must enter all differential equations as 1st-order equations. If you have an nth-order equation, you must transform it into a system of n 1st-order equations.

Transforming an Equation into a 1st-Order System

A system of equations can be defined in various ways, but the following is a general method.

1. Rewrite the original differential equation as necessary.

    $$y'' + y' + y = e^x$$

    a. Solve for the highest-ordered derivative.

    $$y'' = e^x - y' - y$$

    b. Express it in terms of y and t.

    $$y'' = e^t - y' - y$$

    Note: *To produce a 1st-order equation, the right side must contain non-derivative variables only.*

    c. On the right side of the equation only, substitute to eliminate any references to derivative values.

In place of:	Substitute:
y	y1
y'	y2
y"	y3
y'"	y4
$y^{(4)}$	y5
⋮	⋮

    Do not substitute on the left side at this time.

    $$y'' = e^t - y2 - y1$$

    d. On the left side of the equation, substitute for the derivative value as shown below.

In place of:	Substitute:
y'	y1'
y"	y2'
y'"	y3'
$y^{(4)}$	y4'
⋮	⋮

    $$y2' = e^t - y2 - y1$$

    Note: *Based on the above substitutions, the y' lines in the Y= Editor represent:*
    y1' = y'
    y2' = y"
    etc.
    So, this example's 2nd-order equation is entered on the y2' line.

2. On the applicable lines in the Y= Editor, define the system of equations as:

    y1' = y2
    y2' = y3
    y3' = y4
    – up to –
    yn' = *your nth-order equation*

    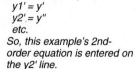

In a system such as this, the solution to the y1' equation is the solution to the nth-order equation. You may want to deselect any other equations in the system.

Example of a 2nd-Order Equation

The 2nd-order differential equation $y''+y = 0$ represents a simple harmonic oscillator. Transform this into a system of equations for the Y= Editor. Then, graph the solution for initial conditions $y(0) = 0$ and $y'(0) = 1$.

Example

1. Press $\boxed{\text{MODE}}$ and set Graph=DIFF EQUATIONS.

2. Define a system of equations for the 2nd-order equation as described on page 44.

   Rewrite the equation and make the necessary substitutions.

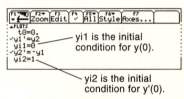

$y'' + y = 0$
$y'' = {}^-y$
$y'' = {}^-y1$
$y2' = {}^-y1$

Note: *t0 is the time at which the initial conditions occur. It is also the first t evaluated for the graph. By default, t0=0.*

3. In the Y= Editor ($\boxed{\bullet}$ [Y=]), enter the system of equations.

4. Enter the initial conditions:

   yi1=0 and yi2=1

yi1 is the initial condition for y(0).

yi2 is the initial condition for y'(0).

Important: *For 2nd-order equations, you must set Fields=DIRFLD or FLDOFF.*

5. Press $\boxed{\bullet}$ F and set Axes = ON, Labels = OFF, Solution Method = RK, and Fields = DIRFLD.

Important: *Fields=DIRFLD cannot plot a time axis. An Invalid Axes error occurs if Axes=TIME or if t is set as a CUSTOM axis.*

6. In the Y= Editor, press $\boxed{\text{F7}}$ and make sure Axes = CUSTOM with y1 and y2 as the axes.

7. In the Window Editor ($\boxed{\bullet}$ [WINDOW]), set the Window variables.

t0=0.	xmin=⁻2.	ncurves=0.
tmax=10.	xmax=2.	diftol=.001
tstep=.1	xscl=1.	fldres=20.
tplot=0.	ymin=⁻2.	dtime=0.
	ymax=2.	
	yscl=1.	

8. Display the Graph screen ($\boxed{\bullet}$ [GRAPH]).

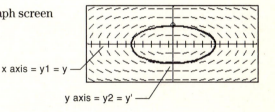

x axis = y1 = y

y axis = y2 = y'

If you select ZoomSqr ($\boxed{\text{F2}}$ 5), you can see that the phase-plane orbit is actually a circle. However, ZoomSqr will change your Window variables.

Example of a 2nd-Order Equation (Continued)

To examine this harmonic oscillator in more detail, use a split screen to graph the manner in which y and y' change with respect to time (t).

Note: To display different graphs in both parts of a split screen, you must use the 2-graph mode.

9. Press MODE and change the mode settings on Page 2 as shown. Then close the MODE dialog box, which redraws the graph.

    Split Screen = LEFT-RIGHT
    Split 1 App = Graph
    Split 2 App = Y=Editor
    Number of Graphs = 2
    Graph 2 = DIFF EQUATIONS
    Split Screen Ratio = 1:1

10. Press 2nd [⊞] to switch to the right side of the split screen.

11. Use F4 to select y1' and y2'.

    The right side uses the same equations as the left side. However, no equations are selected initially in the right side.

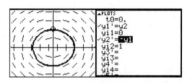

Important: Because Fields=DIRFLD cannot plot a time axis, you must change the Fields setting. FLDOFF turns off all fields.

12. Press ♦ F and set Fields = FLDOFF.

13. In the Y= Editor, press F7 and make sure Axes = TIME.

Note: When you enter 2-graph mode, Window variables for the right side are set to their defaults.

14. In the Window Editor, change ymin and ymax as shown to the right.

    ymin= -2.
    ymax=2.

15. Press ♦ [GRAPH] to display the Graph screen for graph #2.

    The left side shows the phase-plane orbit. The right side shows the solution curve and its derivative.

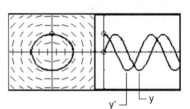

y' ⌐ └ y

Split Screen = FULL

16. To return to a full screen of the original graph, press 2nd [⊞] to switch to the left side. Then press MODE and change the Split Screen setting.

Example of a 3rd-Order Equation

For the 3rd-order differential equation y'''+2y''+2y'+y = sin(x), write a system of equations to enter in the Y= Editor. Then graph the solution as a function of time. Use initial conditions y(0) = 0, y'(0) = 1, and y''(0) = 1.

Example

1. Press MODE and set Graph=DIFF EQUATIONS.

2. Define a system of equations for the 3rd-order equation as described on page 44.

   Rewrite the equation and make the necessary substitutions.

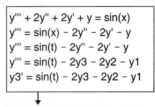

$$y''' + 2y'' + 2y' + y = \sin(x)$$
$$y''' = \sin(x) - 2y'' - 2y' - y$$
$$y''' = \sin(t) - 2y'' - 2y' - y$$
$$y''' = \sin(t) - 2y3 - 2y2 - y1$$
$$y3' = \sin(t) - 2y3 - 2y2 - y1$$

Note: *t0 is the time at which the initial conditions occur. By default, t0=0.*

3. In the Y= Editor (◆ [Y=]), enter the system of equations.

4. Enter the initial conditions:

   yi1=0, yi2=1, and yi3=1

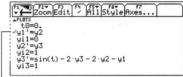

Important: The solution to the y1' equation is the solution to the 3rd-order equation.

5. Be sure that only y1' is selected. Use F4 to deselect any other equations.

Important: *For 3rd- or higher-order equations, you must set Fields=FLDOFF. Otherwise, an Undefined variable error occurs when graphing.*

6. Press ◆ F and set Axes = ON, Labels = ON, Solution Method = RK, and Fields = FLDOFF.

Note: *With Axes=TIME, the solution to the selected equation is plotted against time (t).*

7. In the Y= Editor, press F7 and set Axes = TIME.

8. In the Window Editor (◆ [WINDOW]), set the Window variables.

t0=0.　　xmin=⁻1.　ncurves=0.
tmax=10.　xmax=10.　diftol=.001
tstep=.1　xscl=1.
tplot=0.　ymin=⁻3.
　　　　　ymax=3.
　　　　　yscl=1.

Tip: *To find the solution at a particular time, use F3 to trace the graph.*

9. Display the Graph screen (◆ [GRAPH]).

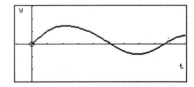

Setting Axes for Time or Custom Plots

Setting the axes can give you great flexibility in graphing differential equations. Custom axes are particularly effective for showing different kinds of relationships.

Displaying the AXES Dialog Box

From the Y= Editor, press F7.

If Fields = SLPFLD, F7 Axes is unavailable.

Item	Description
Axes	TIME — Plots t on the x axis and y (solutions to all selected differential equations) on the y axis.
	CUSTOM — Lets you select the x and y axes.
X Axis, Y Axis	Active only when Axes = CUSTOM, these let you select what you want to plot on the x and y axes.

Axes:
X Axis:
Y Axis:

1:t
2:y
3:y'
4:y1
5:y1'
6:y2
7:y2'
8:y3
9:y3'
A:y4
B:y4'
C:y5

Enter=SA   CANCEL

Note: *t is not valid for* X Axis *when* Fields=DIRFLD. *If you select t, an* Invalid axes *error occurs when graphing.*

t — time

y — solutions (y1, y2, etc.) of all selected differential equations

y' — values of all selected differential equations (y1', y2', etc.)

y1, y2, etc. — the solution to the corresponding differential equation, regardless of whether that equation is selected

y1', y2', etc. — the value of the right-hand side of the corresponding differential equation, regardless of whether that equation is selected

Example of Time and Custom Axes

Using the predator-prey model from biology, determine the numbers of rabbits and foxes that maintain population equilibrium in a certain region. Graph the solution using both time and custom axes.

Predator-Prey Model

Use the two coupled 1st-order differential equations:

$y1' = {}^-y1 + 0.1y1 * y2$ and $y2' = 3y2 - y1 * y2$

where:

y1	=	Population of foxes
yi1	=	Initial population of foxes (2)
y2	=	Population of rabbits
yi2	=	Initial population of rabbits (5)

1. Use [MODE] to set Graph = DIFF EQUATIONS.

Tip: *To speed up graphing times, clear any other equations in the Y= Editor. With FLDOFF, all equations are evaluated even if they are not selected.*

2. In the Y= Editor ([♦] [Y=]), define the differential equations and enter the initial conditions.

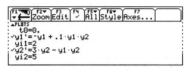

3. Press [♦] F and set Axes = ON, Labels = ON, Solution Method = RK, and Fields = FLDOFF.

4. In the Y= Editor, press [F7] and set Axes = TIME.

5. In the Window Editor ([♦] [WINDOW]), set the Window variables.

t0=0.	xmin=-1.	ncurves=0.
tmax=10.	xmax=10.	diftol=.001
tstep=π/24	xscl=5.	
tplot=0.	ymin=-10.	
	ymax=40.	
	yscl=5.	

6. Graph the differential equations ([♦] [GRAPH]).

Tip: *Use ⊙ and ⊙ to move the trace cursor between the curves for y1 and y2.*

7. Press [F3] to trace. Then press 3 [ENTER] to see the number of foxes (yc for y1) and rabbits (yc for y2) at t=3.

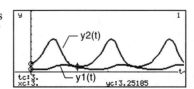

Example of Time and Custom Axes (Continued)

Note: *In this example, DIRFLD is used for two related differential equations that do not represent a 2nd-order equation.*

8. Return to the Y= Editor. Then press ● F and set Fields = DIRFLD.

9. Press F7 and confirm that the axes are set as shown.

10. In the Y= Editor, clear the initial conditions for yi1 and yi2.

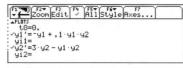

11. Return to the Graph screen, which displays only the direction field.

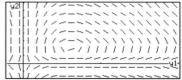

Tip: *Use a list to specify more than one initial condition.*

12. To graph a family of solutions, return to the Y= Editor and enter the initial conditions shown below.

    yi1={2,6,7} and yi2={5,12,18}

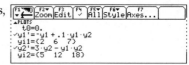

13. Return to the Graph screen, which displays a curve for each pair of initial conditions.

Tip: *Use 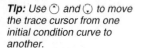 and to move the trace cursor from one initial condition curve to another.*

14. Press F3 to trace. Then press 3 ENTER to see the number of foxes (xc) and rabbits (yc) at t=3.

    Because t0=0 and tmax=10, you can trace in the range 0≤t≤10.

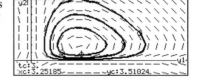

Example Comparison of RK and Euler

Consider a logistic growth model dP/dt = .001∗P∗(100−P), with the initial condition P(0) = 10. Use the new **BldData** instruction to compare the graphing points calculated by the RK and Euler solution methods. Then plot those points along with a graph of the equation's exact solution.

Example

1. Press MODE and set Graph=DIFF EQUATIONS.

2. Express the 1st-order equation in terms of y1' and y1.

   y1'=.001y1∗(100−y1)

   Do not use implied multiplication between ─── the variable and parentheses. If you do, it is treated as a function call.

Tip: *To speed up graphing times, clear any other equations in the Y= Editor. With FLDOFF, all equations are evaluated even if they are not selected.*

3. Enter the equation in the Y= Editor (◆ [Y=]).

4. Enter the initial condition:

   yi1=10

```
┌─F1──┐F2─┐F3─┐F4─┐F5─┐F6─┐F7
│ ▾─▾ │Zoom│Edit│ ✓ │All│Style│▶ ⋯ ⋯
├─PLOTS─────────────────────────
├─ t0=0.
│✓y1'=.001·y1·(100 − y1)
│  yi1=10
```

   └─ t0 is the time at which the initial condition occurs. By default, t0=0.

5. Press ◆ F and set Solution Method = RK and Fields = FLDOFF.

```
┌──────GRAPH FORMATS──────┐
│ Coordinates...... RECT→ │
│ ░░░░░░ ░░░░░░.... ░░░→  │
│ Grid............ OFF→    │
│ Axes............ ON→     │
│ Leading Cursor... OFF→   │
│ Labels.......... ON→     │
│ Solution Method.. ▓▓→    │
│ Fields.......... FLDOFF→ │
├─────────────────────────┤
│ ⟨Enter=SAVE⟩  ⟨ESC=CANCEL⟩│
```

6. In the Window Editor (◆ [WINDOW]), set the Window variables.

   t0=0.   xmin=⁻1.   ncurves=0.
   tmax=100.   xmax=100.   diftol=.001
   ┌─ tstep=1.   xscl=1.
   │ tplot=0.   ymin=⁻10.
   │   ymax=10.
   │   yscl=1.
   │
   └─ **Important:** Change tstep from .1 (its default) to 1. Otherwise, **BldData** calculates too many rows for the data variable and a Dimension error occurs.

Note: *You do not need to graph the equation before using **BldData**. For more information about **BldData**, refer to Appendix A.*

7. In the Home screen (◆ [HOME]), use **BldData** to create a data variable containing the RK graphing points.

```
┌──────────────────────────┐
│ BldData rklog            │
└──────────────────────────┘
```

8. Return to the Y= Editor, press ◆ F, and set Solution Method = EULER.

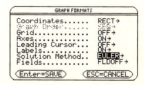

Example Comparison of RK and Euler (Continued)

9. Return to the Home screen, and use **BldData** to create a data variable containing the Euler graphing points.

Note: errorlog *lets you combine the data in* rklog *and* eulerlog *so that you can view the two sets of data side by side.*

10. Use the Data/Matrix Editor ([APPS] 6 3) to create a new data variable named errorlog.

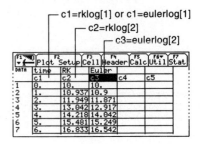

Note: rklog[1] *and* rklog[2] *refer to column 1 and 2 in* rklog, *respectively. Likewise with* eulerlog[2].

Tip: Scroll through the data variable to see how the RK and Euler values differ for the same time value.

11. In this new data variable, define the c1, c2, and c3 column headers to refer to data in rklog and eulerlog. Also, enter column titles as shown.

To define a column header, move the cursor to that column, press [F4], type the reference expression (such as rklog[1] for c1), and press [ENTER].

- c1=rklog[1] or c1=eulerlog[1]
- c2=rklog[2]
- c3=eulerlog[2]

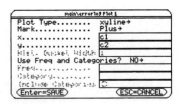

12. In the Data/Matrix Editor, press [F2]. Then press [F1] and define Plot 1 for the RK data, as shown to the right.

13. Define Plot 2 for the Euler data. Use the values shown to the right.

Plot Type=xyline
Mark=Cross
x=c1
y=c3

14. Return to the Y= Editor, press [MODE], and set Graph = FUNCTION.

Note: To see how to use **deSolve()** *to find this exact, general solution, refer to page 54.*

15. The exact solution to the differential equation is given below. Enter it as y1.

$$y1 = (100*e^{(x/10)})/(e^{(x/10)}+9)$$

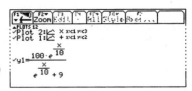

You can use ⊙ to scroll up to see Plot 1 and Plot 2.

16. In the Window Editor, set the Window variables.

xmin=⁻10.   ymin=⁻10.   xres=2.
xmax=100.   ymax=120.
xscl=10.   yscl=10.

Note: *The fuzzy line on the graph indicates differences between the RK and Euler values.*

17. Display the Graph screen (◆ [GRAPH]).

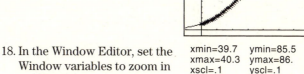

18. In the Window Editor, set the Window variables to zoom in so that you can examine the differences in more detail.

xmin=39.7   ymin=85.5   xres=2.
xmax=40.3   ymax=86.
xscl=.1   yscl=.1

19. Return to the Graph screen.

20. Press [F3] to trace, and then press ⊙ or ⊙ until y1 is selected. (1 shows in upper right corner.) Then enter 40.

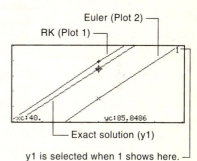

By moving the trace cursor to trace each solution to xc = 40, you can find that:

• The exact solution (y1) is 85.8486, rounded to six digits.

• The RK solution (Plot 1) is 85.8952.

• The Euler solution (Plot 2) is 85.6527.

You can also use the Data/Matrix Editor to open the errorlog data variable and scroll to time = 40.

Example of the deSolve( ) Function

The new **deSolve( )** function lets you solve many 1st- and 2nd-order ordinary differential equations exactly.

Example

For a general solution, use the following syntax. For a particular solution, refer to Appendix A.

deSolve(*1stOr2ndOrderODE*, *independentVar*, *dependentVar***)**

Using the logistic 1st-order differential equation from the example on page 34, find the general solution for y with respect to t.

Tip: For maximum accuracy, use 1/1000 instead of .001. A floating-point number can introduce round-off errors.

deSolve(y' = 1/1000 y*(100−y),t,y)

└─ Do not use implied multiplication between the variable and parentheses. If you do, it will be treated as a function call.

└─ For ', type [2nd] B.

Note: This example does not involve graphing, so you can use any Graph mode.

Before using **deSolve( )**, clear any existing t and y variables. Otherwise, an error occurs.

1. In the Home screen ([♦] [HOME]), use **deSolve( )** to find the general solution.

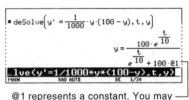

@1 represents a constant. You may get a different constant (@2, etc.).

2. Use the solution to define a function.

   a. Press ⊙ to highlight the solution in the history area. Then press [ENTER] to autopaste it into the entry line.

Tip: Press [2nd] ⊙ to move to the beginning of the entry line.

   b. Insert the **Define** instruction at the beginning of the line. Then press [ENTER].

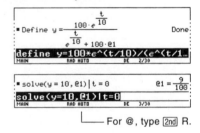

Note: If you got a different constant (@2, etc.), solve for that constant.

3. For an initial condition y=10 with t=0, use **solve( )** to find the @1 constant.

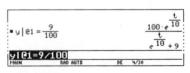

└─ For @, type [2nd] R.

4. Evaluate the general solution (y) with the constant @1=9/100 to obtain the particular solution shown.

You can also use **deSolve( )** to solve this problem directly. Enter:

deSolve(y' = 1/1000 y*(100−y) and y(0)=10,t,y)

Troubleshooting with the Fields Graph Format

If you have difficulties graphing a differential equation, this section can help you correct the problem. Many problems may be related to your Fields graph format setting.

Setting the Fields Graph Format

From the Y= Editor, Window Editor, or Graph screen, press ♦ F.

What Order Equation Are You Graphing?

If the equation is:	Valid Fields settings are:
1st-order	SLPFLD or FLDOFF
2nd-order (system of two 1st-order equations)	DIRFLD or FLDOFF
3rd- or higher-order (system of three or more 1st-order equations)	FLDOFF

Because Fields = SLPFLD is the default setting, a common error message is shown to the right.

When you see this or any other error message:

- For your order of equation, use the previous table to find the valid Fields settings. Change to the applicable setting.

- For a particular Fields setting, check the following for information that applies to that setting.

Fields=SLPFLD

In the Y= Editor	Use F4 to select one and only one 1st-order equation. You can enter multiple equations, but only one at a time can be selected.
	The selected equation must not refer to any other equation in the Y= Editor. For example:

If y1'=y2, an Undefined variable error occurs when you graph.

```
              ERROR
Undefined variable
  (Enter=GOTO)  (ESC=CANCEL)
```

In the Graph screen	If the slope field is drawn but no solution curve is plotted, specify an initial condition as described on page 42.

Fields=DIRFLD

In the Y= Editor

Enter a valid system of two 1st-order equations. For information about defining a valid system for a 2nd-order equation, refer to page 44.

Use [F7] Axes to set Axes = CUSTOM. If Axes = TIME, an Invalid axes error occurs when you graph.

If you enter initial conditions in the Y= Editor, the equations referenced by the custom axes must have the same number of initial conditions.

Otherwise, a Dimension error occurs when you graph.

With custom axes

Set axes that are valid for your system of equations.

Do not select t for either axis. Otherwise, an Invalid axes error occurs when you graph.

The two axes must refer to different equations in your system of equations. For example, y1 vs. y2 is valid, but y1 vs. y1' gives an Invalid axes error.

In the Graph screen

If the direction field is drawn but no curve is plotted, enter initial conditions in the Y= Editor or select one interactively from the Graph screen as described starting on page 42. If you did enter initial conditions, select ZoomFit ([F2] A).

The ncurves Window variable is ignored with DIRFLD. Default curves are not drawn automatically.

Notes

With DIRFLD, the equations referenced by the custom axes determine which equations are graphed, regardless of which equations are selected in the Y= Editor.

If your system of equations refers to t, the direction field (not the plotted curves) is drawn with respect to one particular time, which is set by the dtime Window variable.

Fields=FLDOFF	In the Y= Editor	If you enter a 2nd- or higher-order equation, enter it as a valid system of equations as described on page 44.

All equations (selected or not) must have the same number of initial conditions. Otherwise, a Dimension error occurs when you graph.

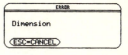

You can use F7 Axes to set Axes = TIME or CUSTOM.

With custom axes

If X Axis is not t, you must enter at least one initial condition for each equation in the Y= Editor (whether the equation is selected or not).

Otherwise, a Diff Eq setup error occurs when you graph.

In the Graph screen

If no curve is graphed, set an initial condition as described on page 42. If you did enter initial conditions in the Y= Editor, select ZoomFit (F2 A).

A 1st-order equation may look different with FLDOFF than with SLPFLD. This is because FLDOFF uses the tplot and tmax Window variables (page 39), which are ignored with SLPFLD.

Notes

For 1st-order equations, use FLDOFF and Axes = Custom to plot axes that are not possible with SLPFLD. For example, you can plot t vs. y1' (where SLPFLD plots t vs. y1). If you enter multiple 1st-order equations, you can plot one equation or its solution vs. another by specifying them as the axes.

If You Use the Table Screen to View Differential Equations

You can use the Table screen to view the points for a differential equation graph. However, the table may show different equations than those graphed. The table shows only the selected equations, regardless of whether those equations will be plotted with your current Fields and Axes settings.

Numeric Solver

4

The Numeric Solver lets you enter an expression or equation, define values for all but one unknown variable, and then solve for the unknown variable.

Note: To solve for the unknown variable from the Home screen or a program, use **nSolve()** *as described in Appendix A.*

After entering an equation and its known values, place the cursor on the unknown variable and press [F2].

You can also graph the solution.

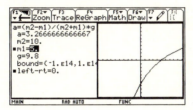

The x axis is the unknown variable. The y axis is the left–rt value, which gives the solution's accuracy.

The solution is precise where the curve crosses the x axis.

As in the example above, the Numeric Solver is often used to solve closed-form equations. But it also gives you a quick way to solve equations such as transcendental equations in which there is no closed form.

For example, you could rearrange the following equation manually to solve for any of the variables.

$a = (m2 - m1) / (m2 + m1) * g \longrightarrow m1 = (g - a) / (g + a) * m2$

With an equation such as the following, however, it may not be as easy to solve for x manually.

$y = x + e^x$

The Numeric Solver is particularly useful for such equations.

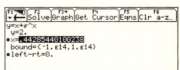

Preview of the Numeric Solver

Consider the equation a=(m2−m1)/(m2+m1)*g, where the known values are m2=10 and g=9.8. If you assume that a=1/3 g, find the value of m1.

Steps	Keystrokes	Display
1. Display the Numeric Solver.	[APPS] A	
2. Enter the equation. _When you press_ [ENTER] _or_ ⊙, _the screen lists the variables used in the equation._	A [=] [(] M 2 [−] M 1 [)] [÷] [(] M 2 [+] M 1 [)] [×] G [ENTER]	
3. Enter values for each variable, except the unknown variable m1. _Define m2 and g first. Then define a. (You must define g before you can define a in terms of g.) Accept the default for bound._ _If a variable has been defined previously, its value is shown as a default._	⊙ 10 ⊙ ⊙ 9 . 8 ⊙ ⊙ ⊙ G [÷] 3	
4. Move the cursor to the unknown variable m1. _Optionally, you can enter an initial guess for m1. Even if you enter a value for all variables, the Numeric Solver solves for the variable marked by the cursor._	⊙ ⊙	g/3 is evaluated when you move the cursor off the line.
5. Solve for the unknown variable. _To check the solution's accuracy, the left and right sides of the equation are evaluated separately. The difference is shown as left−rt. If the solution is precise, left−rt=0._	[F2]	▪ marks the calculated values.
6. Graph the solution using a ZoomStd viewing window. _The graph is displayed in a split screen. You can explore the graph by tracing, zooming, etc._	[F3] 3	
7. Return to the Numeric Solver and exit the split screen. _You can press_ [ENTER] _or_ ⊙ _to redisplay the list of variables._	[2nd] [⊞] [F3] 2	The variable marked by the cursor (unknown variable m1) is on the x axis, and left−rt is on the y axis.

Displaying the Solver and Entering an Equation

After you display the Numeric Solver, start by entering the equation that you want to solve.

Displaying the Numeric Solver

Press [APPS] and then select A:Numeric Solver.

The Numeric Solver screen shows the last entered equation, if any.

Entering an Equation

On the **eqn:** line, type in your equation.

You can:	For example:
Tips: In your equation: • Do not use system function names (such as y1(x) or r1(θ)) as simple variables (y1 or r1). • Be careful with implied multiplication. For example, a(m2+m1) is treated as a function reference, not as a∗(m2+m1).	
Type an equation directly.	a=(m2−m1)/(m2+m1)∗g a+b=c+sin(d)
Refer to a function or equation defined elsewhere.	Suppose you defined y1(x) on either the: • Y= Editor: y1(x)=1.25x∗cos(x) – or – • Home screen: Define y1(x)=1.25x∗cos(x) In the Numeric Solver, you then would enter: y1(x)=0 or y1(t)=0, etc. └─────┴──The argument does not have to match the one used to define the function or equation.
Note: When you define the variables, you can either define exp *or solve for it.* Type an expression without an = sign.	e+f−ln(g) After you press [ENTER], the expression is set equal to a system variable called exp and entered as: exp=e+f−ln(g)
Note: After you press [ENTER], *the current equation is stored automatically to the system variable* eqn. Recall a previously entered equation or open a saved equation.	Refer to the applicable heading later in this section.

Displaying the Solver and Entering an Equation (Continued)

Recalling Previously Entered Equations

Your most recently entered equations (up to 11 with the default setting) are retained in memory. To recall one of these equations:

1. From the Numeric Solver screen, press F5.

   A dialog box displays the most recently entered equation.

Tip: *You can specify how many equations are retained. From the Numeric Solver, press* F1 *and select* 9:Format *(or use* ◆ F*). Then select a number from 1 through 11.*

2. Select an equation.

   • To select the displayed equation, press ENTER.

   • To select a different equation, press ⊙ to display a list. Then select the one you want.

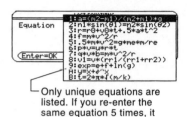

   — Only unique equations are listed. If you re-enter the same equation 5 times, it appears only once.

3. Press ENTER.

Saving Equations for Future Use

Because the number of equations that you can recall with F5 Eqns is limited, a particular equation may not be retained indefinitely.

To store the current equation for future use, save it to a variable.

1. From the Numeric Solver screen, press F1 and select 2:Save Copy As (or press ◆ S instead of using the F1 toolbar menu).

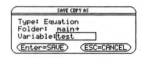

Note: *An equation variable has an EXPR data type, as shown on the MEMORY and VAR-LINK screens.*

2. Specify a folder and a variable name for the equation.

3. Press ENTER twice.

Opening a Saved Equation

To open a previously saved equation variable:

1. From the Numeric Solver screen, press F1 and select 1:Open (or press ◆ O instead of using the F1 toolbar menu).

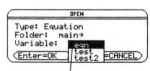

2. Select the applicable folder and equation variable.

3. Press ENTER.

Variable eqn contains the current — equation; it always appears alphabetically in the list.

Defining the Known Variables

After you type an equation in the Numeric Solver, enter the applicable values for all variables except the unknown variable.

Defining the List of Variables

After typing your equation on the **eqn:** line, press ENTER or ⌄.

The screen lists the variables in the order they appear in the equation. If a variable is already defined, its value is shown. You can edit these variable values.

Note: *If an existing variable is locked or archived, you cannot edit its value.*

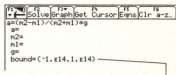

The solution must be within the specified bounds, which you can edit.

Enter a number or expression for all variables except the one you want to solve for.

Notes and Common Errors

• If you define a variable:

  – In terms of another variable in the equation, that variable must be defined first.

  – In terms of another variable that is not in the equation, that variable must already have a value; it cannot be undefined.

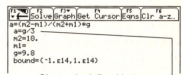

Since a is defined in terms of g, you must define g before a. When you move the cursor to another line, g/3 is evaluated.

  – As an expression, it is evaluated when you move the cursor off the line. The expression must evaluate to a real number.

Note: *When you assign a value to a variable in the Numeric Solver, that variable is defined globally. It still exists after you leave the solver.*

• If the equation contains a variable already defined in terms of other variables, those other variables are listed.

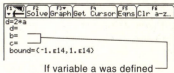

If variable a was defined previously as b+c→a, then b and c are listed instead of a.

• If you refer to a previously defined function, any variables used as arguments in the function call are listed, not the variables used to define the function.

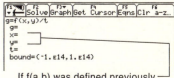

If f(a,b) was defined previously as √(a^2+b^2) and your equation contains f(x,y), then x and y are listed, not a and b.

Defining the Known Variables (Continued)

Note: *You cannot solve for a system variable other than* exp. *Also, if the equation contains a system variable, you cannot use* F3 *to graph.*

- If the equation contains a system variable (xmin, xmax, etc.), that variable is not listed. The solver uses the system variable's existing value.

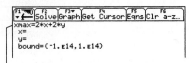

In the standard viewing window, xmax=10.

- Although you can use a system variable in the equation, an error occurs if you use F3 to graph the solution.

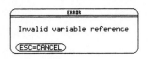

Note: *This error occurs if you use a reserved name incorrectly or refer to an undefined system function as a simple variable without parentheses.*

- If you see the error shown to the right, delete the entered variable value. Then edit the equation to use a different variable.

For example, y1(x) is undefined and you use y1.

Editing the Equation

In the Numeric Solver, press ⊙ until the cursor is on the equation. The screen automatically changes to show only the **eqn:** line. Make your changes, and then press ENTER or ⊙ to return to the list of variables.

Specifying an Initial Guess and/or Bounds (Optional)

To find a solution more quickly or to find a particular solution (if multiple solutions exist), you can optionally:

- Enter an initial guess for the unknown variable. The guess must be within the specified bounds.

Tip: *To select an initial guess graphically, refer to pages 66 and 67.*

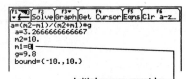

Initial guess must be within the bounds.

- Enter lower and upper bounds close to the solution.

For the bounds, you can also enter variables that evaluate to appropriate values (bound={*lower,upper*}) or a valid list variable that contains a two-element list (bound=*list*).

Solving for the Unknown Variable

After you type an equation in the Numeric Solver and enter values for the known variables, you are ready to solve for the unknown variable.

Finding the Solution

With all known variables defined:

1. Move the cursor to the unknown variable.

Note: *To stop (break) a calculation, press* ON. *The unknown variable shows the value being tested when the break occurred.*

2. Press F2 Solve.

A ■ marks the solution and left-rt. The ■ disappears when you edit a value, move the cursor to the equation, or leave the solver.

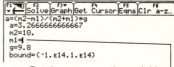

Put the cursor on the variable you want to solve for.

Using the solution and your entered values, the left and right sides of the equation are evaluated separately. left-rt shows the difference, which indicates the solution's accuracy. The smaller the value, the more accurate the solution. If the solution is precise, left-rt=0.

If you:	Do this:
Want to solve for other values	Edit the equation or variable values.
Want to find a different solution for an equation with multiple solutions	Enter an initial guess and/or a new set of bounds close to the other solution.
See the message:	Press ESC. The unknown variable shows the value being tested when the error occurred.

Note: *An iterative process is used to solve an equation. If the iterative process cannot converge on a solution, this error occurs.*

```
            ERROR
  Excessive iteration
   ( ESC=CANCEL )
```

- The left-rt value may be small enough for you to accept the result.

- If not, enter a different set of bounds.

Graphing the Solution

You can graph an equation's solutions any time after defining the known variables, either before or after you solve for the unknown variable. By graphing the solutions, you can see how many solutions exist and use the cursor to select an accurate initial guess and bounds.

Displaying the Graph

In the Numeric Solver, leave the cursor on the unknown variable. Press F3 and select:

1:Graph View

– or –

3:ZoomStd

– or –

4:ZoomFit

Graph View uses the current Window variable values.

For information about ZoomStd and ZoomFit, refer to Chapter 3 in the *TI-92 Guidebook*.

Tips: *With split screens:*

- *Use* 2nd [⊞] *to switch between sides.*
- *The active side has a thick border.*
- *The toolbar belongs to the active side.*

For more information, refer to Chapter 5 in the TI-92 *Guidebook.*

The graph is shown in a split screen, where:

- The unknown variable is plotted on the x axis.

- left-rt is plotted on the y axis.

Solutions for the equation exist at left-rt=0, where the graph crosses the x axis.

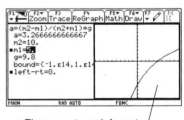

The current graph format settings are used.

You can explore the graph by using the free-moving cursor, tracing, zooming, etc., as described in Chapter 3 in the *TI-92 Guidebook*.

How the Graph Affects Various Settings

When you use the Numeric Solver to display a graph:

- The following modes are changed automatically to these settings:

Note: *If you were previously using different mode settings, you will need to reselect those settings manually.*

Mode	Setting	
Graph	FUNCTION	Any functions selected in the Y= Editor will not be graphed.
Split Screen	LEFT-RIGHT	
Split Screen Ratio	1:1	
Number of Graphs	1	

- All stat plots are deselected.

- After you leave the Numeric Solver, the Graph screen may continue to display the equation's solution, ignoring any selected Y= functions. If so, display the Y= Editor and then return to the Graph screen. Also, the graph is reset when you change the Graph mode or use **ClrGraph** from the Home screen (F4 5) or a program.

Selecting a New Initial Guess from the Graph

To use the graph cursor to select an initial guess:

1. Move the cursor (either free-moving or trace) to the point that you want to use as the new guess.

2. Use [2nd] [⊞] to make the Numeric Solver screen active.

3. Make sure the cursor is on the unknown variable, and press [F4].

4. Press [F2] to re-solve the equation.

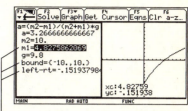

[F4] sets the graph cursor's xc value as an initial guess and the yc value as left–rt. The graph's xmin and xmax values are set as the bounds.

Returning to a Full Screen

From the split screen:

- To display the Numeric Solver full screen, use [2nd] [⊞] to make the solver screen active, press [F3], and then select 2:Clear Graph View.

  – or –

- To display the Home screen, press [2nd] [QUIT] twice.

Clearing Variables Before Leaving the Numeric Solver

When you solve an equation, its variables still exist after you leave the Numeric Solver. If the equation contains single-character variables, their values may inadvertently affect later symbolic calculations. Before leaving the Numeric Solver, you may want to:

1. Press [F6] Clr a–z to clear all single-character variables in the current folder.

2. Press [ENTER] to confirm the action.

The screen returns to the solver's **eqn:** line.

Constants and Measurement Units

Note: Constant and unit names always begin with an underscore _ ([2nd] P).

The UNITS dialog box ([♦] P) lets you select the available constants or units from different categories.

This category lists constant values. ——

Remaining categories list available units. ——

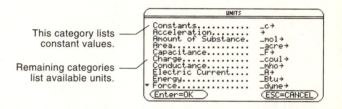

The MODE dialog box, Page 3, lets you select from three systems of measurement to specify the default units for displayed results.

*Note: You can also use **getUnits()** to get a list of the default units or **setUnits()** to set the default units. Refer to Appendix A.*

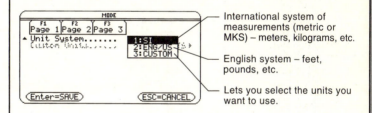

International system of measurements (metric or MKS) – meters, kilograms, etc.

English system – feet, pounds, etc.

Lets you select the units you want to use.

By using the unit features, you can:

*   Enter a unit for values in an expression, such as 6_m * 4_m or 23_m/_s * 10_s. The result is displayed in the selected default units.

*   Convert values from one unit to another within the same category.

*   Create your own user-defined units. These can be a combination of existing units or unique "standalone" units.

Preview of Constants and Measurement Units

Using the equation f = m∗a, calculate the force when m = 5 kilograms and a = 20 meters/second^2. What is the force when a = 9.8 meters/second^2. (This is the acceleration due to gravity, which is a constant named _g). Convert the result from newtons to kilograms of force.

Steps	Keystrokes	Display
1. Display the MODE dialog box, Page 3. For Unit System mode, select SI for the metric system of measurements. *Results are displayed according to these default units.*	[MODE] [F3] ⊙ 1 [ENTER]	
2. Create an acceleration unit for meters/second^2 named _ms2. [♦] P *displays the UNITS dialog box, which lets you select units from an alphabetical list of categories. You can use* [2nd] ⊙ *and* [2nd] ⊙ *to scroll one page at a time through the categories.* *Now, instead of re-entering _m/_s^2 each time you need it, you can use _ms2.* *Also, you can now use* [♦] P *to select _ms2 from the* Acceleration *category.*	[♦] P (scroll to Length category) ⊙ M [ENTER] ÷ [♦] P (scroll to Time category) ⊙ S [ENTER] [^] 2 [STO▶] [2nd] P M S 2 [ENTER]	└─ If you use [♦] P to select a unit, the _ is entered automatically.
3. Calculate the force when m = 5 kilograms (_kg) and a = 20 meters/second^2 (_ms2). *If you know the abbreviation for a unit, you can type it from the keyboard. For _ , press* [2nd] P.	5 [2nd] P K G [×] 2 0 [2nd] P M S 2 [ENTER]	
4. Using the same m, calculate the force for an acceleration due to gravity (the constant _g). *For _g, you can use the pre-defined constant available from* [♦] P *or you can type _g.*	5 [2nd] P K G [×] [♦] P ⊙ G [ENTER] [ENTER]	
5. Convert to kilograms of force (_kgf). [2nd] Y *displays the ▶ conversion operator.*	⊙ [2nd] Y [2nd] P K G F [ENTER]	

Entering Constants or Units

You can use a menu to select from a list of available constants and units, or you can type them directly from the keyboard.

From a Menu

The following shows how to select a unit, but you can use the same general procedure to select a constant.

From the Home screen:

1. Type the value or expression.

```
6.3
```

Tip: Press [•] P (instead of using [F4]) to display the UNITS dialog box.

2. Press [F4] and select C:Units.

   The UNITS dialog box is displayed.

Tip: Use [2nd] ⊙ and [2nd] ⊙ to scroll one page at a time through the categories.

3. Use ⊙ and ⊙ to move the cursor to the applicable category.

Note: If you created a user-defined unit for an existing category (page 76), it is listed in the menu.

4. To select the highlighted unit, press [ENTER].

   – or –

   To select a different unit, press ⊙. Then highlight the applicable unit, and press [ENTER].

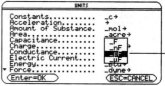

   The selected unit is placed in the entry line. Constant and unit names always begin with an underscore (_).

You can also move the cursor by—typing the first letter of a unit.

```
6.3_pF
```

From the Keyboard

If you know the abbreviation that the TI-92 Plus uses for a particular constant or unit (refer to the list that begins on page 77), you can type it directly from the keyboard. For example:

Note: You can type units in either uppercase or lowercase characters.

   256_m

   └──For _ , press [2nd] P.

• The first character must be an underscore (_).

• A space or a multiplication symbol (*) before the underscore is optional. For example, 256_m, 256 _m, and 256*_m are equivalent.

   – However, if you are adding units to a variable, you must put a space or * before the underscore. For example, x_m is treated as a variable, not as x with a unit.

Combining Multiple Units

You may need to combine two or more units from different categories.

For example, suppose you want to enter a velocity in meters per second. In the UNITS dialog box, however, the Velocity category does not contain this unit.

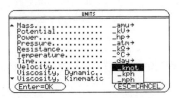

Tip: *Create a user-defined unit (page 76) for frequently used combinations.*

You can enter meters per second by combining _m and _s from the Length and Time categories, respectively.

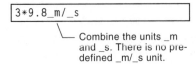

Combine the units _m and _s. There is no predefined _m/_s unit.

Using Parentheses with Units in a Calculation

In a calculation, you may need to use parentheses ( ) to group a value and its units so that they are evaluated properly. This is particularly true for division problems. For example:

Tip: *If you have any doubt about how a value and its units will be evaluated, group them within parentheses ( ).*

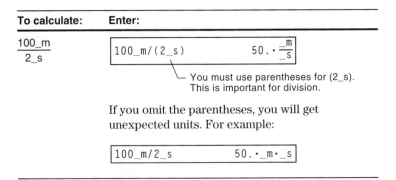

To calculate:	Enter:
$\dfrac{100\_m}{2\_s}$	$100\_m/(2\_s)$ $50.\cdot\dfrac{\_m}{\_s}$

You must use parentheses for (2_s). This is important for division.

If you omit the parentheses, you will get unexpected units. For example:

$$100\_m/2\_s \qquad 50.\cdot\_m\cdot\_s$$

Here's why you get unexpected units if you do not use parentheses. In a calculation, a unit is treated similar to a variable. For example:

100_m is treated as 100*_m
and
2_s is treated as 2*_s

Without parentheses, the entry is calculated as:

$$100*\_m\ /\ 2*\_s = \frac{100*\_m}{2}*\_s = 50.\cdot\_m\cdot\_s$$

Converting from One Unit to Another

You can convert from one unit to another in the same category, including any user-defined units (page 76).

For All Units Except Temperature

Note: *For a list of pre-defined units, see page 77.*

Tip: *Press ◆ P to select available units from a menu.*

If you use a unit in a calculation, it is converted and displayed automatically in the current default unit for that category, unless you use the ▶ conversion operator as described later. The following examples assume that your default units are set to the SI system of metric units (page 75).

To multiply 20 times 6 kilometers.

    20*6_km
    └──For _, press 2nd P.

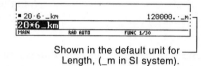

Shown in the default unit for Length, (_m in SI system).

If you want to convert to a unit other than the default, use the ▶ conversion operator.

    expression_unit1 ▶ *_unit2*
                          └──For ▶, press 2nd Y.

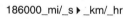

To convert 4 light years to kilometers:

    4_ltyr ▶ _km

To convert 186000 miles/second to kilometers/hour:

    186000_mi/_s ▶ _km/_hr

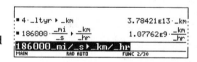

If an expression uses a combination of units, you can specify a conversion for some of the units only. Any units for which you do not specify a conversion will be displayed according to your defaults.

To convert 186000 miles/second from miles to kilometers:

    186000_mi/_s ▶ _km

To convert 186000 miles/second from seconds to hours:

    186000_mi/_s ▶ 1/_hr

Because a Time conversion is not specified, it is shown in its default unit (_s in this example).

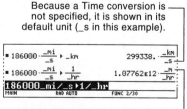

Because a Length conversion is not specified, it is shown in its default unit (_m in this example).

Converting from One Unit to Another (Continued)

For Temperature Values

To convert a temperature value, you must use **tmpCnv()** instead of the ▶ operator.

$$\textbf{tmpCnv}(expression\_°tempUnit1,\ \_°tempUnit2)$$

└──────── For °, press 2nd D.
└──────────── For _, press 2nd P.

For example, to convert 100_°C to _°F:

tmpCnv(100_°c, _°f)

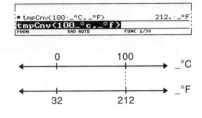

For Temperature Ranges

To convert a temperature range (the difference between two temperature values), use Δ**tmpCnv()**.

$$\Delta\textbf{tmpCnv}(expression\_°tempUnit1,\ \_°tempUnit2)$$

└── For Δ, press 2nd G 1 D.

For example, to convert a 100_°C range to its equivalent range in _°F:

ΔtmpCnv(100_°c, _°f)

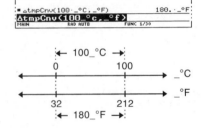

Setting the Default Units for Displayed Results

All results involving units are displayed in the default unit for that category. For example, if the default unit for Length is _m, any length result is displayed in meters (even if you entered _km or _ft in the calculation).

If You're Using the SI or ENG/US System

The SI and ENG/US systems of measurement (set from Page 3 of the MODE screen) use built-in default units, which you cannot change.

To find the default units for these systems, refer to page 77.

If Unit System=SI or ENG/US, the Custom Units item is dimmed. You cannot set a default for individual categories.

Setting Custom Defaults

Note: You can also use **setUnits()** or **getUnits()** to set or return information about default units. Refer to Appendix A.

Tip: When the CUSTOM UNIT DEFAULTS dialog box first appears, it shows the current default units.

To set custom defaults:

1. Press [MODE] [F3] ⊙ 3 to set Unit System = CUSTOM.

2. Press ⊙ to highlight SET DEFAULTS.

3. Press ⊙ to display the CUSTOM UNIT DEFAULTS dialog box.

4. For each category, you can highlight its default, press ⊙, and select a unit from the list.

5. Press [ENTER] twice to save your changes and exit the MODE screen.

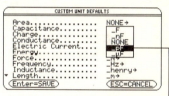

You can also move the cursor by typing the first letter of a unit.

What is the NONE Default?

Note: NONE is not available for base categories such as Length and Mass that have no components.

Many categories let you select NONE as the default unit.

This means that results in that category are displayed in the default units of its components.

For example, Area = Length^2, so Length is the component of Area.

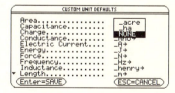

- If the defaults are Area = _acre and Length = _m (meters), area results are shown with _acre units.

- If you set Area = NONE, area results are shown with _m^2 units.

Creating Your Own User-Defined Units

In any category, you can expand the list of available units by defining a new unit in terms of one or more pre-defined units. You can also use "standalone" units.

Why Use Your Own Units?

Some example reasons to create a unit are:

- You want to enter length values in dekameters. Define 10_m as a new unit named _dm.

Note: If you create a user-defined unit for an existing category, you can select it from the ● P menu. But you cannot use MODE to select the unit as a default for displayed results.

- Instead of entering _m/_s² as an acceleration unit, you define that combination of units as a single unit named _ms2.

- You want to calculate how many times someone blinks. You can use _blinks as a valid unit without defining it. This "standalone" unit is treated similar to a variable that is not defined. For instance, 3_blinks is treated the same as 3a.

Rules for User-Defined Unit Names

The naming rules for units are similar to variables.

- Can have up to 8 characters.

- First character must be an underscore. (For _, press 2nd P.)

- Second character can be any valid variable name character except _ or a digit. For example, _9f is not valid.

- Remaining characters (up to 6) can be any valid variable name character except an underscore.

Defining a Unit

Define a unit the same way you store to a variable.

$$definition \rightarrow \_newUnit$$

For _, press 2nd P.

For →, press STO▶.

Note: User-defined units are displayed in lowercase characters, regardless of the case you use to define them.

Note: User-defined units such as _dm are stored as variables. You can delete them the same as you would any variable.

For example, to define a dekameter unit:

10_m → _dm

To define an acceleration unit:

_m/_s^2 → _ms2

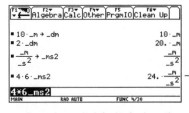

Assuming unit defaults for Length and Time are set to _m and _s.

To calculate 195 blinks in 5 minutes as _blinks/_min:

195_blinks/(5_min)

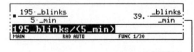

Assuming unit default for Time is set to _min.

List of Pre-Defined Constants and Units

This section lists the pre-defined constants and units by category. You can select any of these from the UNITS dialog box (◆ P). If you use MODE to set default units, note that categories with only one defined unit are not listed.

Defaults for SI and ENG/US

The SI and ENG/US systems of measurement use built-in default units. In this section, the built-in defaults are indicated by (SI) and (ENG/US). In some categories, both systems use the same default.

For a description of the NONE default, refer to page 75. Notice that some categories do not have default units.

Constants

Note: The TI-92 Plus simplifies unit expressions and displays results according to your default units. Therefore, constant values displayed on your screen may appear different from the values in this table.

_c .... speed of light .... $2.99792458\text{E}8\_m/\_s$
_Cc .... coulomb constant .... $8.9875517873682\text{E}9\_N \cdot \_m^2/\_coul^2$
_g .... acceleration of gravity .... $9.80665\_m/\_s^2$
_Gc .... gravitational constant .... $6.67259\text{E}-11\_m^3/\_kg/\_s^2$
_h .... Planck's constant .... $6.6260755\text{E}-34\_J \cdot \_s$
_k .... Boltzmann's constant .... $1.380658\text{E}-23\_J/\_°K$
_Me .... electron rest mass .... $9.1093897\text{E}-31\_kg$
_Mn .... neutron rest mass .... $1.6749286\text{E}-27\_kg$
_Mp .... proton rest mass .... $1.6726231\text{E}-27\_kg$
_Na .... Avogadro's number .... $6.0221367\text{E}23\ /\_mol$
_q .... electron charge .... $1.60217733\text{E}-19\_coul$
_Rb .... Bohr radius .... $5.29177249\text{E}-11\_m$
_Rc .... molar gas constant .... $8.31451\_J/\_mol/\_°K$
_Rdb .... Rydberg constant .... $10973731.53413\ /\_m$
_Vm .... molar volume .... $2.241409\text{E}-2\_m^3/\_mol$

Note: For µ, press 2nd G M. For ε, press 2nd G E.

_ε0 .... permittivity of a vacuum ..... $8.8541878176204\text{E}-12\_F/\_m$
_σ .... Stefan-Boltzmann constant .. $5.6705119\text{E}-8\_W/\_m^2/\_°K^4$
_φ0 .... magnetic flux quantum ...... $2.0678346161\text{E}-15\_Wb$
_µ0 .... permeability of a vacuum.... $1.2566370614359\text{E}-6\_N/\_A^2$
_µb .... Bohr magneton .... $9.2740154\text{E}-24\_J \cdot \_m^2/\_Wb$

Acceleration

no pre-defined units

Amount of Substance

_mol .... mole
(no default)

Area

_acre .... acre
_ha .... hectare

NONE (SI) (ENG/US)

Capacitance

_F .... farad (SI) (ENG/US)
_nF .... nanofarad
_pF .... picofarad

_µF .... microfarad
For µ, press 2nd G M.

List of Pre-Defined Constants and Units (Continued)

Charge
_coul....... coulomb (SI) (ENG/US)

Conductance
_mho ...... mho (ENG/US)   _siemens.. siemens (SI)
_mmho ... millimho   _μmho .... micromho

Electric Current
_A .... ampere (SI) (ENG/US)   _μA .... microampere
_kA .... kiloampere   For μ, press 2nd G M.
_mA .... milliampere

Energy
_Btu .... British thermal unit   _ftlb .... foot-pound
          (ENG/US)   _J.............. joule (SI)
_cal .... calorie   _kcal .... kilocalorie
_erg.......... erg   _kWh ...... kilowatt-hour
_eV .... electron volt   _latm....... liter-atmosphere

Force
_dyne...... dyne   _N............. newton (SI)
_kgf......... kilogram force   _tonf .... ton force
_lbf .... pound force (ENG/US)

Frequency
_GHz....... gigahertz   _kHz........ kilohertz
_Hz .... hertz (SI) (ENG/US)   _MHz ...... megahertz

Inductance
_henry .... henry (SI) (ENG/US)   _μH .... microhenry
_mH .... millihenry   For μ, press 2nd G M.
_nH .... nanohenry

Length
_Ang .... angstrom   _mi .... mile
_au .... astronomical unit   _mil......... 1/1000 inch
_cm .... centimeter   _mm........ millimeter
_fath .... fathom   _Nmi .... nautical mile
_fm .... fermi   _pc .... parsec
_ft .... foot (ENG/US)   _rod .... rod
_in........... inch   _yd .... yard
_km......... kilometer   _μ .... micron
_ltyr .... light year   _Å .... angstrom
_m........... meter (SI)

Luminous Intensity
_cd .... candela
(no default)

Mag Field Strength
_Oe .... oersted   NONE (SI) (ENG/US)

Mag Flux Density
_Gs .... gauss   _T............ tesla (SI) (ENG/US)

Magnetic Flux
_Wb .... weber (SI) (ENG/US)

Mass

_amu....... atomic mass unit
_gm......... gram
_kg.......... kilogram (SI)
_lb........... pound (ENG/US)
_mg......... milligram
_mton ..... metric ton
_oz .... ounce
_slug .... slug
_ton......... ton
_tonne..... metric ton
_tonUK ... long ton

Potential

_kV .... kilovolt
_mV .... millivolt
_V .... volt (SI) (ENG/US)
_volt........ volt

Power

_hp.......... horsepower (ENG/US)
_kW .... kilowatt
_W .... watt (SI)

Pressure

_atm .... atmosphere
_bar .... bar
_inH2O ... inches of water
_inHg...... inches of mercury
_mmH2O . millimeters of water
_mmHg... millimeters of mecury
_Pa.......... pascal (SI)
_psi .... pounds per square
          inch (ENG/US)
_torr........ millimeters of mecury

Resistance

_kΩ......... kilo ohm
For Ω, press
2nd [CHAR] 1 K.
_MΩ........ megaohm
_ohm....... ohm
_Ω .... ohm (SI) (ENG/US)

Temperature

_°C.......... °Celsius
For °, press 2nd D.
_°F .... °Fahrenheit
_°K .... °Kelvin
_°R .... °Rankine
(no default)

Time

_day........ day
_hr .... hour
_min .... minute
_ms......... millisecond
_ns .... nanosecond
_s.............. second (SI) (ENG/US)
_week ..... week
_yr........... year
_μs .... microsecond
          For μ, press 2nd G M.

Velocity

_knot ...... knot
_kph .... kilometers per hour
_mph....... miles per hour
NONE (SI) (ENG/US)

Viscosity, Dynamic

_P............ poise (SI) (ENG/US)

Viscosity, Kinematic

_St........... stokes (SI) (ENG/US)

Volume

_cup........ cup
_floz........ fluid ounce
_flozUK .. British fluid ounce
_gal .... gallon
_galUK.... British gallon
_l............. liter
_ml.......... milliliter
_pt........... pint
_qt .... quart
_tbsp .... tablespoon
_tsp .... teaspoon
NONE (SI) (ENG/US)

Number Bases

Note: *The new* MATH/Base *menu lets you select from a list of operations related to number bases.*

Wherever you enter an integer in a TI-92 Plus calculation, you can enter it in decimal, binary, or hexadecimal form. You can also set the Base mode to specify the form for displaying integer results. Fractional and floating-point results are always displayed in decimal form.

Binary numbers use 0 and 1 in the base 2 format:

100

$2^0 * 0 = +0$
$2^1 * 0 = +0$
$2^2 * 1 = +4$

Hexadecimal numbers use $0 - 9$ and $A - F$ in the base 16 format:

A8F

$16^0 * F = +15$
$16^1 * 8 = +128$
$16^2 * A = +2560$

Dec Base 10	Bin Base 2	Hex Base 16
0	0000	0
1	0001	1
2	0010	2
3	0011	3
4	0100	4
5	0101	5
6	0110	6
7	0111	7
8	1000	8
9	1001	9
10	1010	A
11	1011	B
12	1100	C
13	1101	D
14	1110	E
15	1111	F
16	10000	10

You can use the TI-92 Plus to convert a number from one base to another. For example, 100 binary = 4 decimal and A8F hex = 2703 decimal.

Hexadecimal numbers are often used as a shorthand notation for longer, hard-to-remember binary numbers. For example:

1010 1111 0011 0111
  A   F   3   7

AF37 hexadecimal is usually easier to work with than 1010111100110111 binary.

The TI-92 Plus also lets you compare or manipulate binary numbers bit-by-bit.

Preview of Number Bases

Calculate 10 binary (base 2) + F hexadecimal (base 16) + 10 decimal (base 10). Then, use the ▶ operator to convert an integer from one base to another. Finally, see how changing the Base mode affects the displayed results.

Steps	Keystrokes	Display
1. Display the MODE dialog box, Page 2. For Base mode, select DEC as the default number base. *Integer results are displayed according to the Base mode. Fractional and floating-point results are always displayed in decimal form.*	[MODE] [F2] (use ⊙ to move to Base mode) ⊙ 1 [ENTER]	MODE dialog box, Page 2 F1 Page 1 F2 Page 2 F3 Page 3 Split Screen...... FULL→ Split 1 App...... Home→ Split 2 App...... Number of Graphs.. Split Screen Ratio Exact/Approx..... AUTO→ Base............ DEC→ Enter=SAVE ESC=CANCEL
2. Calculate 0b10+0hF+10. *To enter a binary or hex number, you must use the 0b or 0h prefix (zero and the letter B or H). Otherwise, the entry is treated as a decimal number.*	0 B 1 0 ⊞ 0 H F ⊞ 1 0 [ENTER]	■0b10 + 0hF + 10 27 0b10+0hf+10 MAIN RAD AUTO FUNC 1/30 **Important:** The 0b or 0h prefix is a zero, not the letter O, followed by B or H.
3. Add 1 to the result and convert it to binary. *[2nd] Y displays the ▶ conversion operator.*	⊞ 1 [2nd] Y B I N [ENTER]	
4. Add 1 to the result and convert it to hexadecimal.	⊞ 1 [2nd] Y H E X [ENTER]	
5. Add 1 to the result and leave it in the default decimal base.	⊞ 1 [ENTER]	■0b10 + 0hF + 10 27 ■(27 + 1)▶bin 0b11100 ■(0b11100 + 1)▶hex 0h1D ■0h1D + 1 30 ans(1)+1 MAIN RAD AUTO FUNC 4/30
6. Change the Base mode to HEX. *When Base = HEX or BIN, the magnitude of a result is restricted to certain size limitations. Refer to page 84.*	[MODE] [F2] (use ⊙ to move to Base mode) ⊙ 2 [ENTER]	Results use the 0b or 0h prefix to identify the base.
7. Calculate 0b10+0hF+10.	0 B 1 0 ⊞ 0 H F ⊞ 1 0 [ENTER]	■0b10 + 0hF + 10 0h1B 0b10+0hf+10 MAIN RAD AUTO FUNC 5/30
8. Change the Base mode to BIN.	[MODE] [F2] (use ⊙ to move to Base mode) ⊙ 3 [ENTER]	
9. Re-enter 0b10+0hF+10.	[ENTER]	■0b10 + 0hF + 10 0h1B ■0b10 + 0hF + 10 0b11011 0b10+0hf+10 MAIN RAD AUTO FUNC 6/30

Entering and Converting Number Bases

Regardless of the Base mode, you must always use the appropriate prefix when entering a binary or hexadecimal number.

Entering a Binary or Hexadecimal Number

To enter a binary number, use the form:

0b *binaryNumber* (for example: 0b11100110)

- Binary number with up to 32 digits
- Zero, not the letter O, and the letter b

Note: *You can type the b or h in the prefix, as well as hex characters A – F, in uppercase or lowercase.*

To enter a hexadecimal number, use the form:

0h *hexadecimalNumber* (for example: 0h89F2C)

- Hexadecimal number with up to 8 digits
- Zero, not the letter O, and the letter h

If you enter a number without the 0b or 0h prefix, such as 11, it is always treated as a decimal number. If you omit the 0h prefix on a hexadecimal number containing A – F, all or part of the entry is treated as a variable.

Converting between Number Bases

Use the ▶ conversion operator.

integerExpression ▶ Bin
integerExpression ▶ Dec
integerExpression ▶ Hex

For ▶, press [2nd] Y. Also, you can select base conversions from the MATH/Base menu.

Note: *If your entry is not an integer, a Domain error is displayed.*

For example, to convert 256 from decimal to binary:

256 ▶ Bin

To convert 101110 from binary to hexadecimal:

0b101110 ▶ Hex

For a binary or hex entry, you must use the 0b or 0h prefix.

```
■ 256▶bin                    0b100000000
■ 0b101110▶hex                       0h2E
0b101110▶hex
MAIN        RAD AUTO      FUNC 2/30
```

Results use the 0b or 0h prefix to identify the base.

Alternate Method for Conversions

Instead of using ▶, you can:

1. Use [MODE] (page 84) to set the Base mode to the base that you want to convert to.

2. From the Home screen, type the number that you want to convert (using the correct prefix) and press [ENTER].

If Base mode = BIN:

```
■ 256                     0b100000000
256
MAIN        RAD AUTO      FUNC 1/30
```

If Base mode = HEX:

```
■ 0b101110                        0h2E
0b101110
MAIN        RAD AUTO      FUNC 1/30
```

Performing Math Operations with Hex or Bin Numbers

For any operation that uses an integer number, you can enter a hexadecimal or binary number. Results are displayed according to the Base mode. However, results are restricted to certain size limits when Base = HEX or BIN.

Setting the Base Mode for Displayed Results

1. Press MODE F2 to display Page 2 of the MODE screen.

2. Scroll to the Base mode, press ⊙, and select the applicable setting.

3. Press ENTER to close the MODE screen.

Note: *The* Base *mode affects output only. You must always use the* 0h *or* 0b *prefix to enter a hex or binary number.*

The Base mode controls the displayed format of integer results only.

Fractional and floating-point results are always shown in decimal form.

If Base mode = HEX:

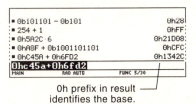

0h prefix in result
identifies the base.

Dividing When Base = HEX or BIN

When Base=HEX or BIN, a division result is displayed in hexadecimal or binary form only if the result is an integer.

To ensure that division always produces an integer, use **intDiv()** instead of ÷.

If Base mode = HEX:

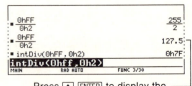

Press ◆ ENTER to display the result in APPROXIMATE form.

Size Limitations When Base = HEX or BIN

When Base=HEX or BIN, an integer result is stored internally as a signed, 32-bit binary number, which uses the range (shown in hexadecimal and decimal):

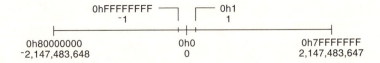

If a result's magnitude is too large to be stored in a signed, 32-bit binary form, a symmetric modulo operation brings the result into the range. Any number greater than 0h7FFFFFFF is affected. For example, 0h80000000 through 0hFFFFFFFF become negative numbers.

Comparing or Manipulating Bits

The following operators and functions let you compare or manipulate bits in a binary number. You can enter an integer in any number base. Your entries are converted to binary automatically for the bitwise operation, and results are displayed according to the Base mode.

Boolean Operations

Operator with syntax	Description
not *integer*	Returns the one's complement, where each bit is flipped.
[-] *integer*	Returns the two's complement, which is the one's complement + 1.
integer1 **and** *integer2*	In a bit-by-bit **and** comparison, the result is 1 if both bits are 1; otherwise, the result is 0. The returned value represents the bit results.
integer1 **or** *integer2*	In a bit-by-bit **or** comparison, the result is 1 if either bit is 1; the result is 0 only if both bits are 0. The returned value represents the bit results.
integer1 **xor** *integer2*	In a bit-by-bit **xor** comparison, the result is 1 if either bit (but not both) is 1; the result is 0 if both bits are 0 or both bits are 1. The returned value represents the bit results.

Note: *You can select these operators from the MATH/Base menu. For an example using each operator, refer to Appendix A in this book.*

Suppose you enter:

    0h7AC36 **and** 0h3D5F

Internally, the hexadecimal integers are converted to a signed, 32-bit binary number.

Then corresponding bits are compared.

If Base mode = HEX:

```
• 0h7AC36 and 0h3D5F          0h2C16
0h7AC36 and 0h3D5F
MAIN        RAD AUTO         FUNC 1/30
```

If Base mode = BIN:

```
• 0h7AC36 and 0h3D5F    0b10110000010110
0h7AC36 and 0h3D5F
MAIN        RAD AUTO         FUNC 1/30
```

Note: *If you enter an integer that is too large to be stored in a signed, 32-bit binary form, a symmetric modulo operation brings the value into the range (page 84).*

0h7AC36 = 0b00000000000000111101011000110110
  and   **and**
0h3D5F = 0b00000000000000000000011110101011111
         0b00000000000000000000010110000010110 = 0h2C16

└──── Leading zeros are not shown in the result.

The result is displayed according to the Base mode.

Comparing or Manipulating Bits (Continued)

**Rotating and
Shifting Bits**

*Note: You can select these
functions from the
MATH/Base menu. For an
example using each
function, refer to Appendix A
in this book.*

Function with syntax	Description
rotate(*integer*) – or – **rotate**(*integer*,*#ofRotations*)	If *#ofRotations* is: • omitted — bits rotate once to the right (default is ⁻1). • negative — bits rotate the specified number of times to the right. • positive — bits rotate the specified number of times to the left. In a right rotation, the rightmost bit rotates to the leftmost bit; vice versa for a left rotation.
shift(*integer*) – or – **shift**(*integer*,*#ofShifts*)	If *#ofShifts* is: • omitted — bits shift once to the right (default is ⁻1). • negative — bits shift the specified number of times to the right. • positive — bits shift the specified number of times to the left. In a right shift, the rightmost bit is dropped and 0 or 1 is inserted to match the leftmost bit. In a left shift, the leftmost bit is dropped and 0 is inserted as the rightmost bit.

Suppose you enter:

shift(0h7AC36)

Internally, the hexadecimal integer is converted to a signed, 32-bit binary number.

Then the shift is applied to the binary number.

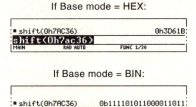

If Base mode = HEX:

If Base mode = BIN:

*Note: If you enter an integer
that is too large to be stored
in a signed, 32-bit binary
form, a symmetric modulo
operation brings the value
into the range (page 84).*

→ Each bit shifts to the right.

0h7AC36 = 0b00000000000000111101011000011 0110

Inserts 0 if leftmost bit is 0,
or 1 if leftmost bit is 1.

Dropped

0b0000000000000001111010110000 11011 = 0h3D61B

Leading zeros are not shown
in the result.

The result is displayed according to the Base mode.

User Data Archive

The TI-92 Plus module contains two separate memory areas: RAM (random-access memory) and user data archive. When you install the module:

- The module's RAM automatically becomes an extension of your TI-92's built-in RAM.

- The user data archive remains as a separate area of memory where you can store variables that you select.

Note: *Remember that variables include programs, functions, geometry figures, graph figures, etc.*

Note: *You cannot archive variables with reserved names or system variables.*

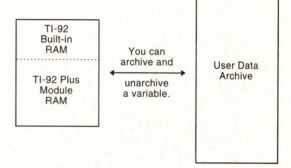

The user data archive lets you:

- Store data, programs, or any other variables to a safe location where they cannot be edited or deleted inadvertently.

- Create additional free RAM by archiving variables. For example:

  - You can archive variables that you need to access but do not need to edit or change, or variables that you are not using currently but need to retain for future use.

  - If you acquire additional programs for your TI-92 Plus, particularly if they are large, you may need to create additional free RAM before you can install those programs.

  - Additional free RAM can improve performance times for certain types of calculations.

Note: *Archiving large amounts of information can be very useful. However, if you do not need the benefits of the user data archive, you do not need to use it.*

Preview of the User Data Archive

Create a variable and move it to the user data archive memory. Then explore the ways in which you can and cannot access an archived variable. You will find that an archived variable is treated as a locked variable, as described in the *TI-92 Guidebook*.

Steps	Keystrokes	Display
1. Store a value to a variable.	5 [STO▶] A [ENTER]	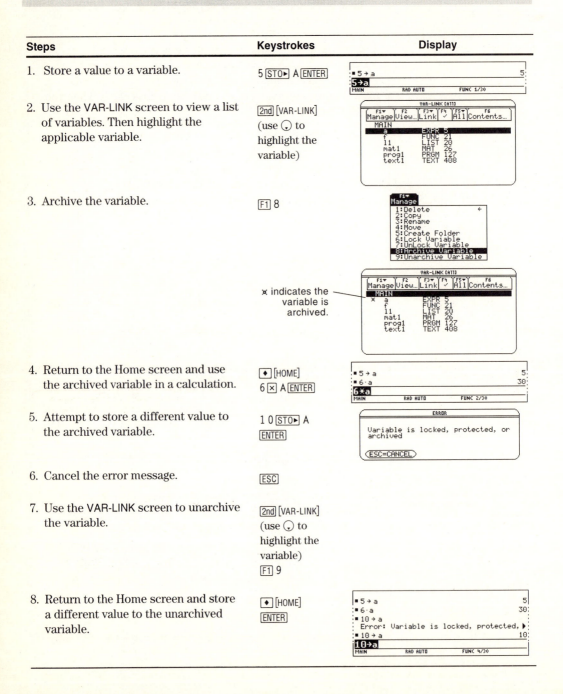
2. Use the VAR-LINK screen to view a list of variables. Then highlight the applicable variable.	[2nd] [VAR-LINK] (use ☉ to highlight the variable)	
3. Archive the variable.	[F1] 8	
	✗ indicates the variable is archived.	
4. Return to the Home screen and use the archived variable in a calculation.	[♦] [HOME] 6 [×] A [ENTER]	
5. Attempt to store a different value to the archived variable.	1 0 [STO▶] A [ENTER]	
6. Cancel the error message.	[ESC]	
7. Use the VAR-LINK screen to unarchive the variable.	[2nd] [VAR-LINK] (use ☉ to highlight the variable) [F1] 9	
8. Return to the Home screen and store a different value to the unarchived variable.	[♦] [HOME] [ENTER]	

Changes to the MEMORY and VAR-LINK Screens

The MEMORY and VAR-LINK screens have been modified to include information about the user data archive.

Changes to the MEMORY Screen

Tip: To display the size of individual variables and determine if they are in the user data archive, use the VAR-LINK screen.

To display the MEMORY screen, press [2nd] [MEM]. For each data type, the screen shows the total size for all variables of that type, regardless of whether they are stored in RAM or in the user data archive.

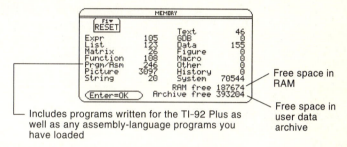

Free space in RAM

Free space in user data archive

Includes programs written for the TI-92 Plus as well as any assembly-language programs you have loaded

[F1] Reset affects the user data archive in the same way that it affects RAM.

1:All and 2:Memory delete all user-defined variables and functions, including those in the user data archive.

3:Default does not affect any user-defined variables and functions.

Changes to the VAR-LINK Screen

To display the VAR-LINK screen, press [2nd] [VAR-LINK].

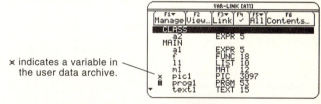

✕ indicates a variable in the user data archive.

Note: [F3] Link contains new items used to send and receive TI-92 Plus information. Refer to the sections about transmitting variables and upgrading product code in Chapter 1 in this book.

[F1] Manage now includes items that let you archive or unarchive a variable. For information about the other menu items, refer to Chapter 18 in the *TI-92 Guidebook*.

Archiving and Unarchiving a Variable

To archive or unarchive one or more variables interactively, use the VAR-LINK screen. You can also perform these operations from the Home screen or a program.

Checking for Available Space

Before archiving or unarchiving variables, particularly those with a large byte size (such as large programs):

1. Use the VAR-LINK screen to find the size of the variable.

2. Use the MEMORY screen to see if there is enough free space.

Note: *If there is not enough space, unarchive or delete variables as necessary.*

For an:	Sizes must be such that:
Archive	Archive free size > variable size
Unarchive	RAM free size > variable size

From the VAR-LINK Screen

To archive or unarchive:

1. Press [2nd] [VAR-LINK] to display the VAR-LINK screen.

Tip: *To select a single variable, highlight it. To select multiple variables, highlight each variable and press* [F4] ✓.

2. Select one or more variables, which can be in different folders. (You can select an entire folder by selecting the folder name.)

3. Press [F1] and select either:

   8:Archive Variable
   – or –
   9:Unarchive Variable

Note: *If you get a Garbage Collection message, refer to page 91.*

If you select 8:Archive Variable, the variables are moved to the user data archive.

archived variables

Note: *An archived variable is locked automatically. You can access the variable, but you cannot edit or delete it. Refer to page 93.*

You can access an archived variable just as you would any locked variable. For all purposes, an archived variable is still in its original folder; it is simply stored in the user data archive instead of RAM.

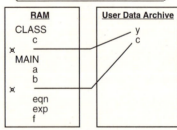

From the Home Screen or a Program

Use the **Archive** and **Unarchiv** commands (Appendix A).

Archive *variable1, variable2, ...*
Unarchiv *variable1, variable2, ...*

If a Garbage Collection Message Is Displayed

If you use the user data archive extensively, you may see a Garbage Collection message. This occurs if you try to archive a variable when there is not enough free archive memory. However, the TI-92 Plus will attempt to rearrange the archived variables to make additional room.

Responding to the Garbage Collection Message

When you see the message to the right:

• To continue archiving, press ENTER.
 – or –
• To cancel, press ESC.

After garbage collection, depending on how much additional space is freed, the variable may or may not be archived. If not, you can unarchive some variables and try again.

Why not Perform Garbage Collection Automatically, without a Message?

The message:

• Lets you know why an archive will take longer than usual. It also alerts you that the archive may fail if there is not enough memory.

• Can alert you when a program is caught in a loop that repetitively fills the user data archive. Cancel the archive and investigate the reason.

Why Is Garbage Collection Necessary?

The user data archive is divided into sectors. When you first begin archiving, variables are stored consecutively in sector 1. This continues to the end of the sector. If there is not enough space left in the sector, the next variable is stored at the beginning of the next sector. Typically, this leaves an empty block at the end of the previous sector.

Note: *An archived variable is stored in a continuous block within a single sector; it cannot cross a sector boundary.*

Each variable that you archive is stored in the first empty block large enough to hold it.

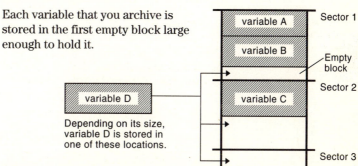

Depending on its size, variable D is stored in one of these locations.

Note: *Garbage collection occurs when the variable you are archiving is larger than any empty block.*

This process continues to the end of the last sector. Depending on the size of individual variables, the empty blocks may account for a significant amount of space.

How Unarchiving a Variable Affects the Process

When you unarchive a variable, it is copied to RAM but is not actually deleted from the user data archive memory.

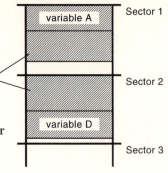

After you unarchive variables B and C, they continue to take up space.

Unarchived variables are "marked for deletion," meaning they will be deleted during the next garbage collection.

If the MEMORY Screen Shows Enough Free Space

Even if the MEMORY screen shows enough free space to archive a variable, you may still get a Garbage Collection message.

Shows free space that will be available after all "marked for deletion" variables are deleted.

When you unarchive a variable, the Archive free amount increases immediately, but the space is not actually available until after the next garbage collection.

If the Archive free amount shows enough available space for your variable, however, there probably will be enough space to archive it after garbage collection (depending on the usability of any empty blocks).

The Garbage Collection Process

The garbage collection process:

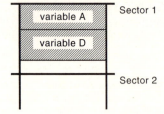

• Deletes unarchived variables from the user data archive.

• Rearranges the remaining variables into consecutive blocks.

Memory Error When Accessing an Archived Variable

An archived variable is treated the same as a locked variable. You can access the variable, but you cannot edit or delete it. In some cases, however, you may get a Memory Error when you try to access an archived variable.

What Causes the Memory Error?

The Memory Error message is displayed if there is not enough free RAM to access the archived variable. This may cause you to ask, "If the variable is in the user data archive, why does it matter how much RAM is available?" The answer is that the following operations can be performed only if a variable is in RAM.

Note: *As described below, a temporary copy lets you open or execute an archived variable. However, you cannot save any changes to the variable.*

- Opening a text variable in the Text Editor.

- Opening a data variable, list, or matrix in the Data/Matrix Editor.

- Opening a geometry figure or executing a macro in the Geometry application.

- Opening a program or function in the Program Editor.

- Running a program or referring to a function.

So that you don't have to unarchive variables unnecessarily, the TI-92 Plus performs a "behind-the-scenes" copy. For example, if you run a program that is in the user data archive, the TI-92 Plus:

Note: *Except for programs and functions, referring to an archived variable does not copy it. If variable ab is archived, it is not copied if you perform 6∗ab.*

1. Copies the program to RAM.

2. Runs the program.

3. Deletes the copy from RAM when the program is finished.

The error message is displayed if there is not enough free RAM for the temporary copy.

Correcting the Error

To free up enough RAM to access the variable:

1. Use the VAR-LINK screen ([2nd] [VAR-LINK]) to determine the size of the archived variable that you want to access.

2. Use the MEMORY screen ([2nd] [MEM]) to check the RAM free size.

Note: *Typically, the RAM free size must be larger than the archived variable.*

3. Free up the needed amount of memory by:

   - Deleting unnecessary variables from RAM.

   - Archiving large variables or programs (moving them from RAM to the user data archive).

TI-92 Plus Functions and Instructions

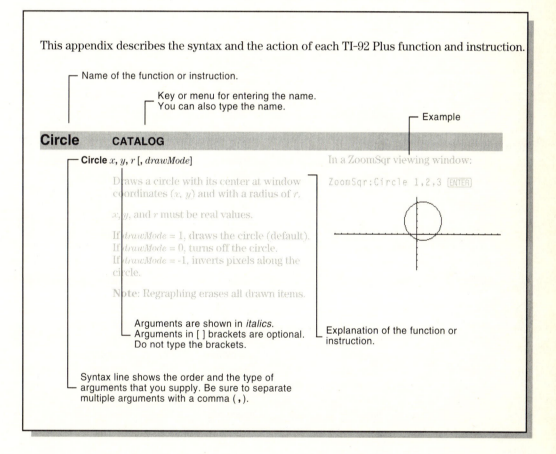

This appendix describes the syntax and the action of each TI-92 Plus function and instruction.

— Name of the function or instruction.

— Key or menu for entering the name.
You can also type the name.

— Example

Circle   CATALOG

Circle *x, y, r* [, *drawMode*]

Draws a circle with its center at window coordinates (*x, y*) and with a radius of *r*.

x, y, and *r* must be real values.

If *drawMode* = 1, draws the circle (default).
If *drawMode* = 0, turns off the circle.
If *drawMode* = -1, inverts pixels along the circle.

Note: Regraphing erases all drawn items.

In a ZoomSqr viewing window:

ZoomSqr:Circle 1,2,3 [ENTER]

Arguments are shown in *italics*.
— Arguments in [ ] brackets are optional. Do not type the brackets.

— Explanation of the function or instruction.

Syntax line shows the order and the type of arguments that you supply. Be sure to separate multiple arguments with a comma (**,**).

Quick-Find Locator

This section lists the TI-92 Plus functions and instructions in functional groups along with the page numbers where they are described in this appendix.

Algebra

| ("with")	222	cFactor()	105	comDenom()	108
cSolve()	112	cZeros	116	expand()	130
factor()	131	getDenom()	137	getNum()	138
nSolve()	159	propFrac()	167	randPoly()	172
solve()	188	tCollect()	197	tExpand()	198
zeros()	204				

Calculus

∫() (integrate)	216	Π() (product)	217	Σ() (sum)	217
arcLen()	102	avgRC()	103	*d()*	118
deSolve()	120	fMax()	133	fMin()	134
limit()	145	nDeriv()	155	nInt()	158
' (prime)	220	seq()	178	taylor()	197

Graphics

AndPic	101	BldData	104	Circle	106
ClrDraw	106	ClrGraph	106	CyclePic	116
DrawFunc	124	DrawInv	125	DrawParm	125
DrawPol	125	DrawSlp	125	DrwCtour	126
FnOff	134	FnOn	134	Graph	140
Line	146	LineHorz	146	LineTan	146
LineVert	146	NewPic	156	PtChg	167
PtOff	167	PtOn	167	ptTest()	167
PtText	168	PxlChg	168	PxlCrcl	168
PxlHorz	168	PxlLine	168	PxlOff	169
PxlOn	169	pxlTest()	169	PxlText	169
PxlVert	169	RclGDB	172	RclPic	173
RplcPic	177	Shade	182	StoGDB	191
StoPic	192	Style	192	Trace	200
XorPic	204	ZoomBox	206	ZoomData	206
ZoomDec	206	ZoomFit	207	ZoomIn	207
ZoomInt	207	ZoomOut	208	ZoomPrev	208
ZoomRcl	208	ZoomSqr	208	ZoomStd	209
ZoomSto	209	ZoomTrig	209		

Lists

+ (add)	210	– (subtract)	210	* (multiply)	211
/ (divide)	211	⁻ (negate)	212	^ (power)	218
augment()	103	crossP()	111	cumSum()	114
dim()	123	dotP()	124	exp▶list()	129
left()	145	list▶mat()	147	mat▶list()	151
max()	151	mid()	153	min()	153
newList()	156	polyEval()	165	product()	166
right()	175	rotate()	175	shift()	183
SortA	190	SortD	190	sum()	193

Math

+ (add)	210	– (subtract)	210	* (multiply)	211
/ (divide)	211	⁻ (negate)	212	% (percent)	212
! (factorial)	215	√() (sqr. root)	217	^ (power)	218
° (degree)	219	∠ (angle)	219	°, ', "	220
_ (underscore)	220	▶ (convert)	221	10^()	221
0b, 0h	223	▶Bin	103	▶Cylind	116
▶DD	118	▶Dec	119	▶DMS	124
▶Hex	140	▶Polar	165	▶Rect	173
▶Sphere	190	abs()	100	and	100
angle()	101	approx()	102	ceiling()	104
conj()	108	cos	109	cos⁻¹()	110
cosh()	110	cosh⁻¹()	111	E	126
e^()	127	exact()	129	floor()	133
fpart()	135	gcd()	136	imag()	142
int()	143	intDiv()	143	iPart()	143
isPrime()	144	lcm()	144	ln()	148
log()	149	max()	151	min()	153
mod()	154	nCr()	155	nPr()	159
P▶Rx()	161	P▶Ry()	161	ʳ (radian)	219
R▶Pθ()	171	R▶Pr()	171	real()	173
remain()	174	rotate()	175	round()	176
shift()	183	sign()	184	sin()	185
sin⁻¹()	185	sinh()	186	sinh⁻¹()	186
tan()	195	tan⁻¹()	195	tanh()	196
tanh⁻¹()	196	tmpCnv()	199	ΔtmpCnv()	199
x⁻¹	221				

Matrices

+ (add)	210	– (subtract)	210	* (multiply)	211
/ (divide)	211	⁻ (negate)	212	.+ (dot add)	214
.- (dot subt.)	214	.* (dot mult.)	215	. / (dot divide)	215
.^ (dot power)	215	^ (power)	218	augment()	103
colDim()	107	colNorm()	107	crossP()	111
cumSum()	114	det()	122	diag()	122
dim()	123	dotP()	124	eigVc()	127
eigVl()	127	Fill	133	identity()	141
list▶mat()	147	LU	151	mat▶list()	151
max()	151	mean()	152	median()	152
min()	153	mRow()	154	mRowAdd()	154
newMat()	156	norm()	158	product()	166
QR	170	randMat()	172	ref()	174
rowAdd()	176	rowDim()	176	rowNorm()	177
rowSwap()	177	rref()	177	simult()	184
stdDev()	191	subMat()	193	sum()	193
ᵀ (transpose)	194	unitV()	201	variance()	202
x⁻¹	221				

Quick-Find Locator (Continued)

Programming

=	212	/= (not equal)	213	<	213
<=	213	>	214	>=	214
# (indirection)	218	→ (store)	222	© (comment)	223
and	100	ans()	102	Archive	102
ClrErr	106	ClrGraph	106	ClrHome	107
ClrIO	107	ClrTable	107	CopyVar	109
CustmOff	115	CustmOn	115	Custom	115
Cycle	115	Define	119	DelFold	120
DelVar	120	Dialog	122	Disp	123
DispG	123	DispHome	123	DispTbl	124
DropDown	126	Else	128	ElseIf	128
EndCustm	128	EndDlog	128	EndFor	128
EndFunc	128	EndIf	128	EndLoop	128
EndPrgm	128	EndTBar	128	EndTry	128
EndWhile	128	entry()	128	Exec	129
Exit	129	For	135	format()	135
Func	136	Get	136	GetCalc	136
getConfg()	137	getFold()	137	getKey()	137
getMode()	138	getType()	138	getUnits()	139
Goto	139	If	141	Input	142
InputStr	142	Item	144	Lbl	144
left()	145	Local	149	Lock	149
Loop	150	MoveVar	154	NewFold	156
NewProb	157	not	158	or	160
Output	161	part()	162	PassErr	163
Pause	164	PopUp	165	Prgm	166
Prompt	166	Rename	174	Request	174
Return	175	right()	175	Send	178
SendCalc	178	setFold()	178	setGraph()	179
setMode()	180	setTable()	181	setUnits()	181
Stop	191	Style	192	switch()	193
Table	194	Text	198	Then	198
Title	198	Toolbar	200	Try	200
Unarchiv	201	Unlock	201	when()	202
While	203	xor	203		

Statistics

! (factorial)	215	BldData	104	CubicReg	114
cumSum()	114	ExpReg	131	LinReg	147
LnReg	148	Logistic	150	mean()	152
median()	152	MedMed	152	nCr()	155
NewData	156	NewPlot	157	nPr()	159
OneVar	160	PlotsOff	164	PlotsOn	164
PowerReg	166	QuadReg	170	QuartReg	171
rand()	172	randNorm()	172	RandSeed	172
ShowStat	184	SinReg	187	SortA	190
SortD	190	stdDev()	191	TwoVar	201
variance()	202				

Strings

& (append)	215	**#** (indirection)	218	**char()**	105
dim()	123	**expr()**	131	**format()**	135
inString()	143	**left()**	145	**mid()**	153
ord()	161	**right()**	175	**rotate()**	175
shift()	183	**string()**	192		

Alphabetical Listing of Operations

Operations whose names are not alphabetic (such as +, !, and >) are listed at the end of this appendix, starting on page 210. Unless otherwise specified, all examples in this section were performed in the default reset mode, and all variables are assumed to be undefined. Additionally, due to formatting restraints, approximate results are truncated at three decimal places (3.14159265359 is shown as 3.141...).

abs()   MATH/Number menu

abs(*expression1*) ⇒ *expression*
abs(*list1*) ⇒ *list*
abs(*matrix1*) ⇒ *matrix*

Returns the absolute value of the argument.

If the argument is a complex number, returns the number's modulus.

Note: All undefined variables are treated as real variables.

abs({π/2,⁻π/3}) [ENTER] $\{\frac{\pi}{2} \quad \frac{\pi}{3}\}$

abs(2-3*i*) [ENTER] $\sqrt{13}$

abs(z) [ENTER] $|z|$

abs(x+y*i*) [ENTER] $\sqrt{x^2+y^2}$

and   MATH/Test and MATH/Base menus

Boolean expression1 **and** *expression2* ⇒ *Boolean expression*
Boolean list1 **and** *list2* ⇒ *Boolean list*
Boolean matrix1 **and** *matrix2* ⇒ *Boolean matrix*

Returns true or false or a simplified form of the original entry.

x≥3 and x≥4 [ENTER]   x≥4

{x≥3,x≤0} and {x≥4,x≤⁻2} [ENTER]
                    {x ≥ 4   x ≤ ⁻2}

---

integer1 **and** *integer2* ⇒ *integer*

Compares two real integers bit-by-bit using an **and** operation. Internally, both integers are converted to signed, 32-bit binary numbers. When corresponding bits are compared, the result is 1 if both bits are 1; otherwise, the result is 0. The returned value represents the bit results, and is displayed according to the Base mode.

You can enter the integers in any number base. For a binary or hexadecimal entry, you must use the 0b or 0h prefix, respectively. Without a prefix, integers are treated as decimal (base 10).

If you enter a decimal integer that is too large for a signed, 32-bit binary form, a symmetric modulo operation is used to bring the value into the appropriate range.

In Hex base mode:

0h7AC36 and 0h3D5F [ENTER]   0h2C16

└─ **Important:** Zero, not the letter O.

In Bin base mode:

0b100101 and 0b100 [ENTER]   0b100

In Dec base mode:

37 and 0b100 [ENTER]   4

Note: A binary entry can have up to 32 digits (not counting the 0b prefix). A hexadecimal entry can have up to 8 digits.

AndPic   CATALOG

AndPic *picVar*[, *row, column*]

Displays the Graph screen and logically "ANDS" the picture stored in *picVar* and the current graph screen at pixel coordinates (*row, column*).

picVar must be a picture type.

Default coordinates are (0,0), which is the upper left corner of the screen.

In function graphing mode and Y= Editor:

```
y1(x) = cos(x)
F6 Style = 3:Square
F2 Zoom = 7:ZoomTrig
F1 = 2:Save Copy As...
Type = Picture, Variable = PIC1
```

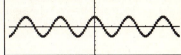

```
y2(x) = sin(x)
F6 Style = 3:Square
y1 = no checkmark (F4 to deselect)
F2 Zoom = 7:ZoomTrig
```

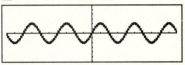

```
◆ [HOME]
AndPic PIC1 [ENTER]                        Done
```

angle()   MATH/Complex menu

angle(*expression1***)** ⇒ *expression*

Returns the angle of *expression1*, interpreting *expression1* as a complex number.

Note: All undefined variables are treated as real variables.

In Degree angle mode:

```
angle(0+2i) [ENTER]                          90
```

In Radian angle mode:

```
angle(1+i) [ENTER]                          π/4
```

```
angle(z) [ENTER]
angle(x+ iy) [ENTER]
```

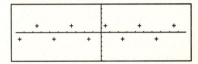

angle(*list1***)** ⇒ *list*
angle(*matrix1***)** ⇒ *matrix*

Returns a list or matrix of angles of the elements in *list1* or *matrix1*, interpreting each element as a complex number that represents a two-dimensional rectangular coordinate point.

In Radian angle mode:
```
angle({1+2i,3+0i,0-4i}) [ENTER]
```

■ angle({1 + 2·**i** 3 + 0·**i** 0 - 4·**i**})
$$\left\{ \text{-tan}^{-1}(1/2) + \frac{\pi}{2} \quad 0 \quad \frac{\text{-}\pi}{2} \right\}$$

ans()   [2nd] [ANS] key

ans() ⇒ *value*
ans(*integer***)** ⇒ *value*

Returns a previous answer from the
Home screen history area.

integer, if included, specifies which previous
answer to recall. Valid range for *integer* is
from 1 to 99 and cannot be an expression.
Default is 1, the most recent answer.

To use **ans()** to generate the Fibonacci
sequence on the Home screen, press:

```
1 [ENTER]                                          1
1 [ENTER]                                          1
[2nd] [ANS] [+] [2nd] [ANS] [◌] [←] 2 [ENTER]      2
[ENTER]                                            3
[ENTER]                                            5
```

approx()   MATH/Algebra menu

approx(*expression***)** ⇒ *value*

Returns the evaluation of *expression* as a
decimal value, when possible, regardless of
the current Exact/Approx mode.

This is equivalent to entering *expression* and
pressing [♦] [ENTER] on the Home screen.

```
approx(π) [ENTER]                            3.141...
```

approx(*list1***)** ⇒ *list*
approx(*matrix1***)** ⇒ *matrix*

Returns a list or matrix where each element
has been evaluated to a decimal value, when
possible.

```
approx({sin(π),cos(π)}) [ENTER]
                                       {0.   ⁻1.}
```
```
approx([√(2),√(3)]) [ENTER]
                                [1.414...  1.732...]
```

Archive   CATALOG

Archive *var1* [, *var2*] [, *var3*] ...

Moves the specified variables from RAM to
the user data archive memory.

You can access an archived variable the same
as you would a variable in RAM. However,
you cannot delete, rename, or store to an
archived variable because it is locked
automatically.

To unarchive variables, use **Unarchiv**
(page 201).

```
10→arctest [ENTER]                               10
Archive arctest [ENTER]                        Done
5*arctest [ENTER]                                50
15→arctest [ENTER]
```

```
┌────────────── ERROR ──────────────┐
│                                    │
│ Variable is locked, protected, or  │
│ archived                           │
│                                    │
│  <ESC=CANCEL>                      │
└────────────────────────────────────┘
```

```
[ESC]
Unarchiv arctest [ENTER]                       Done
15→arctest [ENTER]                               15
```

arcLen()   MATH/Calculus menu

arcLen(*expression1,var,start,end***)** ⇒ *expression*

Returns the arc length of *expression1* from
start to *end* with respect to variable *var*.

Regardless of the graphing mode, arc length
is calculated as an integral assuming a
function mode definition.

```
arcLen(cos(x),x,0,π) [ENTER]                  3.820...
```
```
arcLen(f(x),x,a,b) [ENTER]
```
$$\int_{a}^{b}\sqrt{(\frac{d}{dx}(f(x)))^2+1}\ dx$$

arcLen(*list1,var,start,end***)** ⇒ *list*

Returns a list of the arc lengths of each
element of *list1* from *start* to *end* with
respect to *var*.

```
arcLen({sin(x),cos(x)},x,0,π)
                          (3.820...   3.820...)
```

augment() MATH/Matrix menu

augment(list1, list2**)** ⇒ list

    Returns a new list that is list2 appended to the end of list1.

`augment({1,-3,2},{5,4})` [ENTER]
$$\{1 \ -3 \ 2 \ 5 \ 4\}$$

---

augment(matrix1, matrix2**)** ⇒ matrix
augment(matrix1; matrix2**)** ⇒ matrix

    Returns a new matrix that is matrix2 appended to matrix1. When the "," character is used, the matrices must have equal row dimensions, and matrix2 is appended to matrix1 as new columns. When the ";" character is used, the matrices must have equal column dimensions, and matrix2 is appended to matrix1 as new rows. Does not alter matrix1 or matrix2.

`[1,2;3,4]→M1` [ENTER]
$$\begin{bmatrix} 1 & 2 \\ 3 & 4 \end{bmatrix}$$

`[5;6]→M2` [ENTER]
$$\begin{bmatrix} 5 \\ 6 \end{bmatrix}$$

`augment(M1,M2)` [ENTER]
$$\begin{bmatrix} 1 & 2 & 5 \\ 3 & 4 & 6 \end{bmatrix}$$

`[5,6]→M2` [ENTER]
$$\begin{bmatrix} 5 & 6 \end{bmatrix}$$

`augment(M1;M2)` [ENTER]
$$\begin{bmatrix} 1 & 2 \\ 3 & 4 \\ 5 & 6 \end{bmatrix}$$

---

avgRC() CATALOG

avgRC(expression1, var [, h]**)** ⇒ expression

    Returns the forward-difference quotient (average rate of change).

    expression1 can be a user-defined function name (see **Func**, page 136).

    h is the step value. If h is omitted, it defaults to 0.001.

    Note that the similar function **nDeriv()** uses the central-difference quotient.

`avgRC(f(x),x,h)` [ENTER]
$$\frac{f(x+h) - f(x)}{h}$$

`avgRC(sin(x),x,h)|x=2` [ENTER]
$$\frac{\sin(h+2) - \sin(2)}{h}$$

`avgRC(x^2-x+2,x)` [ENTER] $2.\cdot(x-.4995)$

`avgRC(x^2-x+2,x,.1)` [ENTER]
$$2.\cdot(x-.45)$$

`avgRC(x^2-x+2,x,3)` [ENTER] $2\cdot(x+1)$

▶Bin MATH/Base menu

integer1 **▶Bin** ⇒ integer

    Converts integer1 to a binary number. Binary or hexadecimal numbers always have a 0b or 0h prefix, respectively.

    ┌─ Zero, not the letter O, followed by b or h.

0b binaryNumber
0h hexadecimalNumber

       └── A binary number can have up to 32 digits. A hexadecimal number can have up to 8.

    Without a prefix, integer1 is treated as decimal (base 10). The result is displayed in binary, regardless of the Base mode.

    If you enter a decimal integer that is too large for a signed, 32-bit binary form, a symmetric modulo operation is used to bring the value into the appropriate range.

`256 ▶Bin` [ENTER] `0b100000000`

`0h1F ▶Bin` [ENTER] `0b11111`

BldData   CATALOG

BldData [*dataVar*]

Creates data variable *dataVar* based on the information used to plot the current graph. **BldData** is valid in all graphing modes.

If *dataVar* is omitted, the data is stored in the system variable sysData.

Note: The first time you start the Data/Matrix Editor after using **BldData**, *dataVar* or sysData (depending on the argument you used with **BldData**) is set as the current data variable.

The incremental values used for any independent variables (x in the example to the right) are calculated according to the Window variable values.

For information about the increments used to evaluate a graph, refer to the chapter in this book or in the *TI-92 Guidebook* that describes that graphing mode.

3D graphing mode has two independent variables. In the sample data to the right, notice that x remains constant as y increments through its range of values.

Then, x increments to its next value and y again increments through its range. This pattern continues until x has incremented through its range.

In function graphing mode and Radian angle mode:

```
8*sin(x)→y1(x)  ENTER              Done
2*sin(x)→y2(x)  ENTER              Done
ZoomStd  ENTER
```

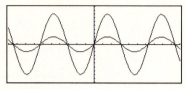

```
♦ [HOME]
BldData  ENTER                     Done
APPS 6 ENTER
```

DATA	x	y1	y2		
	c1	c2	c3	c4	c5
1	-10.	4.3522	1.088		
2	-9.832	3.168	.792		
3	-9.664	1.8945	.47363		
4	-9.496	.56769	.14192		
5	-9.328	-.7752	-.1938		
6	-9.16	-2.096	-.524		
7	-8.992	-3.358	-.8395		

Note: The following sample data is from a 3D graph.

DATA	x	y	z1		
	c1	c2	c3	c4	c5
1	-10.	-10.	142.		
2	-10.	-8.571	128.73		
3	-10.	-7.143	117.51		
4	-10.	-5.714	108.33		
5	-10.	-4.286	101.18		
6	-10.	-2.857	96.082		
7	-10.	-1.429	93.02		

ceiling()   MATH/Number menu

ceiling(*expression1*) $\Rightarrow$ *integer*

Returns the nearest integer that is $\geq$ the argument.

The argument can be a real or a complex number.

Note: See also **floor()** (page 133).

```
ceiling(0.456)  ENTER                1.
```

---

ceiling(*list1*) $\Rightarrow$ *list*
ceiling(*matrix1*) $\Rightarrow$ *matrix*

Returns a list or matrix of the ceiling of each element.

```
ceiling({-3.1,1,2.5})  ENTER
                          {-3.  1  3.}

ceiling([0,-3.2i;1.3,4])  ENTER
                          [ 0   -3.·i ]
                          [ 2.    4   ]
```

cFactor()   MATH/Algebra/Complex menu

cFactor(*expression1*[, *var*]) $\Rightarrow$ *expression*
cFactor(*list1*[,*var*]) $\Rightarrow$ *list*
cFactor(*matrix1*[,*var*]) $\Rightarrow$ *matrix*

    cFactor(*expression1*) returns *expression1* factored with respect to all of its variables over a common denominator.

    expression1 is factored as much as possible toward linear rational factors even if this introduces new non-real numbers. This alternative is appropriate if you want factorization with respect to more than one variable.

```
cFactor(a^3*x^2+a*x^2+a^3+a) ENTER
    a·(a + ⁻i)·(a + i)·(x + ⁻i)·(x + i)

cFactor(x^2+4/9) ENTER
                 (3·x + ⁻2·i)·(3·x + 2·i)
                 ─────────────────────────
                            9

cFactor(x^2+3) ENTER                 x² + 3

cFactor(x^2+a) ENTER                 x² + a
```

    cFactor(*expression1*,*var*) returns *expression1* factored with respect to variable *var*.

    expression1 is factored as much as possible toward factors that are linear in *var*, with perhaps non-real constants, even if it introduces irrational constants or subexpressions that are irrational in other variables.

    The factors and their terms are sorted with *var* as the main variable. Similar powers of *var* are collected in each factor. Include *var* if factorization is needed with respect to only that variable and you are willing to accept irrational expressions in any other variables to increase factorization with respect to *var*. There might be some incidental factoring with respect to other variables.

    For the AUTO setting of the Exact/Approx mode, including *var* also permits approximation with floating-point coefficients where irrational coefficients cannot be explicitly expressed concisely in terms of the built-in functions. Even when there is only one variable, including *var* might yield more complete factorization.

```
cFactor(a^3*x^2+a*x^2+a^3+a,x) ENTER

    a·(a² + 1)·(x + ⁻i)·(x + i)

cFactor(x^2+3,x) ENTER
                 (x + √3·i)·(x + ⁻√3·i)

cFactor(x^2+a,x) ENTER
                 (x + √a·⁻i)·(x + √a·i)
```

```
cFactor(x^5+4x^4+5x^3-6x-3) ENTER
    x⁵ + 4·x⁴ + 5·x³ ⁻6·x-3

cFactor(ans(1),x) ENTER
    (x - .965)·(x + .612)·(x + 2.13)·
    (x + 1.11 - 1.07·i)·(x + 1.11 + 1.07·i)
```

    Note: See also **factor()** (page 131).

char()   MATH/String menu

char(*integer*) $\Rightarrow$ *character*

    Returns a character string containing the character numbered *integer* from the TI-92 Plus character set. See Appendix B for a complete listing of character codes.

    The valid range for *integer* is 0–255.

```
char(38) ENTER                       "&"

char(65) ENTER                       "A"
```

Circle   CATALOG

Circle x, y, r [, *drawMode*]

Draws a circle with its center at window coordinates (x, y) and with a radius of r.

x, y, and r must be real values.

If *drawMode* = 1, draws the circle (default).
If *drawMode* = 0, turns off the circle.
If *drawMode* = -1, inverts pixels along the circle.

Note: Regraphing erases all drawn items. See also **PxlCrcl** (page 168).

In a ZoomSqr viewing window:

```
ZoomSqr:Circle 1,2,3 ENTER
```

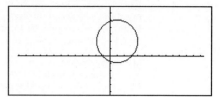

ClrDraw   CATALOG

ClrDraw

Clears the Graph screen and resets the Smart Graph feature so that the next time the Graph screen is displayed, the graph will be redrawn.

While viewing the Graph screen, you can clear all drawn items (such as lines and points) by pressing F4 (ReGraph) or pressing F6 and selecting 1:ClrDraw.

ClrErr   CATALOG

ClrErr

Clears the error status. It sets errornum to zero and clears the internal error context variables.

The **Else** clause of the **Try...EndTry** in the program should use **ClrErr** or **PassErr**. If the error is to be processed or ignored, use **ClrErr**. If what to do with the error is not known, use **PassErr** to send it to the next error handler. If there are no more pending **Try...EndTry** error handlers, the error dialog box will be displayed as normal.

Note: See also **PassErr** (page 163) and **Try** (page 200).

Program listing:

```
:clearerr()
:Prgm
:PlotsOff:FnOff:ZoomStd
:For i,0,238
: Δx*i+xmin→xcord
: Try
:   PtOn xcord,ln(xcord)
: Else
:   If errornum=800 Then
:     ClrErr © clear the error
:   Else
:     PassErr © pass on any other
        error
:   EndIf
: EndTry
:EndFor
:EndPrgm
```

ClrGraph   CATALOG

ClrGraph

Clears any functions or expressions that were graphed with the **Graph** command or were created with the **Table** command. (See **Graph** on page 140 or **Table** on page 194.)

Any previously selected Y= functions will be graphed the next time that the graph is displayed.

ClrHome   CATALOG

ClrHome

Clears all items stored in the **entry()** and **ans()** Home screen history area. Does not clear the current entry line.

While viewing the Home screen, you can clear the history area by pressing [F1] and selecting 8:Clear Home.

For functions such as **solve()** that return arbitrary constants or integers (@1, @2, etc.), **ClrHome** resets the suffix to 1.

ClrIO   CATALOG

ClrIO

Clears the Program I/O screen.

ClrTable   CATALOG

ClrTable

Clears all table values. Applies only to the ASK setting on the Table Setup dialog box.

While viewing the Table screen in Ask mode, you can clear the values by pressing [F1] and selecting 8:Clear Table.

colDim()   MATH/Matrix/Dimensions menu

colDim(*matrix*) ⇒ *expression*

Returns the number of columns contained in *matrix*.

Note: See also **rowDim()** (page 176).

```
colDim([0,1,2;3,4,5]) ENTER          3
```

colNorm()   MATH/Matrix/Norms menu

colNorm(*matrix*) ⇒ *expression*

Returns the maximum of the sums of the absolute values of the elements in the columns in *matrix*.

Note: Undefined matrix elements are not allowed. See also **rowNorm()** (page 177).

```
[1,-2,3;4,5,-6]→mat ENTER
```

$$\begin{bmatrix} 1 & -2 & 3 \\ 4 & 5 & -6 \end{bmatrix}$$

```
colNorm(mat) ENTER                   9
```

comDenom(*expression1*[,*var*]) ⇒ *expression*
comDenom(*list1*[,*var*]) ⇒ *list*
comDenom(*matrix1*[,*var*]) ⇒ *matrix*

comDenom(*expression1*) returns a reduced ratio of a fully expanded numerator over a fully expanded denominator.

comDenom((y^2+y)/(x+1)^2+y^2+y)
[ENTER]

$$\blacksquare \text{comDenom}\left[\frac{y^2+y}{(x+1)^2}+y^2+y\right]$$
$$\frac{x^2 \cdot y^2 + x^2 \cdot y + 2 \cdot x \cdot y^2 + 2 \cdot x \cdot y + 2 \cdot y^2 + 2 \cdot y}{x^2 + 2 \cdot x + 1}$$

comDenom(*expression1,var*) returns a reduced ratio of numerator and denominator expanded with respect to *var*. The terms and their factors are sorted with *var* as the main variable. Similar powers of *var* are collected. There might be some incidental factoring of the collected coefficients. Compared to omitting *var*, this often saves time, memory, and screen space, while making the expression more comprehensible. It also makes subsequent operations on the result faster and less likely to exhaust memory.

comDenom((y^2+y)/(x+1)^2+y^2+y,x)
[ENTER]

$$\blacksquare \text{comDenom}\left[\frac{y^2+y}{(x+1)^2}+y^2+y,x\right]$$
$$\frac{x^2 \cdot y \cdot (y+1) + 2 \cdot x \cdot y \cdot (y+1) + 2 \cdot y \cdot (y+1)}{x^2 + 2 \cdot x + 1}$$

comDenom((y^2+y)/(x+1)^2+y^2+y,y)
[ENTER]

$$\blacksquare \text{comDenom}\left[\frac{y^2+y}{(x+1)^2}+y^2+y,y\right]$$
$$\frac{y^2 \cdot (x^2 + 2 \cdot x + 2) + y \cdot (x^2 + 2 \cdot x + 2)}{x^2 + 2 \cdot x + 1}$$

If *var* does not occur in *expression1*, **comDenom**(*expression1,var*) returns a reduced ratio of an unexpanded numerator over an unexpanded denominator. Such results usually save even more time, memory, and screen space. Such partially factored results also make subsequent operations on the result much faster and much less likely to exhaust memory.

comDenom(exprn,abc)→comden(exprn)
[ENTER]   Done

comden((y^2+y)/(x+1)^2+y^2+y)
[ENTER]

$$\blacksquare \text{comden}\left[\frac{y^2+y}{(x+1)^2}+y^2+y\right]$$
$$\frac{(x^2 + 2 \cdot x + 2) \cdot y \cdot (y+1)}{(x+1)^2}$$

Even when there is no denominator, the **comden** function is often a fast way to achieve partial factorization if **factor()** is too slow or if it exhausts memory.

comden(1234x^2*(y^3-y)+2468x*
(y^2-1)) [ENTER]
$$1234 \cdot x \cdot (x \cdot y + 2) \cdot (y^2 - 1)$$

Hint: Enter this **comden()** function definition and routinely try it as an alternative to **comDenom()** and **factor()**.

conj(*expression1*) ⇒ *expression*
conj(*list1*) ⇒ *list*
conj(*matrix1*) ⇒ *matrix*

Returns the complex conjugate of the argument.

Note: All undefined variables are treated as real variables.

conj(1+2*i*) [ENTER] $1 - 2 \cdot i$

conj([2,1-3*i*; ^-i,$^-7$]) [ENTER] $\begin{bmatrix} 2 & 1+3 \cdot i \\ i & ^-7 \end{bmatrix}$

conj(z)   z

conj(x+*i*y) $x + {}^-i \cdot y$

CopyVar   CATALOG

CopyVar *var1*, *var2*

Copies the contents of variable *var1* to *var2*.
If *var2* does not exist, **CopyVar** creates it.

Note: CopyVar is similar to the store
instruction (→) when you are copying an
expression, list, matrix, or character string
except that no simplification takes place
when using **CopyVar**. You must use **CopyVar**
with non-algebraic variable types such as Pic
and GDB variables.

```
x+y→a ENTER                        x + y
10→x ENTER                            10
CopyVar a,b ENTER                   Done
a→c ENTER                          y + 10
DelVar x ENTER                      Done
b ENTER                            x + y
c ENTER                            y + 10
```

cos()   COS key

cos(*expression1*) ⇒ *expression*
cos(*list1*) ⇒ *list*

cos(*expression1*) returns the cosine of the
argument as an expression.

cos(*list1*) returns a list of the cosines of all
elements in *list1*.

Note: The argument is interpreted as either a
degree or radian angle, according to the
current angle mode setting. You can use °
(page 219) or ʳ (page 219) to override the
angle mode temporarily.

In Degree angle mode:

cos((π/4)ʳ) ENTER $\dfrac{\sqrt{2}}{2}$

cos(45) ENTER $\dfrac{\sqrt{2}}{2}$

cos({0,60,90}) ENTER   {1   1/2   0}

In Radian angle mode:

cos(π/4) ENTER $\dfrac{\sqrt{2}}{2}$

cos(45°) ENTER $\dfrac{\sqrt{2}}{2}$

---

cos(*squareMatrix1*) ⇒ *squareMatrix*

Returns the matrix cosine of *squareMatrix1*.
This is *not* the same as calculating the cosine
of each element.

When a scalar function f(A) operates on
squareMatrix1 (A), the result is calculated by
the algorithm:

1. Compute the eigenvalues (λ_i) and
   eigenvectors (V_i) of A.

   squareMatrix1 must be diagonalizable.
   Also, it cannot have symbolic variables
   that have not been assigned a value.

2. Form the matrices:

$$B = \begin{bmatrix} \lambda_1 & 0 & \ldots & 0 \\ 0 & \lambda_2 & \ldots & 0 \\ 0 & 0 & \ldots & 0 \\ 0 & 0 & \ldots & \lambda_n \end{bmatrix} \text{ and } X = [V_1, V_2, \ldots, V_n]$$

3. Then $A = X B X^{-1}$ and $f(A) = X f(B) X^{-1}$. For
   example, $\cos(A) = X \cos(B) X^{-1}$ where:

$$\cos(B) = \begin{bmatrix} \cos(\lambda_1) & 0 & \ldots & 0 \\ 0 & \cos(\lambda_2) & \ldots & 0 \\ 0 & 0 & \ldots & 0 \\ 0 & 0 & \ldots & \cos(\lambda_n) \end{bmatrix}$$

All computations are performed using
floating-point arithmetic.

In Radian angle mode:

cos([1,5,3;4,2,1;6,-2,1]) ENTER

$$\begin{bmatrix} .212\ldots & .205\ldots & .121\ldots \\ .160\ldots & .259\ldots & .037\ldots \\ .248\ldots & \text{-}.090\ldots & .218\ldots \end{bmatrix}$$

cos⁻¹()   2nd [COS⁻¹] key

cos⁻¹(*expression1*) ⇒ *expression*
cos⁻¹(*list1*) ⇒ *list*

> cos⁻¹ (*expression1*) returns the angle whose cosine is *expression1* as an expression.
>
> cos⁻¹ (*list1*) returns a list of the inverse cosines of each element of *list1*.
>
> **Note:** The result is returned as either a degree or radian angle, according to the current angle mode setting.

In Degree angle mode:

cos⁻¹(1) [ENTER]   0

In Radian angle mode:

cos⁻¹({0,.2,.5}) [ENTER]

$$\{\frac{\pi}{2} \quad 1.369... \quad 1.047...\}$$

---

cos⁻¹(*squareMatrix1*) ⇒ *squareMatrix*

> Returns the matrix inverse cosine of *squareMatrix1*. This is *not* the same as calculating the inverse cosine of each element. For information about the calculation method, refer to **cos()** on page 109.
>
> *squareMatrix1* must be diagonalizable. The result always contains floating-point numbers.

In Radian angle mode and Rectangular complex format mode:

cos⁻¹([1,5,3;4,2,1;6,‑2,1]) [ENTER]

$$\begin{bmatrix} 1.734...+.064...\cdot i & -1.490...+2.105...\cdot i & ... \\ -.725...+1.515...\cdot i & .623...+.778...\cdot i & ... \\ -2.083...+2.632...\cdot i & 1.790...-1.271...\cdot i & ... \end{bmatrix}$$

cosh()   MATH/Hyperbolic menu

cosh(*expression1*) ⇒ *expression*
cosh(*list1*) ⇒ *list*

> cosh (*expression1*) returns the hyperbolic cosine of the argument as an expression.
>
> cosh (*list*) returns a list of the hyperbolic cosines of each element of *list1*.

cosh(1.2) [ENTER]   1.810...

cosh({0,1.2}) [ENTER]   {1   1.810...}

---

cosh(*squareMatrix1*) ⇒ *squareMatrix*

> Returns the matrix hyperbolic cosine of *squareMatrix1*. This is *not* the same as calculating the hyperbolic cosine of each element. For information about the calculation method, refer to **cos()** on page 109.
>
> *squareMatrix1* must be diagonalizable. The result always contains floating-point numbers.

In Radian angle mode:

cosh([1,5,3;4,2,1;6,‑2,1]) [ENTER]

$$\begin{bmatrix} 421.255 & 253.909 & 216.905 \\ 327.635 & 255.301 & 202.958 \\ 226.297 & 216.623 & 167.628 \end{bmatrix}$$

cosh⁻¹()   MATH/Hyperbolic menu

cosh⁻¹(*expression1*) ⇒ *expression*
cosh⁻¹(*list1*) ⇒ *list*

> **cosh⁻¹** (*expression1*) returns the inverse hyperbolic cosine of the argument as an expression.

> **cosh⁻¹** (*list1*) returns a list of the inverse hyperbolic cosines of each element of *list1*.

```
cosh⁻¹(1) ENTER                          0
cosh⁻¹({1,2.1,3}) ENTER
                     {0   1.372...   cosh⁻¹(3)}
```

cosh⁻¹(*squareMatrix1*) ⇒ *squareMatrix*

> Returns the matrix inverse hyperbolic cosine of *squareMatrix1*. This is *not* the same as calculating the inverse hyperbolic cosine of each element. For information about the calculation method, refer to **cos()** on page 109.

> *squareMatrix1* must be diagonalizable. The result always contains floating-point numbers.

In Radian angle mode and Rectangular complex format mode:

```
cosh⁻¹([1,5,3;4,2,1;6,-2,1]) ENTER
```

$$\begin{bmatrix} 2.525...+1.734...\cdot i & -.009...-1.490...\cdot i & ... \\ .486...-.725...\cdot i & 1.662...+.623...\cdot i & ... \\ -.322...-2.083...\cdot i & 1.267...+1.790...\cdot i & ... \end{bmatrix}$$

crossP()   MATH/Matrix/Vector ops menu

crossP(*list1*, *list2*) ⇒ *list*

> Returns the cross product of *list1* and *list2* as a list.

> *list1* and *list2* must have equal dimension, and the dimension must be either 2 or 3.

```
crossP({a1,b1},{a2,b2}) ENTER
                        {0  0  a1·b2-a2·b1}
crossP({0.1,2.2,-5},{1,-.5,0}) ENTER
                        {-2.5  -5.  -2.25}
```

crossP(*vector1*, *vector2*) ⇒ *vector*

> Returns a row or column vector (depending on the arguments) that is the cross product of *vector1* and *vector2*.

> Both *vector1* and *vector2* must be row vectors, or both must be column vectors. Both vectors must have equal dimension, and the dimension must be either 2 or 3.

```
crossP([1,2,3],[4,5,6]) ENTER
                            [-3  6  -3]
crossP([1,2],[3,4]) ENTER
                            [0  0  -2]
```

cSolve(*equation, var***)** $\Rightarrow$ *Boolean expression*

Returns candidate complex solutions of an equation for *var*. The goal is to produce candidates for all real and non-real solutions. Even if *equation* is real, **cSolve()** allows non-real results in real mode.

Although the TI-92 Plus processes all undefined variables as if they were real, **cSolve()** can solve polynomial equations for complex solutions.

cSolve() temporarily sets the domain to complex during the solution even if the current domain is real. In the complex domain, fractional powers having odd denominators use the principal rather than the real branch. Consequently, solutions from **solve()** to equations involving such fractional powers are not necessarily a subset of those from **cSolve()**.

cSolve() starts with exact symbolic methods. Except in EXACT mode, **cSolve()** also uses iterative approximate complex polynomial factoring, if necessary.

Note: See also **cZeros()** (page 116), **solve()** (page 188), and **zeros()** (page 204).

Note: If *equation* is non-polynomial with functions such as **abs()**, **angle()**, **conj()**, **real()**, or **imag()**, you should place an underscore _ (2nd P) at the end of *var*. By default, a variable is treated as a real value. If you use *var_*, the variable is treated as complex.

You should also use *var_* for any other variables in *equation* that might have unreal values. Otherwise, you may receive unexpected results.

cSolve(x^3=-1,x) ENTER
solve(x^3=-1,x) ENTER

$$\blacksquare \text{cSolve}\left(x^3 = -1, x\right)$$
$$x = 1/2 + \frac{\sqrt{3}}{2} \cdot i \text{ or } x = 1/2 - \frac{\sqrt{3}}{2} \cdot i \text{ or } x = -1$$
$$\blacksquare \text{solve}\left(x^3 = -1, x\right) \qquad\qquad x = -1$$

cSolve(x^(1/3)=-1,x) ENTER   false

solve(x^(1/3)=-1,x) ENTER   x = -1

Display Digits mode in Fix 2:

exact(cSolve(x^5+4x^4+5x^3-6x-3=0, x)) ENTER
cSolve(ans(1),x) ENTER

$$\blacksquare \text{exact}\left(\text{cSolve}\left(x^5 + 4 \cdot x^4 + 5 \cdot x^3 - 6 \cdot x - 3 = \blacktriangleright\right.\right.$$
$$x \cdot \left(x^4 + 4 \cdot x^3 + 5 \cdot x^2 - 6\right) = 3$$
$$\blacksquare \text{cSolve}\left(x \cdot \left(x^4 + 4 \cdot x^3 + 5 \cdot x^2 - 6\right) = 3, x\right)$$
$$x = -1.11 + 1.07 \cdot i \text{ or } x = -1.11 - 1.07 \cdot i \blacktriangleright$$

z is treated as real:

cSolve(conj(z)=1+*i*,z) ENTER   z=1+*i*

z_ is treated as complex:

cSolve(conj(z_)=1+*i*,z_) ENTER

z_=1-*i*

cSolve(*equation1* **and** *equation2* [**and** ...],
{*varOrGuess1, varOrGuess2* [, ...]}**)**
⇒ *Boolean expression*

Returns candidate complex solutions to the simultaneous algebraic equations, where each *varOrGuess* specifies a variable that you want to solve for.

Optionally, you can specify an initial guess for a variable. Each *varOrGuess* must have the form:

variable
– or –
variable = real or non-real number

For example, x is valid and so is x=3+*i*.

<u>If all of the equations are polynomials and if you do NOT specify any initial guesses,</u> **cSolve()** uses the lexical Gröbner/Buchberger elimination method to attempt to determine **all** complex solutions.

Complex solutions can include both real and non-real solutions, as in the example to the right.

Note: The following examples use an underscore _ (2nd P) so that the variables will be treated as complex.

```
cSolve(u_*v_-u_=v_ and
v_^2=-u_,{u_,v_})  ENTER
```

$$u\_=1/2 + \frac{\sqrt{3}}{2}\cdot i \text{ and } v\_=1/2 - \frac{\sqrt{3}}{2}\cdot i$$
$$\text{or } u\_=1/2 - \frac{\sqrt{3}}{2}\cdot i \text{ and } v\_=1/2 + \frac{\sqrt{3}}{2}\cdot i$$
$$\text{or } u\_=0 \text{ and } v\_=0$$

You can omit solution variables whose values are not of interest, as in the example to the right.

```
cSolve(u_*v_-u_=v_ and
v_^2=-u_,{u_})  ENTER
```

$$u\_=1/2 + \frac{\sqrt{3}}{2}\cdot i$$
$$\text{or } u\_=1/2 - \frac{\sqrt{3}}{2}\cdot i$$
$$\text{or } u\_=0$$

<u>Simultaneous *polynomial* equations can have extra variables that have no values,</u> but represent given numeric values that could be substituted later.

```
cSolve(u_*v_-u_=c_*v_ and
v_^2=-u_,{u_,v_})  ENTER
```

$$u\_= \frac{-(\sqrt{1-4\cdot c\_}+1)^2}{4} \text{ and } v\_= \frac{\sqrt{1-4\cdot c\_}+1}{2}$$
$$\text{or } u\_= \frac{-(\sqrt{1-4\cdot c\_}-1)^2}{4} \text{ and } v\_= \frac{-(\sqrt{1-4\cdot c\_}-1)}{2}$$
$$\text{or } u\_=0 \text{ and } v\_=0$$

<u>You can also include solution variables that do not appear in the equations.</u> These solutions show how families of solutions might contain arbitrary constants of the form @*k*, where *k* is an integer suffix from 1 through 255. The suffix resets to 1 when you use **ClrHome** or F1 8:Clear Home.

```
cSolve(u_*v_-u_=v_ and
v_^2=-u_,{u_,v_,w_})  ENTER
```

$$u\_=1/2 + \frac{\sqrt{3}}{2}\cdot i \text{ and } v\_=1/2 - \frac{\sqrt{3}}{2}\cdot i$$
$$\text{and } w\_=@1$$
$$\text{or } u\_=1/2 - \frac{\sqrt{3}}{2}\cdot i \text{ and } v\_=1/2 + \frac{\sqrt{3}}{2}\cdot i$$
$$\text{and } w\_=@1$$
$$\text{or } u\_=0 \text{ and } v\_=0 \text{ and } w\_=@1$$

For polynomial systems, computation time or memory exhaustion may depend strongly on the order in which you list solution variables. If your initial choice exhausts memory or your patience, try rearranging the variables in the equations and/or *varOrGuess* list.

If you do not include any guesses and if any equation is non-polynomial in any variable but all equations are linear in all solution variables, **cSolve()** uses Gaussian elimination to attempt to determine all solutions.

```
cSolve(u_+v_=e^(w_) and u_-v_=i,
{u_,v_}) ENTER
```

$$u\_ = \frac{e^{w\_}}{2} +1/2 \cdot i \text{ and } v\_ = \frac{e^{w\_}-i}{2}$$

If a system is neither polynomial in all of its variables nor linear in its solution variables, **cSolve()** determines at most one solution using an approximate iterative method. To do so, the number of solution variables must equal the number of equations, and all other variables in the equations must simplify to numbers.

```
cSolve(e^(z_)=w_ and w_=z_^2,
{w_,z_}) ENTER
          w_=.494... and z_=-.703...
```

A non-real guess is often necessary to determine a non-real solution. For convergence, a guess might have to be rather close to a solution.

```
cSolve(e^(z_)=w_ and w_=z_^2,
{w_,z_=1+i}) ENTER
          w_=.149...+4.891...·i
     and z_=1.588...+1.540...·i
```

CubicReg   MATH/Statistics/Regressions menu

CubicReg *list1*, *list2*[, [*list3*] [, *list4*, *list5*]]

In function graphing mode.

Calculates the cubic polynomial regression and updates all the statistics variables.

All the lists must have equal dimensions except for *list5*.

list1 represents xlist.
list2 represents ylist.
list3 represents frequency.
list4 represents category codes.
list5 represents category include list.

Note: *list1* through *list4* must be a variable name or c1–c99 (columns in the last data variable shown in the Data/Matrix Editor). *list5* does not have to be a variable name and cannot be c1–c99.

```
{0,1,2,3,4,5,6}→L1 ENTER       {0 1 2 ...}
{0,2,3,4,3,4,6}→L2 ENTER       {0 2 3 ...}
CubicReg L1,L2 ENTER               Done
ShowStat ENTER
```

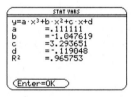

```
ENTER
regeq(x)→y1(x) ENTER               Done
NewPlot 1,1,L1,L2 ENTER            Done
```

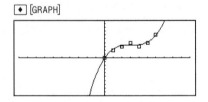

cumSum()   MATH/List menu

cumSum(*list1***)** ⇒ *list*

```
cumSum({1,2,3,4}) ENTER       {1 3 6 10}
```

Returns a list of the cumulative sums of the elements in *list1*, starting at element 1.

cumSum(*matrix1***)** ⇒ *matrix*

Returns a matrix of the cumulative sums of the elements in *matrix1*. Each element is the cumulative sum of the column from top to bottom.

$$[1,2;3,4;5,6] \rightarrow m1 \text{ ENTER} \quad \begin{bmatrix} 1 & 2 \\ 3 & 4 \\ 5 & 6 \end{bmatrix}$$

$$\text{cumSum}(m1) \text{ ENTER} \quad \begin{bmatrix} 1 & 2 \\ 4 & 6 \\ 9 & 12 \end{bmatrix}$$

CustmOff CATALOG

CustmOff

Removes a custom toolbar.

CustmOn and **CustmOff** enable a program to control a custom toolbar. Manually, you can press [2nd] [CUSTOM] to toggle a custom toolbar on and off. Also, a custom toolbar is removed automatically when you change applications.

See **Custom** program listing example on page 115.

CustmOn CATALOG

CustmOn

Activates a custom toolbar that has already been set up in a **Custom...EndCustm** block.

CustmOn and **CustmOff** enable a program to control a custom toolbar. Manually, you can press [2nd] [CUSTOM] to toggle a custom toolbar on and off.

See **Custom** program listing example on page 115.

Custom [2nd] [CUSTOM] key

Custom
  block
EndCustm

Sets up a toolbar that is activated when you press [2nd] [CUSTOM]. It is very similar to the **ToolBar** instruction (page 200) except that Title and Item statements cannot have labels.

block can be either a single statement or a series of statements separated with the ":" character.

Note: [2nd] [CUSTOM] acts as a toggle. The first instance invokes the menu, and the second instance removes the menu. The menu is removed also when you change applications.

Program listing:

```
:Test()
:Prgm
:Custom
:Title    "Lists"
:Item     "List1"
:Item     "Scores"
:Item     "L3"
:Title    "Fractions"
:Item     "f(x)"
:Item     "h(x)"
:Title    "Graph"
:EndCustm
:EndPrgm
```

Cycle CATALOG

Cycle

Transfers program control immediately to the next iteration of the current loop (**For**, **While**, or **Loop**).

Cycle is not allowed outside the three looping structures (**For**, **While**, or **Loop**).

Program listing:

```
:© Sum the integers from 1 to 100
  skipping 50.
:0→temp
:For i,1,100,1
:If i=50
:Cycle
:temp+i→temp
:EndFor
:Disp temp
```

Contents of temp after execution: 5000

CyclePic   CATALOG

CyclePic *picNameString, n* [, [*wait*] , [*cycles*], [*direction*]]

Displays all the PIC variables specified and at the specified interval. The user has optional control over the time between pictures, the number of times to cycle through the pictures, and the direction to go, circular or forward and backwards.

direction is 1 for circular or ⁻1 for forward and backwards. Default = 1.

1. Save three pics named pic1, pic2, and pic3.

2. Enter: `CyclePic "pic",3,.5,4,⁻1`

3. The three pictures (3) will be displayed automatically—one-half second (. 5) between pictures, for four cycles (4), and forward and backwards (⁻1).

▶Cylind   MATH/Matrix/Vector ops menu

vector ▶**Cylind**

Displays the row or column vector in cylindrical form [r∠θ, z].

vector must have exactly three elements. It can be either a row or a column.

$[2,2,3]$ ▶Cylind $\boxed{\text{ENTER}}$ $[2 \cdot \sqrt{2} \ \angle \frac{\pi}{4} \ 3]$

cZeros()   MATH/Algebra/Complex menu

cZeros(*expression, var***)** ⇒ *list*

Returns a list of candidate real and non-real values of *var* that make *expression*=0. **cZeros()** does this by computing **exp▶list(cSolve(***expression*=0,*var***),***var***)**. Otherwise, **cZeros()** is similar to **zeros()**.

Note: See also **cSolve()** (page 112), **solve()** (page 188), and **zeros()** (page 204).

Note: If *expression* is non-polynomial with functions such as **abs()**, **angle()**, **conj()**, **real()**, or **imag()**, you should place an underscore _ ($\boxed{\text{2nd}}$ P) at the end of *var*. By default, a variable is treated as a real value. If you use *var_*, the variable is treated as complex.

You should also use *var_* for any other variables in *expression* that might have unreal values. Otherwise, you may receive unexpected results.

Display Digits mode in Fix 3:

`cZeros(x^5+4x^4+5x^3-6x-3,x)` $\boxed{\text{ENTER}}$
$\{^{-}2.125 \ \ ^{-}.612 \ \ .965$
$^{-}1.114 - 1.073 \cdot i \ \ ^{-}1.114 + 1.073 \cdot i\}$

z is treated as real:

`cZeros(conj(z)-1-i,z)` $\boxed{\text{ENTER}}$ $\{1+i\}$

z_ is treated as complex:

`cZeros(conj(z_)-1-i,z_)` $\boxed{\text{ENTER}}$ $\{1-i\}$

cZeros({*expression1, expression2* [, ...]}, {*varOrGuess1, varOrGuess2* [, ...]}**)** ⇒ *matrix*

Returns candidate positions where the expressions are zero simultaneously. Each *varOrGuess* specifies an unknown whose value you seek.

Optionally, you can specify an initial guess for a variable. Each *varOrGuess* must have the form:

variable
– or –
variable = *real or non-real number*

For example, x is valid and so is x=3+*i*.

If all of the expressions are polynomials and you do NOT specify any initial guesses, **cZeros()** uses the lexical Gröbner/Buchberger elimination method to attempt to determine **all** complex zeros.

Complex zeros can include both real and non-real zeros, as in the example to the right.

Each row of the resulting matrix represents an alternate zero, with the components ordered the same as the *varOrGuess* list. To extract a row, index the matrix by [*row*].

You can omit unknowns whose values are not of interest, as in the example to the right.

Simultaneous *polynomials* can have extra variables that have no values, but represent given numeric values that could be substituted later.

You can also include unknown variables that do not appear in the expressions. These zeros show how families of zeros might contain arbitrary constants of the form @*k*, where *k* is an integer suffix from 1 through 255. The suffix resets to 1 when you use **ClrHome** or F1 8:Clear Home.

For polynomial systems, computation time or memory exhaustion may depend strongly on the order in which you list unknowns. If your initial choice exhausts memory or your patience, try rearranging the variables in the expressions and/or *varOrGuess* list.

If you do not include any guesses and if any expression is non-polynomial in any variable but all expressions are linear in all unknowns, **cZeros()** uses Gaussian elimination to attempt to determine all zeros.

If a system is neither polynomial in all of its variables nor linear in its unknowns, **cZeros()** determines at most one zero using an approximate iterative method. To do so, the number of unknowns must equal the number of expressions, and all other variables in the expressions must simplify to numbers.

A non-real guess is often necessary to determine a non-real zero. For convergence, a guess might have to be rather close to a zero.

Note: The following examples use an underscore _ ([2nd] P) so that the variables will be treated as complex.

cZeros({u_*v_–u_–v_,v_^2+u_}, {u_,v_}) [ENTER]

$$\begin{bmatrix} 1/2 - \frac{\sqrt{3}}{2} \cdot i & 1/2 + \frac{\sqrt{3}}{2} \cdot i \\ 1/2 + \frac{\sqrt{3}}{2} \cdot i & 1/2 - \frac{\sqrt{3}}{2} \cdot i \\ 0 & 0 \end{bmatrix}$$

Extract row 2:

ans(1)[2] [ENTER]

$$\begin{bmatrix} 1/2 + \frac{\sqrt{3}}{2} \cdot i & 1/2 - \frac{\sqrt{3}}{2} \cdot i \end{bmatrix}$$

cZeros({u_*v_–u_–v_,v_^2+u_},{u_}) [ENTER]

$$\begin{bmatrix} 1/2 - \frac{\sqrt{3}}{2} \cdot i \\ 1/2 + \frac{\sqrt{3}}{2} \cdot i \\ 0 \end{bmatrix}$$

cZeros({u_*v_–u_–(c_*v_),v_^2+u_}, {u_,v_}) [ENTER]

$$\begin{bmatrix} \frac{-(\sqrt{1-4\cdot c_}+1)^2}{4} & \frac{\sqrt{1-4\cdot c_}+1}{2} \\ \frac{-(\sqrt{1-4\cdot c_}-1)^2}{4} & \frac{-(\sqrt{1-4\cdot c_}-1)}{2} \\ 0 & 0 \end{bmatrix}$$

cZeros({u_*v_–u_–v_,v_^2+u_}, {u_,v_,w_}) [ENTER]

$$\begin{bmatrix} 1/2 - \frac{\sqrt{3}}{2} \cdot i & 1/2 + \frac{\sqrt{3}}{2} \cdot i & @1 \\ 1/2 + \frac{\sqrt{3}}{2} \cdot i & 1/2 - \frac{\sqrt{3}}{2} \cdot i & @1 \\ 0 & 0 & @1 \end{bmatrix}$$

cZeros({u_+v_–e^(w_),u_–v_– i}, {u_,v_}) [ENTER]

$$\begin{bmatrix} \frac{e^{w_}}{2} +1/2 \cdot i & \frac{e^{w_}-i}{2} \end{bmatrix}$$

cZeros({e^(z_)–w_,w_–z_^2}, {w_,z_}) [ENTER]

$$\begin{bmatrix} .494\ldots & -.703\ldots \end{bmatrix}$$

cZeros({e^(z_)–w_,w_–z_^2}, {w_,z_=1+ i}) [ENTER]

$$\begin{bmatrix} .149\ldots+4.89\ldots\cdot i & 1.588\ldots+1.540\ldots\cdot i \end{bmatrix}$$

$d()$ 2nd [d] key or MATH/Calculus menu

$d(expression1, var\,[,order])\ \Rightarrow\ expression$
$d(list1,var\,[,order])\ \Rightarrow\ list$
$d(matrix1,var\,[,order])\ \Rightarrow\ matrix$

Returns the first derivative of *expression1*
with respect to variable *var. expression1* can
be a list or a matrix.

order, if included, must be an integer. If the
order is less than zero, the result will be an
anti-derivative.

$d()$ does not follow the normal evaluation
mechanism of fully simplifying its arguments
and then applying the function definition to
these fully simplified arguments. Instead, $d()$
performs the following steps:

1. Simplify the second argument only to the
   extent that it does not lead to a non-
   variable.

2. Simplify the first argument only to the
   extent that it does recall any stored value
   for the variable determined by step 1.

3. Determine the symbolic derivative of the
   result of step 2 with respect to the
   variable from step 1.

4. If the variable from step 1 has a stored
   value or a value specified by a "with" (|)
   operator, substitute that value into the
   result from step 3.

$d(3x^3-x+7,x)$ ENTER $9x^2-1$

$d(3x^3-x+7,x,2)$ ENTER $18 \cdot x$

$d(f(x)*g(x),x)$ ENTER

$$\frac{d}{dx}(f(x)) \cdot g(x) + \frac{d}{dx}(g(x)) \cdot f(x)$$

$d(\sin(f(x)),x)$ ENTER

$$\cos(f(x))\frac{d}{dx}(f(x))$$

$d(x^3,x)\,|\,x=5$ ENTER 75

$d(d(x^2*y^3,x),y)$ ENTER $6 \cdot y^2 \cdot x$

$d(x^2,x,\text{-}1)$ ENTER $\dfrac{x^3}{3}$

$d(\{x^2,x^3,x^4\},x)$ ENTER
$$\{2 \cdot x \quad 3 \cdot x^2 \quad 4 \cdot x^3\}$$

▶DD   MATH/Angle menu

$number$ ▶DD $\Rightarrow\ value$
$list1$ ▶DD $\Rightarrow\ list$
$matrix1$ ▶DD $\Rightarrow\ matrix$

Returns the decimal equivalent of the
argument. The argument is a number, list, or
matrix that is interpreted by the Mode
setting in radians or degrees.

Note: ▶DD can also accept input in radians.

In Degree angle mode:

$1.5°$ ▶DD ENTER $1.5°$

$45°22'14.3"$ ▶DD ENTER $45.370...°$

$\{45°22'14.3",60°0'0"\}$ ▶DD ENTER
$$\{45.370... \quad 60\}°$$

In Radian angle mode:

1.5 ▶DD ENTER $85.9°$

▶Dec MATH/Base menu

integer1 ▶**Dec** ⟹ *integer*

Converts *integer1* to a decimal (base 10) number. A binary or hexadecimal entry must always have a 0b or 0h prefix, respectively.

┌─ Zero, not the letter O, followed by b or h.

0b *binaryNumber*
0h *hexadecimalNumber*

└── A binary number can have up to 32 digits. A hexadecimal number can have up to 8.

Without a prefix, *integer1* is treated as decimal. The result is displayed in decimal, regardless of the Base mode.

```
0b10011 ▶Dec ENTER          19

0h1F ▶Dec ENTER             31
```

Define CATALOG

Define *funcName*(*arg1Name, arg2Name, ...*) = *expression*

Creates *funcName* as a user-defined function. You then can use *funcName*(), just as you use built-in functions. The function evaluates *expression* using the supplied arguments and returns the result.

funcName cannot be the name of a system variable or built-in function.

The argument names are placeholders; you should not use those same names as arguments when you use the function.

Note: This form of **Define** is equivalent to executing the expression: *expression*→ *funcName*(*arg1Name*, *arg2Name*).
This command also can be used to define simple variables; for example, Define a=3.

```
Define g(x,y)=2x-3y ENTER     Done
g(1,2) ENTER                   -4
1→a:2→b:g(a,b) ENTER           -4

Define h(x)=when(x<2,2x-3, -2x+3)
ENTER                         Done

h(-3) ENTER                    -9
h(4) ENTER                     -5

Define eigenvl(a)=
  cZeros(det(identity(dim(a)
  [1])-x*a),x) ENTER          Done
eigenvl([-1,2;4,3]) ENTER
```

$$\left\{ \frac{2 \cdot \sqrt{3} - 1}{11} \quad \frac{-(2 \cdot \sqrt{3} + 1)}{11} \right\}$$

Define *funcName*(*arg1Name, arg2Name, ...*) = **Func**
    block
EndFunc

Is identical to the previous form of **Define**, except that in this form, the user-defined function *funcName*() can execute a block of multiple statements.

block can be either a single statement or a series of statements separated with the ":" character. *block* also can include expressions and instructions (such as **If**, **Then**, **Else**, and **For**). This allows the function *funcName*() to use the **Return** instruction to return a specific result.

Note: It is usually easier to author and edit this form of Function in the program editor rather than on the entry line.

```
Define g(x,y)=Func:If x>y Then
:Return x:Else:Return y:EndIf
:EndFunc ENTER               Done

g(3,-7) ENTER                   3
```

Define *progName*(*arg1Name, arg2Name, ...*) **= Prgm**
   block
EndPrgm

   Creates *progName* as a program or
   subprogram, but cannot return a result using
   Return. Can execute a block of multiple
   statements.

   block can be either a single statement or a
   series of statements separated with the ":"
   character. *block* also can include expressions
   and instructions (such as **If**, **Then**, **Else**, and
   For) without restrictions.

   Note: It is usually easier to author and edit a
   program block in the Program Editor rather
   than on the entry line.

```
Define listinpt()=prgm:Local
n,i,str1,num:InputStr "Enter
name of list",str1:Input "No. of
elements",n:For i,1,n,1:Input
"element "&string(i),num:
num→#str1[i]:EndFor:EndPrgm ENTER
                              Done

listinpt() ENTER    Enter name of list
```

DelFold   CATALOG

DelFold *folderName1*[, *folderName2*] [, *folderName3*] ...

   Deletes user-defined folders with the names
   folderName1, *folderName2*, etc. An error
   message is displayed if the folders contain
   any variables.

   Note: You cannot delete the main folder.

```
NewFold games ENTER            Done
(creates the folder games)

DelFold games ENTER            Done
(deletes the folder games)
```

DelVar   CATALOG

DelVar *var1*[, *var2*] [, *var3*] ...

   Deletes the specified variables from memory.

```
2→a ENTER                         2
(a+2)^2 ENTER                    16
DelVar a ENTER                 Done
(a+2)^2 ENTER              (a + 2)²
```

deSolve()   MATH/Calculus menu

deSolve(*1stOr2ndOrderOde, independentVar,*
   *dependentVar***)** ⇒ *a general solution*

   Returns an equation that explicitly or
   implicitly specifies a general solution to the
   1st- or 2nd-order ordinary differential
   equation (ODE). In the ODE:

   • Use a prime symbol (', press 2nd B) to
     denote the 1st derivative of the dependent
     variable with respect to the independent
     variable.

   • Use two prime symbols to denote the
     corresponding second derivative.

   The ' symbol is used for derivatives within
   deSolve() only. In other cases, use *d*().

   The general solution of a 1st-order equation
   contains an arbitrary constant of the form
   @*k*, where *k* is an integer suffix from 1
   through 255. The suffix resets to 1 when you
   use **ClrHome** or F1 8: Clear Home. The
   solution of a 2nd-order equation contains two
   such constants.

Note: To type a prime symbol ('), press
2nd B.

```
deSolve(y''+2y'+y=x^2,x,y) ENTER
        y=(@1·x+@2)·e⁻ˣ+x²-4·x+6

right(ans(1))→temp ENTER
            (@1·x+@2)·e⁻ˣ+x²-4·x+6

d(temp,x,2)+2*d(temp,x)+temp-x^2
ENTER                            0

delVar temp ENTER             Done
```

Apply **solve()** to an implicit solution if you want to try to convert it to one or more equivalent explicit solutions.

When comparing your results with textbook or manual solutions, be aware that different methods introduce arbitrary constants at different points in the calculation, which may produce different general solutions.

```
deSolve(y'=(cos(y))^2*x,x,y) [ENTER]
```
$$\tan(y)=\frac{x^2}{2}+@3$$

```
solve(ans(1),y) [ENTER]
```
$$y=\tan^{-1}\left(\frac{x^2+2\cdot@3}{2}\right)+@n1\cdot\pi$$

Note: To type an @ symbol, press [2nd] R.

```
ans(1)|@3=c-1 and @n1=0 [ENTER]
```
$$y=\tan^{-1}\left(\frac{x^2+2\cdot(c-1)}{2}\right)$$

---

deSolve(1stOrderOde **and** initialCondition, independentVar, dependentVar**)**
⇒ a particular solution

Returns a particular solution that satisfies 1stOrderOde and initialCondition. This is usually easier than determining a general solution, substituting initial values, solving for the arbitrary constant, and then substituting that value into the general solution.

initialCondition is an equation of the form:

dependentVar (initialIndependentValue) = initialDependentValue

The initialIndependentValue and initialDependentValue can be variables such as x0 and y0 that have no stored values. Implicit differentiation can help verify implicit solutions.

```
sin(y)=(y*e^(x)+cos(y))y'→ode [ENTER]
```
$$\sin(y)=(e^x\cdot y+\cos(y))\cdot y'$$

```
deSolve(ode and y(0)=0,x,y)→soln
[ENTER]
```
$$\frac{^-(2\cdot\sin(y)+y^2)}{2}=^-(e^x-1)\cdot e^{-x}\cdot\sin(y)$$

```
soln|x=0 and y=0 [ENTER]                    true
d(right(eq)-left(eq),x)/
(d(left(eq)-right(eq),y))
→impdif(eq,x,y) [ENTER]
                                            Done
ode|y'=impdif(soln,x,y) [ENTER]
                                            true
delVar ode,soln [ENTER]               Done
```

---

deSolve(2ndOrderOde **and** initialCondition1 **and** initialCondition2, independentVar, dependentVar**)** ⇒ a particular solution

Returns a particular solution that satisfies 2ndOrderOde and has a specified value of the dependent variable and its first derivative at one point.

For initialCondition1, use the form:

dependentVar (initialIndependentValue) = initialDependentValue

For initialCondition2, use the form:

dependentVar' (initialIndependentValue) = initial1stDerivativeValue

```
deSolve(y''=y^(-1/2) and y(0)=0
and y'(0)=0,t,y) [ENTER]
```
$$\frac{2\cdot y^{3/4}}{3}=t$$

```
solve(ans(1),y) [ENTER]
```
$$y=\frac{2^{2/3}\cdot(3\cdot t)^{4/3}}{4}\ \text{and}\ t\geq0$$

---

deSolve(2ndOrderOde **and** boundaryCondition1 **and** boundaryCondition2, independentVar, dependentVar**)** ⇒ a particular solution

Returns a particular solution that satisfies 2ndOrderOde and has specified values at two different points.

```
deSolve(w''-2w'/x+(9+2/x^2)w=
x*e^(x) and w(π/6)=0 and
w(π/3)=0,x,w) [ENTER]
```
$$w=\frac{e^{\frac{\pi}{3}}\cdot x\cdot\cos(3\cdot x)}{10}$$

$$-\frac{e^{\frac{\pi}{6}}\cdot x\cdot\sin(3\cdot x)}{10}+\frac{x\cdot e^x}{10}$$

det() MATH/Matrix menu

det(*squareMatrix*[, *tol*]) ⇒ *expression*

Returns the determinant of *squareMatrix*.

Optionally, any matrix element is treated as zero if its absolute value is less than *tol*. This tolerance is used only if the matrix has floating-point entries and does not contain any symbolic variables that have not been assigned a value. Otherwise, *tol* is ignored.

- If you use ◆ ENTER or set the mode to Exact/Approx=APPROXIMATE, computations are done using floating-point arithmetic.

- If *tol* is omitted or not used, the default tolerance is calculated as:

  5ᴇ⁻14 ∗ **max(dim(**squareMatrix**))** ∗ **rowNorm(**squareMatrix**)**

det([a,b;c,d]) ENTER   a·d − b·c

det([1,2;3,4]) ENTER   ⁻2

det(identity(3) − x∗[1,⁻2,3;
⁻2,4,1;⁻6,⁻2,7]) ENTER
                ⁻(98·x^3 − 55·x^2 + 12·x − 1)

[1ᴇ20,1;0,1]→mat1 $\begin{bmatrix} 1.\text{ᴇ}20 & 1 \\ 0 & 1 \end{bmatrix}$

det(mat1) ENTER   0

det(mat1,.1) ENTER   1.ᴇ20

diag() MATH/Matrix menu

diag(*list*) ⇒ *matrix*
diag(*rowMatrix*) ⇒ *matrix*
diag(*columnMatrix*) ⇒ *matrix*

Returns a matrix with the values in the argument list or matrix in its main diagonal.

diag({2,4,6}) ENTER $\begin{bmatrix} 2 & 0 & 0 \\ 0 & 4 & 0 \\ 0 & 0 & 6 \end{bmatrix}$

---

diag(*squareMatrix*) ⇒ *rowMatrix*

Returns a row matrix containing the elements from the main diagonal of *squareMatrix*.

squareMatrix must be square.

[4,6,8;1,2,3;5,7,9] ENTER $\begin{bmatrix} 4 & 6 & 8 \\ 1 & 2 & 3 \\ 5 & 7 & 9 \end{bmatrix}$

diag(ans(1)) ENTER   [4 2 9]

Dialog CATALOG

Dialog
 block
EndDlog

Generates a dialog box when the program is executed.

block can be either a single statement or a series of statements separated with the ":" character. Valid *block* options in the F3 I/O, 1:Dialog menu item in the Program Editor are 1:Text, 2:Request, 4:DropDown, and 7:Title.

The variables in a dialog box can be given values that will be displayed as the default (or initial) value. If ENTER is pressed, the variables are updated from the dialog box and variable ok is set to 1. If ESC is pressed, its variables are not updated, and system variable ok is set to zero.

Program listing:

```
:Dlogtest()
:Prgm
:Dialog
:Title     "This is a dialog box"
:Request   "Your name",Str1
:Dropdown  "Month you were born",
  seq(string(i),i,1,12),Var1
:EndDlog
:EndPrgm
```

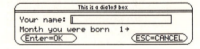

dim()   MATH/Matrix/Dimensions menu

dim(*list***)** ⇒ *integer*   dim({0,1,2}) `ENTER`   3

Returns the dimension of *list*.

---

dim(*matrix***)** ⇒ *list*   dim([1,-1,2;-2,3,5]) `ENTER`   {2 3}

Returns the dimensions of *matrix* as a two-element list {rows, columns}.

---

dim(*string***)** ⇒ *integer*   dim("Hello") `ENTER`   5

Returns the number of characters contained   dim("Hello"&" there") `ENTER`   11
in character string *string*.

Disp   CATALOG

Disp [*exprOrString1*] [, *exprOrString2*] ...   Disp "Hello" `ENTER`   Hello

Displays the current contents of the Program   Disp cos(2.3) `ENTER`   -.666…
I/O screen. If one or more *exprOrString* is
specified, each expression or character string   {1,2,3,4}→L1 `ENTER`
is displayed on a separate line of the Program   Disp L1 `ENTER`   {1   2   3   4}
I/O screen.
                                                                        Disp 180_min▶_hr `ENTER`   3.•_hr

An expression can include conversion
operations such as **▶DD** and **▶Rect**. You can   **Note:** To type an underscore (_), press
also use the ▶ operator (page 221) to perform   `2nd` P. To type ▶, press `2nd` Y.
unit and number base conversions.

If Pretty Print = ON, expressions are displayed
in pretty print.

From the Program I/O screen, you can press
`F5` to display the Home screen, or a program
can use **DispHome** (page 123).

DispG   CATALOG

DispG   In function graphing mode:

Displays the current contents of the Graph   Program segment:
screen.
                                                                          ⋮
                                                                        :5*cos(x)→y1(x)
                                                                        :-10→xmin
                                                                        :10→xmax
                                                                        :-5→ymin
                                                                        :5→ymax
                                                                        :DispG
                                                                          ⋮

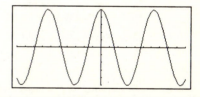

DispHome CATALOG

DispHome   Program segment:

Displays the current contents of the Home   ⋮
screen.   :Disp "The result is: ",xx
                                                                        :Pause "Press Enter to quit"
                                                                        :DispHome
                                                                        :EndPrgm

DispTbl CATALOG

DispTbl

Displays the current contents of the Table screen.

Note: The cursor pad is active for scrolling. Press [ESC] or [ENTER] to resume execution if in a program.

```
5*cos(x)→y1(x) [ENTER]
DispTbl [ENTER]
```

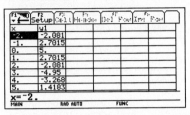

▶DMS MATH/Angle menu

expression ▶DMS
list ▶DMS
matrix ▶DMS

Interprets the argument as an angle and displays the equivalent DMS (*DDDDDD°MM′SS.ss″*) number. See °, ′, ″ on page 220 for DMS (degree, minutes, seconds) format.

Note: ▶DMS will convert from radians to degrees when used in radian mode. If the input is followed by a degree symbol (°), no conversion will occur. You can use ▶DMS only at the end of an entry line.

In Degree angle mode:

```
45.371 ▶DMS [ENTER]              45°22'15.6"

{45.371,60} ▶DMS [ENTER]
                         {45°22'15.6"   60°}
```

dotP() MATH/Matrix/Vector ops menu

dotP(*list1*, *list2*) ⇒ *expression*

Returns the "dot" product of two lists.

```
dotP({a,b,c},{d,e,f}) [ENTER]
                         a·d + b·e + c·f

dotP({1,2},{5,6}) [ENTER]                17
```

---

dotP(*vector1*, *vector2*) ⇒ *expression*

Returns the "dot" product of two vectors.

Both must be row vectors, or both must be column vectors.

```
dotP([a,b,c],[d,e,f]) [ENTER]
                         a·d + b·e + c·f

dotP([1,2,3],[4,5,6]) [ENTER]            32
```

DrawFunc CATALOG

DrawFunc *expression*

Draws *expression* as a function, using x as the independent variable.

Note: Regraphing erases all drawn items.

In function graphing mode and ZoomStd window:

```
DrawFunc 1.25x*cos(x) [ENTER]
```

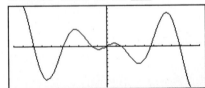

DrawInv CATALOG

DrawInv *expression*

Draws the inverse of *expression* by plotting x values on the y axis and y values on the x axis.

x is the independent variable.

Note: Regraphing erases all drawn items.

In function graphing mode and ZoomStd window:

```
DrawInv 1.25x*cos(x) ENTER
```

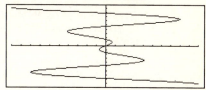

DrawParm CATALOG

DrawParm *expression1*, *expression2* [, *tmin*] [, *tmax*] [, *tstep*]

Draws the parametric equations *expression1* and *expression2*, using t as the independent variable.

Defaults for *tmin*, *tmax*, and *tstep* are the current settings for the Window variables tmin, tmax, and tstep. Specifying values does not alter the window settings. If the current graphing mode is not parametric, these three arguments are required.

Note: Regraphing erases all drawn items.

In function graphing mode and ZoomStd window:

```
DrawParm t*cos(t),t*sin(t),0,10,.1
ENTER
```

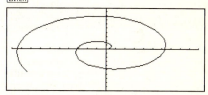

DrawPol CATALOG

DrawPol *expression*[, θ*min*] [, θ*max*] [, θ*step*]

Draws the polar graph of *expression*, using θ as the independent variable.

Defaults for θ*min*, θ*max*, and θ*step* are the current settings for the Window variables θmin, θmax, and θstep. Specifying values does not alter the window settings. If the current graphing mode is not polar, these three arguments are required.

Note: Regraphing erases all drawn items.

In function graphing mode and ZoomStd window:

```
DrawPol 5*cos(3*θ),0,3.5,.1 ENTER
```

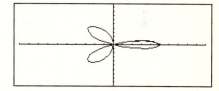

DrawSlp CATALOG

DrawSlp *x1*, *y1*, *slope*

Displays the graph and draws a line using the formula y−y1=slope·(x−x1).

Note: Regraphing erases all drawn items.

In function graphing mode and ZoomStd window:

```
DrawSlp 2,3,⁻2 ENTER
```

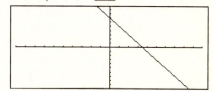

DropDown CATALOG

DropDown *titleString*, {*item1String*, *item2String*, ...}, *varName*

> Displays a drop-down menu with the name *titleString* and containing the items **1:***item1String*, **2:***item2String*, and so forth. **DropDown** must be within a **Dialog...EndDlog** block.
>
> If *varName* already exists and has a value within the range of items, the referenced item is displayed as the default selection. Otherwise, the menu's first item is the default selection.
>
> When you select an item from the menu, the corresponding number of the item is stored in the variable *varName*. (If necessary, **DropDown** creates *varName*.)

See **Dialog** program listing example on page 122.

DrwCtour CATALOG

DrwCtour *expression*
DrwCtour *list*

> Draws contours on the current 3D graph at the z values specified by *expression* or *list*. The 3D graphing mode must already be set. **DrwCtour** automatically sets the graph format style to CONTOUR LEVELS.
>
> By default, the graph automatically contains the number of equally spaced contours specified by the ncontour Window variable. **DrwCtour** draws contours in addition to the defaults.
>
> To turn off the default contours, set ncontour to zero, either by using the Window screen or by storing 0 to the ncontour system variable.

In 3D graphing mode:

```
(1/5)x^2+(1/5)y^2-10→z1(x,y) ENTER
                                  Done
-10→xmin:10→xmax ENTER               10
-10→ymin:10→ymax ENTER               10
-10→zmin:10→zmax ENTER               10
0→ncontour ENTER                      0
DrwCtour {-9,-4.5,-3,0,4.5,9} ENTER
```

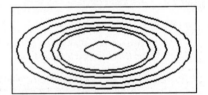

- Use the cursor to change the viewing angle. Press 0 (zero) to return to the original view.

- Press F to toggle between different graph format styles.

- Press X, Y, or Z to look down the corresponding axis.

E

2nd [EE] key

*mantissa***E***exponent*

> Enters a number in scientific notation. The number is interpreted as *mantissa* × 10^{exponent}.
>
> **Hint:** If you want to enter a power of 10 without causing a decimal value result, use 10^*integer*.

```
2.3E4 ENTER                      23000.
2.3E9+4.1E15 ENTER              4.1E15

3*10^4 ENTER                      30000
```

e^( )   [2nd] [e^x] **key**

e^(expression1**)** ⇒ expression

Returns e raised to the *expression1* power.

Note: Pressing [2nd] [e^x] to display e^(is different from accessing the character e from the QWERTY keyboard.

You can enter a complex number in $re^{i\theta}$ polar form. However, use this form in Radian angle mode only; it causes a Domain error in Degree angle mode.

e^(1) [ENTER]	e
e^(1.) [ENTER]	2.718...
e^(3)^2 [ENTER]	e^9

---

e^(list1**)** ⇒ list

Returns e raised to the power of each element in *list1*.

e^({1,1.,0,.5}) [ENTER]

{e 2.718... 1 1.648...}

---

e^(squareMatrix1**)** ⇒ squareMatrix

Returns the matrix exponential of *squareMatrix1*. This is *not* the same as calculating e raised to the power of each element. For information about the calculation method, refer to **cos()** on page 109.

squareMatrix1 must be diagonalizable. The result always contains floating-point numbers.

e^([1,5,3;4,2,1;6,-2,1]) [ENTER]

$$\begin{bmatrix} 782.209 & 559.617 & 456.509 \\ 680.546 & 488.795 & 396.521 \\ 524.929 & 371.222 & 307.879 \end{bmatrix}$$

---

eigVc( )   **MATH/Matrix menu**

eigVc(squareMatrix**)** ⇒ matrix

Returns a matrix containing the eigenvectors for a real or complex *squareMatrix*, where each column in the result corresponds to an eigenvalue. Note that an eigenvector is not unique; it may be scaled by any constant factor. The eigenvectors are normalized, meaning that if V = [$x_1, x_2, \ldots, x_n$], then:

$$\sqrt{x_1{}^2 + x_2{}^2 + \ldots + x_n{}^2} = 1$$

squareMatrix is first balanced with similarity transformations until the row and column norms are as close to the same value as possible. The *squareMatrix* is then reduced to upper Hessenberg form and the eigenvectors are computed via a Schur factorization.

In Rectangular complex format mode:

[-1,2,5;3,-6,9;2,-5,7]→m1 [ENTER]

$$\begin{bmatrix} -1 & 2 & 5 \\ 3 & -6 & 9 \\ 2 & -5 & 7 \end{bmatrix}$$

eigVc(m1) [ENTER]

$$\begin{bmatrix} -.800\ldots & .767\ldots & .767\ldots \\ .484\ldots & .573\ldots+.052\ldots\cdot i & .573\ldots-.052\ldots\cdot i \\ .352\ldots & .262\ldots+.096\ldots\cdot i & .262\ldots-.096\ldots\cdot i \end{bmatrix}$$

---

eigVl( )   **MATH/Matrix menu**

eigVl(squareMatrix**)** ⇒ list

Returns a list of the eigenvalues of a real or complex *squareMatrix*.

squareMatrix is first balanced with similarity transformations until the row and column norms are as close to the same value as possible. The *squareMatrix* is then reduced to upper Hessenberg form and the eigenvalues are computed from the upper Hessenberg matrix.

In Rectangular complex format mode:

[-1,2,5;3,-6,9;2,-5,7]→m1 [ENTER]

$$\begin{bmatrix} -1 & 2 & 5 \\ 3 & -6 & 9 \\ 2 & -5 & 7 \end{bmatrix}$$

eigVl(m1) [ENTER]

{-4.409... 2.204...+.763...·i 2.204...-.763...·i}

Else

See **If**, page 141.

ElseIf

CATALOG See also **If**, page 141.

If *Boolean expression1* **Then**
   block1
ElseIf *Boolean expression2* **Then**
   block2
   ⋮
ElseIf *Boolean expressionN* **Then**
   blockN
EndIf
   ⋮

ElseIf can be used as a program instruction for program branching.

Program segment:

```
 :
:If choice=1 Then
:  Goto option1
:  ElseIf choice=2 Then
:  Goto option2
:  ElseIf choice=3 Then
:  Goto option3
:  ElseIf choice=4 Then
:  Disp "Exiting Program"
:  Return
:EndIf
 :
```

EndCustm

See **Custom**, page 115.

EndDlog

See **Dialog**, page 122.

EndFor

See **For**, page 135.

EndFunc

See **Func**, page 136.

EndIf

See **If**, page 141.

EndLoop

See **Loop**, page 150.

EndPrgm

See **Prgm**, page 166.

EndTBar

See **ToolBar**, page 200.

EndTry

See **Try**, page 200.

EndWhile

See **While**, page 203.

entry()

CATALOG

entry() ⇒ *expression*
entry(*integer***)** ⇒ *expression*

Returns a previous entry-line entry from the Home screen history area.

integer, if included, specifies which entry expression in the history area. The default is 1, the most recently evaluated entry. Valid range is from 1 to 99 and cannot be an expression.

Note: If the last entry is still highlighted on the Home screen, pressing ENTER is equivalent to executing **entry(1)**.

On the Home screen:

1+1/x [ENTER]	$\frac{1}{x} + 1$
1+1/entry(1) [ENTER]	$\frac{-1}{x+1} + 2$
[ENTER]	$\frac{1}{2 \cdot (2 \cdot x+1)} + 3/2$
[ENTER]	$\frac{-1}{3 \cdot (3 \cdot x+2)} + 5/3$
entry(4) [ENTER]	$\frac{1}{x} + 1$

exact()   MATH/Number menu

exact(_expression1_ [, _tol_]**)** ⇒ _expression_
exact(_list1_ [, _tol_]**)** ⇒ _list_
exact(_matrix1_ [, _tol_]**)** ⇒ _matrix_

Uses Exact mode arithmetic regardless of the
Exact/Approx mode setting to return, when
possible, the rational-number equivalent of
the argument.

tol specifies the tolerance for the conversion;
the default is 0 (zero).

```
exact(.25) ENTER                    1/4

exact(.333333) ENTER        333333
                           ──────
                           1000000

exact(.33333,.001)                  1/3

exact(3.5x+y) ENTER         7·x
                            ─── + y
                             2

exact({.2,.33,4.125}) ENTER
                        {1/5  33   33/8}
                              ───
                              100
```

Exec   CATALOG

Exec _string_ [, _expression1_] [, _expression2_] ...

Executes a _string_ consisting of a series of
Motorola 68000 op-codes. These codes act as a
form of an assembly-language program. If
needed, the optional _expressions_ let you pass
one or more arguments to the program.

For more information, check the TI Web site:
http://www.ti.com/calc

Exit   CATALOG

Exit

Exits the current **For**, **While**, or **Loop** block.

Exit is not allowed outside the three looping
structures (**For**, **While**, or **Loop**).

Program listing:

```
:0→temp
:For i,1,100,1
:   temp+i→temp
:   If temp>20
:   Exit
:EndFor
:Disp temp
```

Contents of temp after execution: 21

exp▸list()   CATALOG

exp▸list(_expression,var_**)** ⇒ _list_

Examines _expression_ for equations that are
separated by the word "or," and returns a list
containing the right-hand sides of the
equations of the form _var=expression_. This
gives you an easy way to extract some
solution values embedded in the results of
the **solve()**, **cSolve()**, **fMin()**, and **fMax()**
functions.

Note: exp▸list() is not necessary with the
zeros and **cZeros()** functions because they
return a list of solution values directly.

```
solve(x^2-x-2=0,x) ENTER   x=2 or x=-1

exp▸list(solve(x^2-x-2=0,x),x) ENTER
                              {-1   2}
```

expand(*expression1* [, *var*]) ⇒ *expression*
expand(*list1* [,*var*]) ⇒ *list*
expand(*matrix1* [,*var*]) ⇒ *matrix*

expand(*expression1*) returns *expression1* expanded with respect to all its variables. The expansion is polynomial expansion for polynomials and partial fraction expansion for rational expressions.

The goal of **expand()** is to transform *expression1* into a sum and/or difference of simple terms. In contrast, the goal of **factor()** is to transform *expression1* into a product and/or quotient of simple factors.

expand((x+y+1)^2) ENTER
$$x^2 + 2 \cdot x \cdot y + 2 \cdot x + y^2 + 2 \cdot y + 1$$

expand((x^2-x+y^2-y)/(x^2*y^2-x^2
*y-x*y^2+x*y)) ENTER

$$\blacksquare \text{ expand}\left(\frac{x^2 - x + y^2 - y}{x^2 \cdot y^2 - x^2 \cdot y - x \cdot y^2 + x \cdot y}\right)$$
$$\frac{1}{x-1} - \frac{1}{x} + \frac{1}{y-1} - \frac{1}{y}$$

---

expand(*expression1*,*var*) returns *expression* expanded with respect to *var*. Similar powers of *var* are collected. The terms and their factors are sorted with *var* as the main variable. There might be some incidental factoring or expansion of the collected coefficients. Compared to omitting *var*, this often saves time, memory, and screen space, while making the expression more comprehensible.

expand((x+y+1)^2,y) ENTER
$$y^2 + 2 \cdot y \cdot (x + 1) + (x + 1)^2$$

expand((x+y+1)^2,x) ENTER
$$x^2 + 2 \cdot x \cdot (y + 1) + (y + 1)^2$$

expand((x^2-x+y^2-y)/(x^2*y^2-x^2
*y-x*y^2+x*y),y) ENTER

$$\blacksquare \text{ expand}\left(\frac{x^2 - x + y^2 - y}{x^2 \cdot y^2 - x^2 \cdot y - x \cdot y^2 + x \cdot y}, y\right)$$
$$\frac{1}{y-1} - \frac{1}{y} + \frac{1}{x \cdot (x-1)}$$

expand(ans(1),x) ENTER

$$\blacksquare \text{ expand}\left(\frac{1}{y-1} - \frac{1}{y} + \frac{1}{x \cdot (x-1)}, x\right)$$
$$\frac{1}{x-1} - \frac{1}{x} + \frac{1}{y \cdot (y-1)}$$

Even when there is only one variable, using *var* might make the denominator factorization used for partial fraction expansion more complete.

expand((x^3+x^2-2)/(x^2-2)) ENTER
$$\frac{2 \cdot x}{x^2-2} + x+1$$

expand(ans(1),x) ENTER
$$\frac{1}{x-\sqrt{2}} + \frac{1}{x+\sqrt{2}} + x+1$$

Hint: For rational expressions, **propFrac()** (page 167) is a faster but less extreme alternative to **expand()**.

Note: See also **comDenom()** (page 108) for an expanded numerator over an expanded denominator.

expand(*expression1*,[*var*]) also distributes logarithms and fractional powers regardless of *var*. For increased distribution of logarithms and fractional powers, inequality constraints might be necessary to guarantee that some factors are nonnegative.

ln(2x*y)+√(2x*y) ENTER
$$\ln(2 \cdot x \cdot y) + \sqrt{(2 \cdot x \cdot y)}$$

expand(ans(1)) ENTER
$$\ln(x \cdot y) + \sqrt{2} \cdot \sqrt{(x \cdot y)} + \ln(2)$$

expand(ans(1))|y>=0 ENTER
$$\ln(x) + \sqrt{2} \cdot \sqrt{x} \cdot \sqrt{y} + \ln(y) + \ln(2)$$

expand(*expression1*, [*var*]) also distributes absolute values, **sign()**, and exponentials, regardless of *var*.

sign(x*y)+abs(x*y)+ e^(2x+y) ENTER
$$e^{2x+y} + \text{sign}(x \cdot y) + |x \cdot y|$$

Note: See also **tExpand()** (page 198) for trigonometric angle-sum and multiple-angle expansion.

expand(ans(1)) ENTER
$$(e^x)^2 \cdot e^y + \text{sign}(x) \cdot \text{sign}(y) + |x| \cdot |y|$$

expr()   MATH/String menu

expr(*string*) ⇒ *expression*

Returns the character string contained in *string* as an expression and immediately executes it.

```
expr("1+2+x^2+x") ENTER          x² + x + 3
expr("expand((1+x)^2)") ENTER
                                 x² + 2·x + 1
"Define cube(x)=x^3"→funcstr ENTER
                          "Define cube(x)=x^3"
expr(funcstr) ENTER                       Done
cube(2) ENTER                                8
```

ExpReg   MATH/Statistics/Regressions menu

ExpReg *list1*, *list2* [, [*list3*] [, *list4*, *list5*]]

Calculates the exponential regression and updates all the system statistics variables.

All the lists must have equal dimensions except for *list5*.

list1 represents xlist.
list2 represents ylist.
list3 represents frequency.
list4 represents category codes.
list5 represents category include list.

Note: *list1* through *list4* must be a variable name or c1–c99 (columns in the last data variable shown in the Data/Matrix Editor). *list5* does not have to be a variable name and cannot be c1–c99.

In function graphing mode:

```
{1,2,3,4,5,6,7,8}→L1 ENTER        {1 2 ...}
{1,2,2,2,3,4,5,7}→L2 ENTER        {1 2 ...}
ExpReg L1,L2 ENTER                    Done
ShowStat ENTER
```

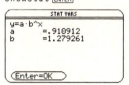

```
ENTER
Regeq(x)→y1(x) ENTER                  Done
NewPlot 1,1,L1,L2 ENTER               Done
```

◆ [GRAPH]

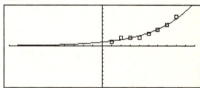

factor()   MATH/Algebra menu

factor(*expression1*[, *var*]) ⇒ *expression*
factor(*list1*[,*var*]) ⇒ *list*
factor(*matrix1*[,*var*]) ⇒ *matrix*

factor(*expression1*) returns *expression1* factored with respect to all of its variables over a common denominator.

expression1 is factored as much as possible toward linear rational factors without introducing new non-real subexpressions. This alternative is appropriate if you want factorization with respect to more than one variable.

```
factor(a^3*x^2-a*x^2-a^3+a) ENTER
                  a·(a − 1)·(a + 1)·(x − 1)·(x + 1)
factor(x^2+1) ENTER                      x² + 1
factor(x^2-4) ENTER              (x − 2)·(x + 2)
factor(x^2-3) ENTER                      x² − 3
factor(x^2-a) ENTER                      x² − a
```

factor(*expression1,var*) returns *expression1* factored with respect to variable *var*.

expression1 is factored as much as possible toward real factors that are linear in *var*, even if it introduces irrational constants or subexpressions that are irrational in other variables.

The factors and their terms are sorted with *var* as the main variable. Similar powers of *var* are collected in each factor. Include *var* if factorization is needed with respect to only that variable and you are willing to accept irrational expressions in any other variables to increase factorization with respect to *var*. There might be some incidental factoring with respect to other variables.

For the AUTO setting of the Exact/Approx mode, including *var* permits approximation with floating-point coefficients where irrational coefficients cannot be explicitly expressed concisely in terms of the built-in functions. Even when there is only one variable, including *var* might yield more complete factorization.

Note: See also **comDenom()** (page 108) for a fast way to achieve partial factoring when **factor()** is not fast enough or if it exhausts memory.

Note: See also **cFactor()** (page 105) for factoring all the way to complex coefficients in pursuit of linear factors.

factor(a^3*x^2-a*x^2-a^3+a,x) ENTER
$$a \cdot (a^2 - 1) \cdot (x - 1) \cdot (x + 1)$$

factor(x^2-3,x) ENTER $(x + \sqrt{3}) \cdot (x - \sqrt{3})$

factor(x^2-a,x) ENTER $(x + \sqrt{a}) \cdot (x - \sqrt{a})$

factor(x^5+4x^4+5x^3-6x-3) ENTER
$$x^5 + 4 \cdot x^4 + 5 \cdot x^3 - 6 \cdot x - 3$$

factor(ans(1),x) ENTER
$$(x - .965) \cdot (x + .612) \cdot$$
$$(x + 2.13) \cdot (x^2 + 2.23 \cdot x + 2.39)$$

---

factor(*rationalNumber*) returns the rational number factored into primes. For composite numbers, the computing time grows exponentially with the number of digits in the second-largest factor. For example, factoring a 30-digit integer could take more than a day, and factoring a 100-digit number could take more than a century.

Note: To stop (break) a computation, press ON.

If you merely want to determine if a number is prime, use **isPrime()** instead. It is much faster, particularly if *rationalNumber* is not prime and if the second-largest factor has more than five digits.

factor(152417172689) ENTER
$$123457 \cdot 1234577$$

isPrime(152417172689) ENTER   false

Fill
MATH/Matrix menu

Fill *expression, matrixVar* ⇒ *matrix*

Replaces each element in variable *matrixVar* with *expression*.

matrixVar must already exist.

```
[1,2;3,4]→amatrx ENTER          [1  2]
Fill 1.01,amatrx ENTER          [3  4]
amatrx ENTER                    Done
                          [1.01 1.01]
                          [1.01 1.01]
```

Fill *expression, listVar* ⇒ *list*

Replaces each element in variable *listVar* with *expression*.

listVar must already exist.

```
{1,2,3,4,5}→alist ENTER    {1 2 3 4 5}
Fill 1.01,alist ENTER           Done
alist ENTER
         {1.01 1.01 1.01 1.01 1.01}
```

floor()
MATH/Number menu

floor(*expression*) ⇒ *integer*

Returns the greatest integer that is ≤ the argument. This function is identical to **int()**.

The argument can be a real or a complex number.

```
floor(-2.14) ENTER              -3.
```

floor(*list1*) ⇒ *list*
floor(*matrix1*) ⇒ *matrix*

Returns a list or matrix of the floor of each element.

Note: See also **ceiling()** (page 104) and **int()** (page 143).

```
floor({3/2,0,-5.3}) ENTER    {1 0 -6.}

floor([1.2,3.4;2.5,4.8]) ENTER
                            [1. 3.]
                            [2. 4.]
```

fMax()
MATH/Calculus menu

fMax(*expression, var*) ⇒ *Boolean expression*

Returns a Boolean expression specifying candidate values of *var* that maximize *expression* or locate its least upper bound.

Use the "|" operator to restrict the solution interval and/or specify the sign of other undefined variables.

For the APPROX setting of the Exact/Approx mode, **fMax()** iteratively searches for one approximate local maximum. This is often faster, particularly if you use the "|" operator to constrain the search to a relatively small interval that contains exactly one local maximum.

Note: See also **fMin()** (page 134) and **max()** (page 151).

```
fMax(1-(x-a)^2-(x-b)^2,x) ENTER
```
$$x = \frac{a+b}{2}$$
```
fMax(.5x^3-x-2,x) ENTER          x = ∞

fMax(.5x^3-x-2,x)|x≤1 ENTER  x = -.816...

fMax(a*x^2,x) ENTER
      x = ∞ or x = -∞ or x = 0 or a = 0

fMax(a*x^2,x)|a<0 ENTER          x = 0
```

fMin()　　MATH/Calculus menu

fMin(*expression, var***)** ⇒ *Boolean expression*

Returns a Boolean expression specifying candidate values of *var* that minimize *expression* or locate its greatest lower bound.

Use the "|" operator to restrict the solution interval and/or specify the sign of other undefined variables.

For the APPROX setting of the Exact/Approx mode, **fMin()** iteratively searches for one approximate local minimum. This is often faster, particularly if you use the "|" operator to constrain the search to a relatively small interval that contains exactly one local minimum.

Note: See also **fMax()** (page 133) and **min()** (page 153).

```
fMin(1-(x-a)^2-(x-b)^2,x) ENTER
                              x = ∞ or x = ⁻∞
fMin(.5x^3-x-2,x)|x≥1 ENTER        x = 1
fMin(a*x^2,x) ENTER
    x = ∞ or x = ⁻∞ or x = 0 or a = 0
fMin(a*x^2,x)|a>0 and x>1 ENTER  x = 1.
fMin(a*x^2,x)|a>0 ENTER             x = 0
```

FnOff　　CATALOG

FnOff

Deselects all Y= functions for the current graphing mode.

In split-screen, two-graph mode, **FnOff** only applies to the active graph.

FnOff [1] [, 2] ... [,99]

Deselects the specified Y= functions for the current graphing mode.

In function graphing mode:
FnOff 1,3 ENTER deselects y1(x) and y3(x).

In parametric graphing mode:
FnOff 1,3 ENTER deselects xt1(t), yt1(t), xt3(t), and yt3(t).

FnOn　　CATALOG

FnOn

Selects all Y= functions that are defined for the current graphing mode.

In split-screen, two-graph mode, **FnOn** only applies to the active graph.

FnOn [1] [, 2] ... [,99]

Selects the specified Y= functions for the current graphing mode.

Note: In 3D graphing mode, only one function at a time can be selected. FnOn 2 selects z2(x,y) and deselects any previously selected function. In the other graph modes, previously selected functions are not affected.

For   CATALOG

For *var, low, high* [*, step*]
　　block
EndFor

Executes the statements in *block* iteratively for each value of *var*, from *low* to *high*, in increments of *step*.

var must not be a system variable.

step can be positive or negative. The default value is 1.

block can be either a single statement or a series of statements separated with the ":" character.

Program segment:

```
    :
:0→tempsum : 1→step
:For i,1,100,step
:  tempsum+i→tempsum
:EndFor
:Disp tempsum
    :
```

Contents of `tempsum` after execution: 5050

Contents of `tempsum` when `step`
is changed to 2:   2500

format()   MATH/String menu

format(expression[, formatString]**)** ⇒ *string*

Returns *expression* as a character string based on the format template.

expression must simplify to a number. *formatString* is a string and must be in the form: "F[n]", "S[n]", "E[n]", "G[n][c]", where [ ] indicate optional portions.

F[n]: Fixed format. *n* is the number of digits to display after the decimal point.

S[n]: Scientific format. *n* is the number of digits to display after the decimal point.

E[n]: Engineering format. *n* is the number of digits after the first significant digit. The exponent is adjusted to a multiple of three, and the decimal point is moved to the right by zero, one, or two digits.

G[n][c]: Same as fixed format but also separates digits to the left of the radix into groups of three. *c* specifies the group separator character and defaults to a comma. If *c* is a period, the radix will be shown as a comma.

[Rc]: Any of the above specifiers may be suffixed with the Rc radix flag, where *c* is a single character that specifies what to substitute for the radix point.

```
format(1.234567,"f3") ENTER    "1.235"

format(1.234567,"s2") ENTER    "1.23E0"

format(1.234567,"e3") ENTER    "1.235E0"

format(1.234567,"g3") ENTER    "1.235"

format(1234.567, "g3") ENTER
                             "1,234.567"

format(1.234567,"g3,r:") ENTER
                             "1:235"
```

fpart()   MATH/Number menu

fpart(expression1**)** ⇒ *expression*
fpart(list1**)** ⇒ *list*
fpart(matrix1**)** ⇒ *matrix*

Returns the fractional part of the argument.

For a list or matrix, returns the fractional parts of the elements.

The argument can be a real or a complex number.

```
fpart(-1.234) ENTER              -.234

fpart({1, -2.3, 7.003}) ENTER
                        {0  -.3  .003}
```

Func   CATALOG

Func
  block
EndFunc

Required as the first statement in a multi-statement function definition.

block can be either a single statement or a series of statements separated with the ":" character.

Note: when() (page 202) also can be used to define and graph piecewise-defined functions.

In function graphing mode, define a piecewise function:

```
Define g(x)=Func:If x<0 Then
 :Return 3*cos(x):Else:Return
 3-x:EndIf:EndFunc ENTER          Done

Graph g(x) ENTER
```

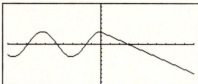

gcd()   MATH/Number menu

gcd(*number1, number2*) ⇒ *expression*

Returns the greatest common divisor of the two arguments. The **gcd** of two fractions is the **gcd** of their numerators divided by the **lcm** of their denominators.

The **gcd** of fractional floating-point numbers is 1.0.

```
gcd(18,33) ENTER                3
```

gcd(*list1, list2*) ⇒ *list*

Returns the greatest common divisors of the corresponding elements in *list1* and *list2*.

```
gcd({12,14,16},{9,7,5}) ENTER {3 7 1}
```

gcd(*matrix1, matrix2*) ⇒ *matrix*

Returns the greatest common divisors of the corresponding elements in *matrix1* and *matrix2*.

```
gcd([2,4;6,8],[4,8;12,16]) ENTER
```
$$\begin{bmatrix} 2 & 4 \\ 6 & 8 \end{bmatrix}$$

Get   CATALOG

Get *var*

Retrieves a CBL (Calculator-Based Laboratory) value from the link port and stores it in variable *var*.

Program segment:

```
    ⋮
:Send {3,1,-1,0}
:For i,1,99
:   Get data[i]
:   PtOn i,data[i]
:EndFor
    ⋮
```

GetCalc   CATALOG

GetCalc *var*

Retrieves a value from the link port and stores it in variable *var*. This is for unit-to-unit linking.

Note: To get a variable to the link port from another unit, use 2nd [VAR-LINK] on the other unit to select and send a variable, or do a **SendCalc** on the other unit.

Program segment:

```
    ⋮
:Disp "Press Enter when ready"
:Pause
:GetCalc L1
:Disp "List L1 received"
    ⋮
```

getConfg() CATALOG

getConfg() ⇒ *ListPairs*

Returns a list of calculator attributes. The
attribute name is listed first, followed by its
value.

```
getConfg() ENTER
    {"Product Name" "Advanced
        Mathematics Software"
"Version" "1.00, 03/03/1998"
    "Product ID" "01-0-0-38"
"Serial #" "01012 34567 ABCD"
        "Cert. Rev. #" 0
    "Screen Width" 240
   "Screen Height" 128
    "Window Width" 240
   "Window Height" 91
      "RAM Size" 262144
      "Free RAM" 191706
  "Archive Size" 393216
 "Free Archive" 393204}
```

Note: Your screen may display different
attribute values. The Cert. Rev. # attribute
appears only if you have purchased and
installed additional software into the
calculator.

getDenom() MATH/Algebra/Extract menu

getDenom(*expression1***)** ⇒ *expression*

Transforms *expression1* into one having a
reduced common denominator, and then
returns its denominator.

```
getDenom((x+2)/(y–3)) ENTER        y – 3

getDenom(2/7) ENTER                     7

getDenom(1/x+(y^2+y)/y^2) ENTER    x•y
```

getFold() CATALOG

getFold() ⇒ *nameString*

Returns the name of the current folder as a
string.

```
getFold() ENTER                  "main"

getFold()→oldfoldr ENTER         "main"

oldfoldr ENTER                   "main"
```

getKey() CATALOG

getKey() ⇒ *integer*

Returns the key code of the key pressed.
Returns 0 if no key is pressed.

The prefix keys (shift ⬆, second function
2nd, option ♦, and drag ✋) are not
recognized by themselves; however, they
modify the keycodes of the key that follows
them. For example: ♦K ≠ K ≠ 2ndK.

For a listing of key codes, see Appendix B in
the *TI-92 Guidebook*.

Program listing:

```
:Disp
:Loop
:  getKey()→key
:  while key=0
:    getKey()→key
:  EndWhile
:  Disp key
:  If key = ord("a")
:  Stop
:EndLoop
```

getMode() CATALOG

getMode(modeNameString**)** ⇒ string
getMode("ALL") ⇒ ListStringPairs

> If the argument is a specific mode name,
> returns a string containing the current setting
> for that mode.
>
> If the argument is **"ALL"**, returns a list of
> string pairs containing the settings of all the
> modes. If you want to restore the mode
> settings later, you must store the
> **getMode("ALL")** result in a variable, and then
> use **setMode()** to restore the modes.
>
> For a listing of mode names and possible
> settings, see **setMode()** on page 180.
>
> **Note:** To set or return information about the
> Unit System mode, use **setUnits()** on page 181
> or **getUnits()** on page 139 instead of **setMode()**
> or **getMode()**.

```
getMode("angle") ENTER          "RADIAN"

getMode("graph") ENTER        "FUNCTION"

getMode("all") ENTER
                      {"Graph" "FUNCTION"
             "Display Digits" "FLOAT 6"
                       "Angle" "RADIAN"
       "Exponential Format" "NORMAL"
            "Complex Format" "REAL"
     "Vector Format" "RECTANGULAR"
                    "Pretty Print" "ON"
                 "Split Screen" "FULL"
                  "Split 1 App" "Home"
                 "Split 2 App" "Graph"
             "Number of Graphs" "1"
                    "Graph 2" "FUNCTION"
       "Split Screen Ratio" "1:1"
            "Exact/Approx" "AUTO"
                        "Base" "DEC"}
```

Note: Your screen may display different
mode settings.

getNum() MATH/Algebra/Extract menu

getNum(expression1**)** ⇒ expression

> Transforms expression1 into one having a
> reduced common denominator, and then
> returns its numerator.

```
getNum((x+2)/(y-3)) ENTER          x + 2

getNum(2/7) ENTER                      2

getNum(1/x+1/y) ENTER              x + y
```

getType() CATALOG

getType(var**)** ⇒ string

> Returns a string indicating the data type of
> variable var.
>
> If var has not been defined, returns the string
> "NONE".

```
{1,2,3}→temp ENTER               {1 2 3}
getType(temp) ENTER               "LIST"

2+3i→temp ENTER                   2 + 3i
getType(temp) ENTER               "EXPR"

DelVar temp ENTER                   Done
getType(temp) ENTER               "NONE"
```

Data Type	Variable Contents
"ASM"	Assembly-language program
"DATA"	Data type
"EXPR"	Expression (includes complex/arbitrary/undefined, ∞, ⁻∞, TRUE, FALSE, pi, e)
"FIG"	Geometry figure
"FUNC"	Function
"GDB"	Graph data base
"LIST"	List
"MAC"	Geometry macro
"MAT"	Matrix
"NONE"	Variable does not exist
"NUM"	Real number
"OTHER"	Miscellaneous data type for future use by software applications
"PIC"	Picture
"PRGM"	Program
"STR"	String
"TEXT"	Text type
"VAR"	Name of another variable

getUnits() CATALOG

getUnits() ⇒ *list*

Returns a list of strings that contain the current default units for all categories except constants, temperature, amount of substance, luminous intensity, and acceleration. *list* has the form:

{*"system"* *"cat1"* *"unit1"* *"cat2"* *"unit2"* ...}

The first string gives the system (SI, ENG/US, or CUSTOM). Subsequent pairs of strings give a category (such as Length) and its default unit (such as _m for meters).

To set the default units, use **setUnits()** on page 181.

```
getUnits()  ENTER
                 {"SI"   "Area"   "NONE"
                  "Capacitance"   "_F"
                  "Charge"   "_coul"
                     … }
```

Note: Your screen may display different default units.

Goto CATALOG

Goto *labelName*

Transfers program control to the label *labelName*.

labelName must be defined in the same program using a **Lbl** instruction. (See page 144.)

Program segment:

```
      ⋮
:0→temp
:1→i
:Lbl TOP
:  temp+i→temp
:  If i<10 Then
:    i+1→i
:    Goto TOP
:  EndIf
:Disp temp
      ⋮
```

Graph   CATALOG

Graph *expression1*[, *expression2*] [, *var1*] [, *var2*]

The Smart Graph feature graphs the requested expressions/ functions using the current graphing mode.

Expressions entered using the **Graph** or **Table** (page 194) commands are assigned increasing function numbers starting with 1. They can be modified or individually deleted using the edit functions available when the table is displayed by pressing F4 Header. The currently selected Y= functions are ignored.

If you omit an optional *var* argument, **Graph** uses the independent variable of the current graphing mode.

Note: Not all optional arguments are valid in all modes because you can never have all four arguments at the same time.

Some valid variations of this instruction are:

Function graphing	**Graph** *expr, x*
Parametric graphing	**Graph** *xExpr, yExpr, t*
Polar graphing	**Graph** *expr, θ*
Sequence graphing	Not allowed.
3D graphing	**Graph** *expr, x, y*
Diff Equations graphing	Not allowed.

Note: Use **ClrGraph** (page 106) to clear these functions, or go to the Y= Editor to re-enable the system Y= functions.

In function graphing mode and ZoomStd window:

`Graph 1.25a*cos(a),a` ENTER

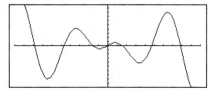

In parametric graphing mode and ZoomStd window:

`Graph time,2cos(time)/time,time` ENTER

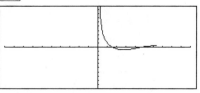

In 3D graphing mode:

`Graph (v^2 – w^2)/4,v,w` ENTER

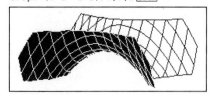

▸Hex   MATH/Base menu

integer1 ▸**Hex** ⇒ *integer*

Converts *integer1* to a hexadecimal number. Binary or hexadecimal numbers always have a 0b or 0h prefix, respectively.

┌─ Zero, not the letter O, followed by b or h.

0b *binaryNumber*
0h *hexadecimalNumber*

└── A binary number can have up to 32 digits. A hexadecimal number can have up to 8.

Without a prefix, *integer1* is treated as decimal (base 10). The result is displayed in hexadecimal, regardless of the Base mode.

If you enter a decimal integer that is too large for a signed, 32-bit binary form, a symmetric modulo operation is used to bring the value into the appropriate range.

`256 ▸Hex` ENTER   `0h100`

`0b111100001111 ▸Hex` ENTER   `0hF0F`

identity()   MATH/Matrix menu

identity(_expression_**)** ⇒ _matrix_

Returns the identity matrix with a dimension of _expression_.

expression must evaluate to a positive integer.

```
identity(4) ENTER
```

$$\begin{bmatrix} 1 & 0 & 0 & 0 \\ 0 & 1 & 0 & 0 \\ 0 & 0 & 1 & 0 \\ 0 & 0 & 0 & 1 \end{bmatrix}$$

If   CATALOG

If _Boolean expression_   **If** _Boolean expression_ **Then**
    statement   _block_
                              Endif

If _Boolean expression_ evaluates to true, executes the single statement _statement_ or the block of statements _block_ before continuing execution.

If _Boolean expression_ evaluates to false, continues execution without executing the statement or block of statements.

block can be either a single statement or a sequence of statements separated with the ":" character.

Program segment:

```
  :
:If x<0
:Disp "x is negative"
  :
```

—or—

```
  :
:If x<0 Then
:   Disp "x is negative"
:   abs(x)→x
:EndIf
  :
```

If _Boolean expression_ **Then**
    block1
Else
    block2
Endif

If _Boolean expression_ evaluates to true, executes _block1_ and then skips _block2_.

If _Boolean expression_ evaluates to false, skips _block1_ but executes _block2_.

block1 and _block2_ can be a single statement.

Program segment:

```
  :
:If x<0 Then
:   Disp "x is negative"
:   Else
:   Disp "x is positive or zero"
:EndIf
  :
```

If _Boolean expression1_ **Then**
    block1
Elseif _Boolean expression2_ **Then**
    block2
      ⋮
Elseif _Boolean expressionN_ **Then**
    blockN
Endif

Allows for program branching. If _Boolean expression1_ evaluates to true, executes _block1_. If _Boolean expression1_ evaluates to false, evaluates _Boolean expression2_, etc.

Program segment:

```
  :
:If choice=1 Then
:   Goto option1
:   ElseIf choice=2 Then
:     Goto option2
:   ElseIf choice=3 Then
:     Goto option3
:   ElseIf choice=4 Then
:     Disp "Exiting Program"
:     Return
:EndIf
  :
```

imag()   MATH/Complex menu

imag(*expression1*) ⇒ *expression*

    imag(*expression1*) returns the imaginary part of the argument.

    Note: All undefined variables are treated as real variables. See also **real()** (page 173).

```
imag(1+2i) ENTER                    2
imag(z) ENTER                       0
imag(x+iy) ENTER                    y
```

imag(*list1*) ⇒ *list*

    Returns a list of the imaginary parts of the elements.

```
imag({-3,4-i,i}) ENTER        {0  -1  1}
```

imag(*matrix1*) ⇒ *matrix*

    Returns a matrix of the imaginary parts of the elements.

```
imag([a,b;ic,id]) ENTER    [0  0]
                           [c  d]
```

Input   CATALOG

Input

    Pauses the program, displays the current Graph screen, and lets you update variables *xc* and *yc* (also *rc* and θ*c* for polar coordinate mode) by positioning the graph cursor.

    When you press ENTER, the program resumes.

Program segment:

```
  :
:© Get 10 points from the Graph
  Screen
:For i,1,10
:  Input
:  xc→XLIST[i]
:  yc→YLIST[i]
:EndFor
  :
```

Input [*promptString,*] *var*

    Input [*promptString*], *var* pauses the program, displays *promptString* on the Program I/O screen, waits for you to enter an expression, and stores the expression in variable *var*.

    If you omit *promptString*, "?" is displayed as a prompt.

Program segment:

```
  :
:For i,1,9,1
:  "Enter x" & string(i)→str1
:  Input str1,#(right(str1,2))
:EndFor
  :
```

InputStr   CATALOG

InputStr [*promptString,*] *var*

    Pauses the program, displays *promptString* on the Program I/O screen, waits for you to enter a response, and stores your response as a string in variable *var*.

    If you omit *promptString*, "?" is displayed as a prompt.

    Note: The difference between **Input** and **InputStr** is that **InputStr** always stores the result as a string so that " " are not required.

Program segment:

```
  :
:InputStr "Enter Your Name",str1
  :
```

inString()　MATH/String menu

inString(*srcString*, *subString*[, *start*])　⇒　*integer*

Returns the character position in string *srcString* at which the first occurrence of string *subString* begins.

start, if included, specifies the character position within *srcString* where the search begins. Default = 1 (the first character of *srcString*).

If *srcString* does not contain *subString* or *start* is > the length of *srcString*, returns zero.

```
inString("Hello there","the")
ENTER                            7

"ABCEFG"→s1:If inString(s1,
"D")=0:Disp "D not found." ENTER
                    D not found.
```

int()　CATALOG

int(*expression*)　⇒　*integer*
int(*list1*)　⇒　*list*
int(*matrix1*)　⇒　*matrix*

Returns the greatest integer that is less than or equal to the argument. This function is identical to **floor()**.

The argument can be a real or a complex number.

For a list or matrix, returns the greatest integer of each of the elements.

```
int(-2.5) ENTER              -3.

int([-1.234,0,0.37]) ENTER
                    [-2. 0 0.]
```

intDiv()　CATALOG

intDiv(*number1*, *number2*)　⇒　*integer*
intDiv(*list1*, *list2*)　⇒　*list*
intDiv(*matrix1*, *matrix2*)　⇒　*matrix*

Returns the signed integer part of argument 1 divided by argument 2.

For lists and matrices returns the signed integer part of argument 1 divided by argument 2 for each element pair.

```
intDiv(-7,2) ENTER           -3

intDiv(4,5) ENTER             0

intDiv({12,-14,-16},{5,4,-3}) ENTER
                    {2 -3 5}
```

integrate　See ∫, page 216.

iPart()　MATH/Number menu

iPart(*number*)　⇒　*integer*
iPart(*list1*)　⇒　*list*
iPart(*matrix1*)　⇒　*matrix*

Returns the integer part of the argument.

For lists and matrices, returns the integer part of each element.

The argument can be a real or a complex number.

```
iPart(-1.234) ENTER          -1.

iPart({3/2,-2.3,7.003}) ENTER
                    {1 -2. 7.}
```

isPrime()   MATH/Test menu

IsPrime(*number*) ⇒ *Boolean constant expression*

Returns true or false to indicate if *number* is a whole number ≥ 2 that is evenly divisible only by itself and 1.

If *number* exceeds about 306 digits and has no factors ≤ 1021, **isPrime**(*number*) displays an error message.

If you merely want to determine if *number* is prime, use **isPrime()** instead of **factor()**. It is much faster, particularly if *number* is not prime and has a second-largest factor that exceeds about five digits.

```
IsPrime(5) ENTER                    true
IsPrime(6) ENTER                    false
```

Function to find the next prime after a specified number:

```
Define nextPrim(n)=Func:Loop:
n+1→n:if isPrime(n):return n:
EndLoop:EndFunc ENTER                Done
```

```
nextPrim(7) ENTER                       11
```

Item   CATALOG

Item *itemNameString*
Item *itemNameString*, *label*

Valid only within a **Custom...EndCustm** or **ToolBar...EndTBar** block. Sets up a drop-down menu element to let you paste text to the cursor position (**Custom**) or branch to a label (**ToolBar**).

Note: Branching to a label is not allowed within a **Custom** block (page 115).

See **Custom** example on page 115.

Lbl   CATALOG

Lbl *labelName*

Defines a label with the name *labelName* in the program.

You can use a **Goto** *labelName* instruction to transfer program control to the instruction immediately following the label.

labelName must meet the same naming requirements as a variable name.

Program segment:

```
   ⋮
:Lbl lbl1
:InputStr "Enter password", str1
:If str1≠password
:  Goto lbl1
:Disp "Welcome to ..."
   ⋮
```

lcm()   MATH/Number menu

lcm(*number1*, *number2*) ⇒ *expression*
lcm(*list1*, *list2*) ⇒ *list*
lcm(*matrix1*, *matrix2*) ⇒ *matrix*

Returns the least common multiple of the two arguments. The **lcm** of two fractions is the **lcm** of their numerators divided by the **gcd** of their denominators. The **lcm** of fractional floating-point numbers is their product.

For two lists or matrices, returns the least common multiples of the corresponding elements.

```
lcm(6,9) ENTER                          18
```

```
lcm({1/3,⁻14,16},{2/15,7,5}) ENTER
                           {2/3 14 80}
```

left()   MATH/String menu

left(*sourceString*[, *num*]) ⇒ *string*

Returns the leftmost *num* characters
contained in character string *sourceString*.

If you omit *num*, returns all of *sourceString*.

`left("Hello",2)` `ENTER`   `"He"`

left(*list1*[, *num*]) ⇒ *list*

Returns the leftmost *num* elements contained
in *list1*.

If you omit *num*, returns all of *list1*.

`left({1,3,-2,4},3)` `ENTER`   `{1  3  -2}`

left(*comparison*) ⇒ *expression*

Returns the left-hand side of an equation or
inequality.

`left(x<3)` `ENTER`   `x`

limit()   MATH/Calculus menu

limit(*expression1*, *var*, *point*[, *direction*]) ⇒
  expression
limit(*list1*, *var*, *point*[, *direction*]) ⇒ *list*
limit(*matrix1*, *var*, *point*[, *direction*]) ⇒ *matrix*

Returns the limit requested.

direction: negative=from left, positive=from
right, otherwise=both. (If omitted, *direction*
defaults to both.)

Limits at positive ∞ and at negative ∞ are
always converted to one-sided limits from the
finite side.

Depending on the circumstances, **limit()**
returns itself or undef when it cannot
determine a unique limit. This does not
necessarily mean that a unique limit does not
exist. undef means that the result is either an
unknown number with finite or infinite
magnitude, or it is the entire set of such
numbers.

limit() uses methods such as L'Hopital's rule,
so there are unique limits that it cannot
determine. If *expression1* contains undefined
variables other than *var*, you might have to
constrain them to obtain a more concise
result.

Limits can be very sensitive to rounding
error. When possible, avoid the APPROX
setting of the Exact/Approx mode and
approximate numbers when computing
limits. Otherwise, limits that should be zero
or have infinite magnitude probably will not,
and limits that should have finite non-zero
magnitude might not.

`limit(2x+3,x,5)` `ENTER`   `13`

`limit(1/x,x,0,1)` `ENTER`   `∞`

`limit(sin(x)/x,x,0)` `ENTER`   `1`

`limit((sin(x+h)-sin(x))/h,h,0)` `ENTER`
                                          `cos(x)`

`limit((1+1/n)^n,n,∞)` `ENTER`   `e`

`limit(a^x,x,∞)` `ENTER`   `undef`

`limit(a^x,x,∞)|a>1` `ENTER`   `∞`

`limit(a^x,x,∞)|a>0 and a<1` `ENTER`   `0`

Line   CATALOG

Line *xStart*, *yStart*, *xEnd*, *yEnd*[, *drawMode*]

Displays the Graph screen and draws, erases, or inverts a line segment between the window coordinates (*xStart*, *yStart*) and (*xEnd*, *yEnd*), including both endpoints.

If *drawMode* = 1, draws the line (default).
If *drawMode* = 0, turns off the line.
If *drawMode* = ‾1, turns a line that is on to off or off to on (inverts pixels along the line).

Note: Regraphing erases all drawn items. See also **PxlLine** (page 168).

In the ZoomStd window, draw a line and then erase it.

Line 0,0,6,9 [ENTER]

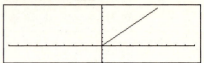

◆ [HOME]
Line 0,0,6,9,0 [ENTER]

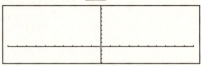

LineHorz   CATALOG

LineHorz *y* [, *drawMode*]

Displays the Graph screen and draws, erases, or inverts a horizontal line at window position *y*.

If *drawMode* = 1, draws the line (default).
If *drawMode* = 0, turns off the line.
If *drawMode* = ‾1, turns a line that is on to off or off to on (inverts pixels along the line).

Note: Regraphing erases all drawn items. See also **PxlHorz** (page 168).

In a ZoomStd window:

LineHorz 2.5 [ENTER]

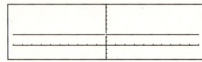

LineTan   CATALOG

LineTan *expression1*, *expression2*

Displays the Graph screen and draws a line tangent to *expression1* at the point specified.

expression1 is an expression or the name of a function, where x is assumed to be the independent variable, and *expression2* is the x value of the point that is tangent.

Note: In the example shown, *expression1* is graphed separately. **LineTan** does not graph *expression1*.

In function graphing mode and a ZoomTrig window:

Graph cos(x)
◆ [HOME]
LineTan cos(x),π/4 [ENTER]

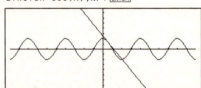

LineVert   CATALOG

LineVert *x* [, *drawMode*]

Displays the Graph screen and draws, erases, or inverts a vertical line at window position *x*.

If *drawMode* = 1, draws the line (default).
If *drawMode* = 0, turns off the line.
If *drawMode* = ‾1, turns a line that is on to off or off to on (inverts pixels along the line).

Note: Regraphing erases all drawn items. See also **PxlVert** (page 169).

In a ZoomStd window:

LineVert ‾2.5 [ENTER]

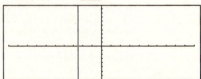

LinReg   MATH/Statistics/Regressions menu

LinReg *list1*, *list2*[, [*list3*] [, *list4*, *list5*]]

Calculates the linear regression and updates all the system statistics variables.

All the lists must have equal dimensions except for *list5*.

list1 represents xlist.
list2 represents ylist.
list3 represents frequency.
list4 represents category codes.
list5 represents category include list.

Note: *list1* through *list4* must be a variable name or c1–c99 (columns in the last data variable shown in the Data/Matrix Editor). *list5* does not have to be a variable name and cannot be c1–c99.

In function graphing mode:

```
{0,1,2,3,4,5,6}→L1 ENTER        {0 1 2 …}
{0,2,3,4,3,4,6}→L2 ENTER        {0 2 3 …}
LinReg L1,L2 ENTER              Done
ShowStat ENTER
```

```
ENTER
Regeq(x)→y1(x) ENTER            Done
NewPlot 1,1,L1,L2 ENTER         Done
```

♦ [GRAPH]

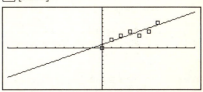

list▶mat()   MATH/List menu

list▶mat(*list* [, *elementsPerRow*]**)**   ⇒   *matrix*

Returns a matrix filled row-by-row with the elements from *list*.

elementsPerRow, if included, specifies the number of elements per row. Default is the number of elements in *list* (one row).

If *list* does not fill the resulting matrix, zeros are added.

```
list▶mat({1,2,3}) ENTER         [1 2 3]

list▶mat({1,2,3,4,5},2) ENTER
```

$$\begin{bmatrix} 1 & 2 \\ 3 & 4 \\ 5 & 0 \end{bmatrix}$$

ln()   [LN] key

ln(_expression1_**)** ⇒ _expression_
ln(_list1_**)** ⇒ _list_

Returns the natural logarithm of the argument.

For a list, returns the natural logarithms of the elements.

```
ln(2.0) [ENTER]                          .693...
```

If complex format mode is REAL:

```
ln({-3,1.2,5}) [ENTER]
                    Error: Non-real result
```

If complex format mode is RECTANGULAR:

```
ln({-3,1.2,5}) [ENTER]
              {ln(3) + π·i   .182...   ln(5)}
```

---

ln(_squareMatrix1_**)** ⇒ _squareMatrix_

Returns the matrix natural logarithm of _squareMatrix1_. This is _not_ the same as calculating the natural logarithm of each element. For information about the calculation method, refer to **cos()** on page 109.

squareMatrix1 must be diagonalizable. The result always contains floating-point numbers.

In Radian angle mode and Rectangular complex format mode:

```
ln([1,5,3;4,2,1;6,-2,1]) [ENTER]
```

$$\begin{bmatrix} 1.831...+1.734...\cdot i & .009...-1.490...\cdot i & ... \\ .448...-.725...\cdot i & 1.064...+.623\cdot i & ... \\ -.266...-2.083...\cdot i & 1.124...+1.790...\cdot i & ... \end{bmatrix}$$

LnReg   MATH/Statistics/Regressions menu

LnReg _list1, list2_[, [_list3_] [, _list4, list5_]]

Calculates the logarithmic regression and updates all the system statistics variables.

All the lists must have equal dimensions except for _list5_.

list1 represents xlist.
list2 represents ylist.
list3 represents frequency.
list4 represents category codes.
list5 represents category include list.

Note: _list1_ through _list4_ must be a variable name or c1–c99 (columns in the last data variable shown in the Data/Matrix Editor). _list5_ does not have to be a variable name and cannot be c1–c99.

In function graphing mode:

```
{1,2,3,4,5,6,7,8}→L1 [ENTER]   {1 2 3 ...}
{1,2,2,3,3,3,4,4}→L2 [ENTER]   {1 2 2 ...}
LnReg L1,L2 [ENTER]                  Done
ShowStat [ENTER]
```

```
[ENTER]
Regeq(x)→y1(x) [ENTER]              Done
NewPlot 1,1,L1,L2 [ENTER]           Done
```

[♦] [GRAPH]

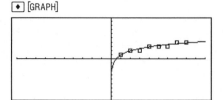

Local   CATALOG

Local *var1*[, *var2*] [, *var3*] ...

Declares the specified *vars* as local variables. Those variables exist only during evaluation of a program or function and are deleted when the program or function finishes execution.

Note: Local variables save memory because they only exist temporarily. Also, they do not disturb any existing global variable values. Local variables must be used for **For** loops and for temporarily saving values in a multi-line function since modifications on global variables are not allowed in a function.

Program listing:

```
:prgmname()
:Prgm
:Local x,y
:Input "Enter x",x
:Input "Enter y",y
:Disp x*y
:EndPrgm
```

Note: *x* and *y* do not exist after the program executes.

Lock   CATALOG

Lock *var1*[, *var2*] ...

Locks the specified variables. This prevents you from accidentally deleting or changing the variable without first using the unlock instruction on that variable.

In the example to the right, the variable L1 is locked and cannot be deleted or modified.

Note: The variables can be unlocked using the **Unlock** command (page 201).

```
{1,2,3,4}→L1 ENTER                    {1,2,3,4}

Lock L1 ENTER                              Done

DelVar L1 ENTER
  Error: Variable is locked or protected
```

log()   CATALOG

log(*expression1***)** ⇒ *expression*
log(*list1***)** ⇒ *list*

Returns the base-10 logarithm of the argument.

For a list, returns the base-10 logs of the elements.

```
log(2.0) ENTER                              .301...
```

If complex format mode is REAL:

```
log({-3,1.2,5}) ENTER
                        Error: Non-real result
```

If complex format mode is RECTANGULAR:

```
log({-3,1.2,5}) ENTER
```
$\{\frac{\ln(3)}{\ln(10)} + \frac{\pi}{\ln(10)} \cdot i \quad .079... \quad \frac{\ln(5)}{\ln(10)}\}$

log(*squareMatrix1***)** ⇒ *squareMatrix*

Returns the matrix base-10 logarithm of *squareMatrix1*. This is *not* the same as calculating the base-10 logarithm of each element. For information about the calculation method, refer to **cos()** on page 109.

squareMatrix1 must be diagonalizable. The result always contains floating-point numbers.

In Radian angle mode and Rectangular complex format mode:

```
log([1,5,3;4,2,1;6,-2,1]) ENTER
```
$$\begin{bmatrix} .795...+.753...\cdot i & .003...-.647...\cdot i & ... \\ .194...-.315...\cdot i & .462...+.270\cdot i & ... \\ -.115...-.904...\cdot i & .488...+.777...\cdot i & ... \end{bmatrix}$$

Logistic   MATH/Statistics/Regressions menu

Logistic *list1*, *list2* [, [*iterations*], [*list3*] [, *list4*, *list5*]]

Calculates the logistic regression and updates all the system statistics variables.

All the lists must have equal dimensions except for *list5*.

list1 represents xlist.
list2 represents ylist.
list3 represents frequency.
list4 represents category codes.
list5 represents category include list.

iterations specifies the maximum number of times a solution will be attempted. If omitted, 64 is used. Typically, larger values result in better accuracy but longer execution times, and vice versa.

Note: *list1* through *list4* must be a variable name or c1–c99 (columns in the last data variable shown in the Data/Matrix Editor). *list5* does not have to be a variable name and cannot be c1–c99.

In function graphing mode:

```
{1,2,3,4,5,6}→L1 ENTER        {1 2 3 …}
{1,1.3,2.5,3.5,4.5,4.8}→L2 ENTER
                              {1 1.3 2.5 …}
Logistic L1,L2 ENTER                  Done
ShowStat ENTER
```

```
ENTER
regeq(x)→y1(x) ENTER                  Done
NewPlot 1,1,L1,L2 ENTER               Done
♦ [GRAPH]
F2 9
```

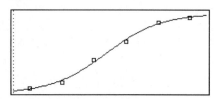

Loop   CATALOG

Loop
   block
EndLoop

Repeatedly executes the statements in *block*. Note that the loop will be executed endlessly, unless a **Goto** or **Exit** instruction is executed within *block*.

block is a sequence of statements separated with the ":" character.

Program segment:

```
  :
:1→i
:Loop
:   Rand(6)→die1
:   Rand(6)→die2
:   If die1=6 and die2=6
:     Goto End
:   i+1→i
:EndLoop
:Lbl End
:Disp "The number of rolls is", i
  :
```

LU *matrix, lMatName, uMatName, pMatName*[*, tol*]

Calculates the Doolittle LU (lower-upper) decomposition of a real or complex *matrix*. The lower triangular matrix is stored in *lMatName*, the upper triangular matrix in *uMatName*, and the permutation matrix (which describes the row swaps done during the calculation) in *pMatName*.

lMatName ∗ *uMatName* = *pMatName* ∗ *matrix*

Optionally, any matrix element is treated as zero if its absolute value is less than *tol*. This tolerance is used only if the matrix has floating-point entries and does not contain any symbolic variables that have not been assigned a value. Otherwise, *tol* is ignored.

- If you use ◆ ENTER or set the mode to Exact/Approx=APPROXIMATE, computations are done using floating-point arithmetic.

- If *tol* is omitted or not used, the default tolerance is calculated as:

  5E⁻14 ∗ **max(dim(***matrix***))** ∗ **rowNorm(***matrix***)**

The **LU** factorization algorithm uses partial pivoting with row interchanges.

[6,12,18;5,14,31;3,8,18]→m1 ENTER

$$\begin{bmatrix} 6 & 12 & 18 \\ 5 & 14 & 31 \\ 3 & 8 & 18 \end{bmatrix}$$

LU m1,lower,upper,perm ENTER   Done

lower ENTER

$$\begin{bmatrix} 1 & 0 & 0 \\ 5/6 & 1 & 0 \\ 1/2 & 1/2 & 1 \end{bmatrix}$$

upper ENTER

$$\begin{bmatrix} 6 & 12 & 18 \\ 0 & 4 & 16 \\ 0 & 0 & 1 \end{bmatrix}$$

perm ENTER

$$\begin{bmatrix} 1 & 0 & 0 \\ 0 & 1 & 0 \\ 0 & 0 & 1 \end{bmatrix}$$

[m,n;o,p]→m1 ENTER $\begin{bmatrix} m & n \\ o & p \end{bmatrix}$

LU m1,lower,upper,perm ENTER   Done

lower ENTER $\begin{bmatrix} 1 & 0 \\ \frac{m}{o} & 1 \end{bmatrix}$

upper ENTER $\begin{bmatrix} o & p \\ 0 & n - \dfrac{m \cdot p}{o} \end{bmatrix}$

perm ENTER $\begin{bmatrix} 0 & 1 \\ 1 & 0 \end{bmatrix}$

---

mat▶list()   MATH/List menu

mat▶list(*matrix***)** ⇒ *list*

Returns a list filled with the elements in *matrix*. The elements are copied from *matrix* row by row.

mat▶list([1,2,3]) ENTER   {1 2 3}

[1,2,3;4,5,6]→M1 ENTER $\begin{bmatrix} 1 & 2 & 3 \\ 4 & 5 & 6 \end{bmatrix}$

mat▶list(M1) ENTER   {1 2 3 4 5 6}

---

max()   MATH/List menu

max(*expression1, expression2***)** ⇒ *expression*
max(*list1, list2***)** ⇒ *list*
max(*matrix1, matrix2***)** ⇒ *matrix*

Returns the maximum of the two arguments. If the arguments are two lists or matrices, returns a list or matrix containing the maximum value of each pair of corresponding elements.

max(2.3,1.4) ENTER   2.3

max({1,2},{⁻4,3}) ENTER   {1 3}

---

max(*list***)** ⇒ *expression*

Returns the maximum element in *list*.

max({0,1,⁻7,1.3,.5}) ENTER   1.3

---

max(*matrix1***)** ⇒ *matrix*

Returns a row vector containing the maximum element of each column in *matrix1*.

Note: See also **fMax()** (page 133) and **min()** (page 153).

max([1,⁻3,7;⁻4,0,.3]) ENTER   [1 0 7]

mean()   MATH/Statistics menu

mean(list**)** ⇒ *expression*

Returns the mean of the elements in *list*.

mean({.2,0,1,⁻.3,.4}) [ENTER]   .26

---

mean(matrix1**)** ⇒ *matrix*

Returns a row vector of the means of all the columns in *matrix1*.

In vector format rectangular mode:

mean([.2,0;⁻1,3;.4,⁻.5]) [ENTER]
                        [⁻.133... .833...]

mean([1/5,0;⁻1,3;2/5,⁻1/2]) [ENTER]
                        [⁻2/15   5/6]

median()   MATH/Statistics menu

median(list**)** ⇒ *expression*

Returns the median of the elements in *list1*.

median({.2,0,1,⁻.3,.4}) [ENTER]   .2

---

median(matrix1**)** ⇒ *matrix*

Returns a row vector containing the medians of the columns in *matrix1*.

Note: All entries in the list or matrix must simplify to numbers.

median([.2,0;1,⁻.3;.4,⁻.5]) [ENTER]
                        [.4 ⁻.3]

MedMed   MATH/Statistics/Regressions menu

MedMed *list1*, *list2*[, [*list3*] [, *list4*, *list5*]]

Calculates the median-median line and updates all the system statistics variables.

All the lists must have equal dimensions except for *list5*.

list1 represents xlist.
list2 represents ylist.
list3 represents frequency.
list4 represents category codes.
list5 represents category include list.

Note: *list1* through *list4* must be a variable name or c1–c99 (columns in the last data variable shown in the Data/Matrix Editor). *list5* does not have to be a variable name and cannot be c1–c99.

In function graphing mode:

{0,1,2,3,4,5,6}→L1 [ENTER]   {0 1 2 ...}
{0,2,3,4,3,4,6}→L2 [ENTER]   {0 2 3 ...}
MedMed L1,L2 [ENTER]   Done
ShowStat [ENTER]

```
              STAT VARS
 y=a·x+b
 a       =.8
 b       =.6


 Enter=OK
```

[ENTER]
Regeq(x)→y1(x) [ENTER]   Done
NewPlot 1,1,L1,L2 [ENTER]   Done

[♦] [GRAPH]

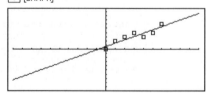

mid()   MATH/String menu

mid(sourceString, start[, count]**)** ⇒ string

Returns count characters from character string sourceString, beginning with character number start.

If count is omitted or is greater than the dimension of sourceString, returns all characters from sourceString, beginning with character number start.

count must be ≥ 0. If count = 0, returns an empty string.

```
mid("Hello there",2) ENTER
                       "ello there"
mid("Hello there",7,3) ENTER    "the"
mid("Hello there",1,5) ENTER   "Hello"
mid("Hello there",1,0) ENTER      ""
```

mid(sourceList, start [, count]**)** ⇒ list

Returns count elements from sourceList, beginning with element number start.

If count is omitted or is greater than the dimension of sourceList, returns all elements from sourceList, beginning with element number start.

count must be ≥ 0. If count = 0, returns an empty list.

```
mid({9,8,7,6},3) ENTER          {7 6}
mid({9,8,7,6},2,2) ENTER        {8 7}
mid({9,8,7,6},1,2) ENTER        {9 8}
mid({9,8,7,6},1,0) ENTER          {}
```

mid(sourceStringList, start[, count]**)** ⇒ list

Returns count strings from the list of strings sourceStringList, beginning with element number start.

```
mid({"A","B","C","D"},2,2) ENTER
                       {"B" "C"}
```

min()   MATH/List menu

min(expression1, expression2**)** ⇒ expression
min(list1, list2**)** ⇒ list
min(matrix1, matrix2**)** ⇒ matrix

Returns the minimum of the two arguments. If the arguments are two lists or matrices, returns a list or matrix containing the minimum value of each pair of corresponding elements.

```
min(2.3,1.4) ENTER              1.4
min({1,2},{-4,3}) ENTER       {-4 2}
```

min(list**)** ⇒ expression

Returns the minimum element of list.

```
min({0,1,-7,1.3,.5}) ENTER       -7
```

min(matrix1**)** ⇒ matrix

Returns a row vector containing the minimum element of each column in matrix1.

Note: See also **fMin()** (page 134) and **max()** (page 151).

```
min([1,-3,7;-4,0,.3]) ENTER
                       [-4 -3 .3]
```

mod()   MATH/Number menu

mod(*expression1, expression2***)** ⇒ *expression*
mod(*list1, list2***)** ⇒ *list*
mod(*matrix1, matrix2***)** ⇒ *matrix*

    Returns the first argument modulo the
    second argument as defined by the identities:

        mod(x,0) ≡ x
        mod(x,y) ≡ x−y floor(x/y)

    When the second argument is non-zero, the
    result is periodic in that argument. The result
    is either zero or has the same sign as the
    second argument.

    If the arguments are two lists or two
    matrices, returns a list or matrix containing
    the modulo of each pair of corresponding
    elements.

    Note: See also **remain()** (page 174).

mod(7,0) ENTER	7
mod(7,3) ENTER	1
mod(-7,3) ENTER	2
mod(7,-3) ENTER	-2
mod(-7,-3) ENTER	-1

mod({12,-14,16},{9,7,-5}) ENTER
                        {3 0 -4}

MoveVar   CATALOG

MoveVar *var, oldFolder, newFolder*

    Moves variable *var* from *oldFolder* to
    newFolder. If *newFolder* does not exist,
    MoveVar creates it.

{1,2,3,4}→L1 ENTER   {1 2 3 4}
MoveVar L1,Main,Games ENTER   Done

mRow()   MATH/Matrix/Row ops menu

mRow(*expression, matrix1, index***)** ⇒ *matrix*

    Returns a copy of *matrix1* with each element
    in row *index* of *matrix1* multiplied by
    expression.

mRow(-1/3,[1,2;3,4],2) ENTER
$$\begin{bmatrix} 1 & 2 \\ -1 & -4/3 \end{bmatrix}$$

mRowAdd() MATH/Matrix/Row ops menu

mRowAdd(*expression, matrix1, index1, index2***)**
    ⇒ *matrix*

    Returns a copy of *matrix1* with each element
    in row *index2* of *matrix1* replaced with:

    expression × row *index1* + row *index2*

mRowAdd(-3,[1,2;3,4],1,2) ENTER
$$\begin{bmatrix} 1 & 2 \\ 0 & -2 \end{bmatrix}$$

mRowAdd(n,[a,b;c,d],1,2) ENTER
$$\begin{bmatrix} a & b \\ a \cdot n+c & b \cdot n+d \end{bmatrix}$$

nCr() MATH/Probability menu

nCr(*expression1, expression2***)** $\Rightarrow$ *expression*

For integer *expression1* and *expression2* with *expression1* $\geq$ *expression2* $\geq$ 0, **nCr()** is the number of combinations of *expression1* things taken *expression2* at a time. (This is also known as a binomial coefficient.) Both arguments can be integers or symbolic expressions.

$$\text{nCr}(z,3) \qquad \frac{z\cdot(z-2)\cdot(z-1)}{6}$$

$$\text{ans}(1)|z=5 \qquad 10$$

$$\text{nCr}(z,c) \qquad \frac{z!}{c!(z-c)!}$$

$$\text{ans}(1)/\text{nPr}(z,c) \qquad \frac{1}{c!}$$

nCr(*expression*, 0**)** $\Rightarrow$ 1

nCr(*expression, negInteger***)** $\Rightarrow$ 0

nCr(*expression, posInteger***)** $\Rightarrow$ *expression* · (*expression*–1)... (*expression* –*posInteger*+1)/ *posInteger*!

nCr(*expression, nonInteger***)** $\Rightarrow$ *expression*!/ ((*expression* –*nonInteger*)! · *nonInteger*!)

nCr(*list1, list2***)** $\Rightarrow$ *list*

Returns a list of combinations based on the corresponding element pairs in the two lists. The arguments must be the same size list.

nCr({5,4,3},{2,4,2}) [ENTER] {10 1 3}

nCr(*matrix1, matrix2***)** $\Rightarrow$ *matrix*

Returns a matrix of combinations based on the corresponding element pairs in the two matrices. The arguments must be the same size matrix.

nCr([6,5;4,3],[2,2;2,2]) [ENTER]
$$\begin{bmatrix} 15 & 10 \\ 6 & 3 \end{bmatrix}$$

nDeriv() MATH/Calculus menu

nDeriv(*expression1, var*[, *h*]**)** $\Rightarrow$ *expression*

Returns the numerical derivative as an expression. Uses the central difference quotient formula.

h is the step value. If *h* is omitted, it defaults to 0.001.

Note: See also **avgRC()** (page 103) and ***d*()** (page 118).

nDeriv(cos(x),x,h) [ENTER]
$$\frac{-(\cos(x-h)-\cos(x+h))}{2\cdot h}$$

limit(nDeriv(cos(x),x,h),h,0) [ENTER]
$$-\sin(x)$$

nDeriv(x^3,x,0.01) [ENTER]
$$3.\cdot(x^2+.000033)$$

nDeriv(cos(x),x)|x=π/2 [ENTER]
$$-1.$$

NewData CATALOG

NewData *dataVar, list1[, list2] [, list3]...*

Creates data variable *dataVar*, where the columns are the lists in order.

Must have at least one list.

list1, list2, ..., listn can be lists as shown, expressions that resolve to lists, or list variable names.

NewData makes the new variable current in the Data/Matrix Editor.

```
NewData mydata,{1,2,3},{4,5,6} ENTER
                                Done
```

(Go to the Data/Matrix Editor and open the *var* mydata to display the data variable below.)

DATA	c1	c2	c3	c4	c5
1	1	4			
2	2	5			
3	3	6			
4					
5					
6					
7					

NewData *dataVar, matrix*

Creates data variable *dataVar* based on *matrix*.

NewData sysData, *matrix*

Loads the contents of *matrix* into the system data variable sysData.

NewFold CATALOG

NewFold *folderName*

Creates a user-defined folder with the name *folderName*, and then sets the current folder to that folder. After you execute this instruction, you are in the new folder.

```
NewFold games ENTER              Done
```

newList() CATALOG

newList(*numElements* **)** ⇒ *list*

Returns a list with a dimension of *numElements*. Each element is zero.

```
newList(4) ENTER            {0 0 0 0}
```

newMat() CATALOG

newMat(*numRows, numColumns* **)** ⇒ *matrix*

Returns a matrix of zeros with the dimension *numRows* by *numColumns*.

```
newMat(2,3) ENTER           [0 0 0]
                            [0 0 0]
```

NewPic CATALOG

NewPic *matrix, picVar [, maxRow][, maxCol]*

Creates a pic variable *picVar* based on *matrix*. *matrix* must be an *n×2* matrix in which each row represents a pixel. Pixel coordinates start at 0,0. If *picVar* already exists, **NewPic** replaces it.

The default for *picVar* is the minimum area required for the matrix values. The optional arguments, *maxRow* and *maxCol*, determine the maximum boundary limits for *picVar*.

```
NewPic [1,1;2,2;3,3;4,4;5,5;
      5,1;4,2;2,4;1,5],xpic ENTER   Done

RclPic xpic ENTER
```

NewPlot CATALOG

NewPlot *n*, *type*, *xList* [,[*yList*], [*frqList*], [*catList*],
[*includeCatList*], [*mark*] [, *bucketSize*]]

Creates a new plot definition for plot number *n*.

type specifies the type of the graph plot.
1 = scatter plot
2 = xyline plot
3 = box plot
4 = histogram
5 = modified box plot

mark specifies the display type of the mark.
1 = ▫ (box)
2 = × (cross)
3 = + (plus)
4 = ▪ (square)
5 = · (dot)

bucketSize is the width of each histogram
"bucket" (*type* = 4), and will vary based on
the window variables xmin and xmax.
bucketSize must be >0. Default = 1.

Note: *n* can be 1–9. Lists must be variable
names or c1–c99 (columns in the last data
variable shown in the Data/Matrix Editor),
except for *includeCatList*, which does not
have to be a variable name and cannot be
c1–c99.

```
FnOff ENTER                          Done
PlotsOff ENTER                       Done
{1,2,3,4}→L1 ENTER              {1 2 3 4}
{2,3,4,5}→L2 ENTER              {2 3 4 5}
NewPlot 1,1,L1,L2,,,,4 ENTER         Done
```

Press ♦ [GRAPH] to display:

NewProb CATALOG

NewProb

Performs a variety of operations that let you
begin a new problem from a cleared state
without resetting the memory.

- Clears all single-character variable names
  (Clear a–z) in the current folder, unless the
  variables are locked or archived.

- Turns off all functions and stat plots
  (**FnOff** and **PlotsOff**) in the current
  graphing mode.

- Perfoms **ClrDraw**, **ClrErr**, **ClrGraph**,
  ClrHome, **ClrIO**, and **ClrTable**.

```
NewProb ENTER                        Done
```

nInt()   MATH/Calculus menu

nInt(_expression1, var, lower, upper_**)** $\Rightarrow$ _expression_

If the integrand _expression1_ contains no variable other than _var_, and if _lower_ and _upper_ are constants, positive ∞, or negative ∞, then **nInt()** returns an approximation of ∫(_expression1, var, lower, upper_). This approximation is a weighted average of some sample values of the integrand in the interval _lower<var<upper_.

The goal is six significant digits. The adaptive algorithm terminates when it seems likely that the goal has been achieved, or when it seems unlikely that additional samples will yield a worthwhile improvement.

A warning is displayed ("Questionable accuracy") when it seems that the goal has not been achieved.

Nest **nInt()** to do multiple numeric integration. Integration limits can depend on integration variables outside them.

Note: See also ∫() (page 216).

`nInt(e^(⁻x^2),x,⁻1,1)` ENTER   1.493...

`nInt(cos(x),x,⁻π,π+1ε⁻12)` ENTER
$$⁻1.041...ε⁻12$$

`∫(cos(x),x,⁻π,π+10^(⁻12))` ENTER
$$⁻\sin(\frac{1}{1000000000000})$$

`ans(1)`◆ ENTER   ⁻1.ε⁻12

`nInt(nInt(e^(⁻x*y)/√(x^2-y^2),`
`   y,⁻x,x),x,0,1)` ENTER   3.304...

norm()   MATH/Matrix/Norms menu

norm(_matrix_**)** $\Rightarrow$ _expression_

Returns the Frobenius norm.

`norm([a,b;c,d])` ENTER $\sqrt{a^2+b^2+c^2+d^2}$

`norm([1,2;3,4])` ENTER $\sqrt{30}$

not   MATH/Test menu

not _Boolean expression1_ $\Rightarrow$ _Boolean expression_

Returns true, false, or a simplified _Boolean expression1_.

`not 2>=3` ENTER   true

`not x<2` ENTER   x ≥ 2

`not not innocent` ENTER   innocent

---

not _integer1_ $\Rightarrow$ _integer_

Returns the one's complement of a real integer. Internally, _integer1_ is converted to a signed, 32-bit binary number. The value of each bit is flipped (0 becomes 1, and vice versa) for the one's complement. Results are displayed according to the Base mode.

You can enter the integer in any number base. For a binary or hexadecimal entry, you must use the 0b or 0h prefix, respectively. Without a prefix, the integer is treated as decimal (base 10).

If you enter a decimal integer that is too large for a signed, 32-bit binary form, a symmetric modulo operation is used to bring the value into the appropriate range.

In Hex base mode:

`not 0h7AC36` ENTER   0hFFF853C9

└─ **Important:** Zero, not the letter O.

In Bin base mode:

`0b100101▶dec` ENTER   37

`not 0b100101` ENTER
`0b11111111111111111111111111011010`

`ans(1)▶dec` ENTER   ⁻38

Note: A binary entry can have up to 32 digits (not counting the 0b prefix). A hexadecimal entry can have up to 8 digits.

Note: To type the ▶ conversion operator, press 2nd Y. You can also select base conversions from the MATH/Base menu.

nPr()   MATH/Probability menu

nPr(*expression1*, *expression2***)** $\Rightarrow$ *expression*

For integer *expression1* and *expression2* with
expression1 $\geq$ *expression2* $\geq$ 0, **nPr()** is the
number of permutations of *expression1* things
taken *expression2* at a time. Both arguments
can be integers or symbolic expressions.

nPr(*expression*, 0**)** $\Rightarrow$ 1

nPr(*expression*, *negInteger***)** $\Rightarrow$ 1/((*expression*+1) ·
(*expression*+2)... (*expression* − *negInteger*))

nPr(*expression*, *posInteger***)** $\Rightarrow$ *expression* ·
(*expression* − 1)... (*expression* − *posInteger*+1)

nPr(*expression*, *nonInteger***)** $\Rightarrow$ *expression*!/
(*expression* − *nonInteger*)!

nPr(z,3) [ENTER]	$z \cdot (z-2) \cdot (z-1)$
ans(1)|z=5 [ENTER]	60
nPr(z,-3) [ENTER]	$\dfrac{1}{(z+1) \cdot (z+2) \cdot (z+3)}$
nPr(z,c) [ENTER]	$\dfrac{z!}{(z-c)!}$
ans(1)*nPr(z-c,-c) [ENTER]	1

nPr(*list1*, *list2***)** $\Rightarrow$ *list*

Returns a list of permutations based on the
corresponding element pairs in the two lists.
The arguments must be the same size list.

nPr({5,4,3},{2,4,2}) [ENTER]   {20 24 6}

nPr(*matrix1*, *matrix2***)** $\Rightarrow$ *matrix*

Returns a matrix of permutations based on
the corresponding element pairs in the two
matrices. The arguments must be the same
size matrix.

nPr([6,5;4,3],[2,2;2,2]) [ENTER]
$$\begin{bmatrix} 30 & 20 \\ 12 & 6 \end{bmatrix}$$

nSolve()   MATH/Algebra menu

nSolve(*equation*, *varOrGuess***)** $\Rightarrow$ *number or*
error_string

Iteratively searches for one approximate real
numeric solution to *equation* for its one
variable. Specify *varOrGuess* as:

variable
– or –
variable = *real number*

For example, x is valid and so is x=3.

nSolve() is often much faster than **solve()** or
zeros(), particularly if the "|" operator is used
to constrain the search to a small interval
containing exactly one simple solution.

nSolve() attempts to determine either one
point where the residual is zero or two
relatively close points where the residual has
opposite signs and the magnitude of the
residual is not excessive. If it cannot achieve
this using a modest number of sample points,
it returns the string "no solution found."

If you use **nSolve()** in a program, you can use
getType() (page 138) to check for a numeric
result before using it in an algebraic expression.

Note: See also **cSolve()** (page 112), **cZeros()**
(page 116), **solve()** (page 188), and **zeros()**
(page 204).

nSolve(x^2+5x−25=9,x) [ENTER]
3.844...

nSolve(x^2=4,x=−1) [ENTER]   -2
nSolve(x^2=4,x=1) [ENTER]   2

Note: If there are multiple solutions, you
can use a guess to help find a particular
solution.

nSolve(x^2+5x−25=9,x)|x<0 [ENTER]
-8.844...

nSolve(((1+r)^24−1)/r=26,r)|r>0
and r<.25 [ENTER]   .0068...

nSolve(x^2=−1,x) [ENTER]
"no solution found"

OneVar   MATH/Statistics menu

OneVar *list1* [[, *list2*] [, *list3*] [, *list4*]]

Calculates 1-variable statistics and updates all the system statistics variables.

All the lists must have equal dimensions except for *list4*.

list1 represents xlist.
list2 represents frequency.
list3 represents category codes.
list4 represents category include list.

Note: *list1* through *list3* must be a variable name or c1–c99 (columns in the last data variable shown in the Data/Matrix Editor). *list4* does not have to be a variable name and cannot be c1–c99.

```
{0,2,3,4,3,4,6}→L1 ENTER
OneVar L1 ENTER                     Done
ShowStat ENTER
```

or   MATH/Test menu

Boolean expression1 **or** *Boolean expression2* ⇒
   Boolean expression

Returns true or false or a simplified form of the original entry.

Returns true if either or both expressions simplify to true. Returns false only if both expressions evaluate to false.

Note: See **xor** (page 203).

x≥3 or x≥4 ENTER   x ≥ 3

Program segment:

```
 :
If x<0 or x≥5
  Goto END

If choice=1 or choice=2
  Disp "Wrong choice"
 :
```

integer1 **or** *integer2* ⇒ *integer*

Compares two real integers bit-by-bit using an **or** operation. Internally, both integers are converted to signed, 32-bit binary numbers. When corresponding bits are compared, the result is 1 if either bit is 1; the result is 0 only if both bits are 0. The returned value represents the bit results, and is displayed according to the Base mode.

You can enter the integers in any number base. For a binary or hexadecimal entry, you must use the 0b or 0h prefix, respectively. Without a prefix, integers are treated as decimal (base 10).

If you enter a decimal integer that is too large for a signed, 32-bit binary form, a symmetric modulo operation is used to bring the value into the appropriate range.

Note: See **xor** (page 203).

In Hex base mode:

0h7AC36 or 0h3D5F ENTER   0h7BD7F

└─ **Important:** Zero, not the letter O.

In Bin base mode:

0b100101 or 0b100 ENTER   0b100101

Note: A binary entry can have up to 32 digits (not counting the 0b prefix). A hexadecimal entry can have up to 8 digits.

ord()   MATH/String menu

ord(*string*) ⇒ *integer*
ord(*list1*) ⇒ *list*

Returns the numeric code of the first character in character string *string*, or a list of the first characters of each list element.

See Appendix B for a complete listing of character codes.

```
ord("hello") ENTER            104
char(104) ENTER               "h"
ord(char(24)) ENTER            24
ord({"alpha","beta"}) ENTER  {97  98}
```

Output   CATALOG

Output *row*, *column*, *exprOrString*

Displays *exprOrString* (an expression or character string) on the Program I/O screen at the text coordinates (*row*, *column*).

An expression can include conversion operations such as ▸**DD** and ▸**Rect**. You can also use the ▸ operator (page 221) to perform unit and number base conversions.

If Pretty Print = ON, *exprOrString* is "pretty printed."

From the Program I/O screen, you can press F5 to display the Home screen, or a program can use **DispHome** (page 123).

Program segment:

```
    ⋮
:randseed(1147)
:ClrIO
:For i,1,100,10
:  Output i, rand(200),"Hello"
:EndFor
    ⋮
```

Result after execution:

```
Hello
                    Hello
         Hello
   Hello
             Hello
      Hello
                Hello
   Hello
                       Hello
        Hello
```

P▸Rx()   MATH/Angle menu

P▸Rx(*rExpression*, *θExpression*) ⇒ *expression*
P▸Rx(*rList*, *θList*) ⇒ *list*
P▸Rx(*rMatrix*, *θMatrix*) ⇒ *matrix*

Returns the equivalent x-coordinate of the (r, θ) pair.

Note: The θ argument is interpreted as either a degree or radian angle, according to the current angle mode. If the argument is an expression, you can use ° (page 219) or ᶜ (page 219) to override the angle mode setting temporarily.

In Radian angle mode:

```
P▸Rx(r,θ) ENTER           cos(θ)·r
P▸Rx(4,60°) ENTER                2
P▸Rx({-3,10,1.3},{π/3,-π/4,0}) ENTER
              { -3/2  5·√2  1.3 }
```

P▸Ry()   MATH/Angle menu

P▸Ry(*rExpression*, *θExpression*) ⇒ *expression*
P▸Ry(*rList*, *θList*) ⇒ *list*
P▸Ry(*rMatrix*, *θMatrix*) ⇒ *matrix*

Returns the equivalent y-coordinate of the (r, θ) pair.

Note: The θ argument is interpreted as either a degree or radian angle, according to the current angle mode. If the argument is an expression, you can use ° (page 219) or ᶜ (page 219) to override the angle mode setting temporarily.

In Radian angle mode:

```
P▸Ry(r,θ) ENTER           sin(θ)·r
P▸Ry(4,60°) ENTER              2·√3
P▸Ry({-3,10,1.3},{π/3,-π/4,0}) ENTER
         { -3·√3/2  -5·√2  0. }
```

part()   CATALOG

part(*expression1*[,*nonNegativeInteger*]**)**

> This advanced programming function lets you identify and extract all of the sub-expressions in the simplified result of *expression1*.
>
> For example, if *expression1* simplifies to cos(π*x+3), the:
>
> - The **cos()** function has one argument: (π*x+3).
> - The sum of (π*x+3) has two operands: π*x and 3.
> - The number 3 has no arguments or operands.
> - The product π*x has two operands: π and x.
> - The variable x and the symbolic constant π have no arguments or operands.
>
> If x has a numeric value and you press ● [ENTER], the numeric value of π*x is calculated, the result is added to 3, and then the cosine is calculated. **cos()** is the **top-level** operator because it is applied **last**.

---

part(*expression1***)** ⇒ *number*

> Simplifies *expression1* and returns the number of top-level arguments or operands. This returns 0 if *expression1* is a number, variable, or symbolic constant such as π, *e*, *i*, or ∞.

part(cos(π*x+3)) [ENTER]   1

Note: cos(π*x+3) has one argument.

part(*expression1*, **0)** ⇒ *string*

> Simplifies *expression1* and returns a string that contains the top-level function name or operator. This returns **string(***expression1***)** if *expression1* is a number, variable, or symbolic constant such as π, *e*, *i*, or ∞.

part(cos(π*x+3),0) [ENTER]   "cos"

part(*expression1*, *n***)** ⇒ *expression*

> Simplifies *expression1* and returns the *n*th argument or operand, where *n* is > 0 and ≤ the number of top-level arguments or operands returned by **part(***expression1***)**. Otherwise, an error is returned.

part(cos(π*x+3),1) [ENTER]   3+π·x

Note: Simplification changed the order of the argument.

> By combining the variations of **part()**, you can extract all of the sub-expressions in the simplified result of *expression1*. As shown in the example to the right, you can store an argument or operand and then use **part()** to extract further sub-expressions.
>
> **Note:** When using **part()**, do not rely on any particular order in sums and products.

```
part(cos(π*x+3)) [ENTER]                1
part(cos(π*x+3),0) [ENTER]          "cos"
part(cos(π*x+3),1)→temp [ENTER]
                                    3+π·x
temp [ENTER]                        π·x+3
part(temp,0) [ENTER]                  "+"
part(temp) [ENTER]                      2
part(temp,2) [ENTER]                    3
part(temp,1)→temp [ENTER]             π·x
part(temp,0) [ENTER]                  "*"
part(temp) [ENTER]                      2
part(temp,1) [ENTER]                    π
part(temp,2) [ENTER]                    x
```

Expressions such as (x+y+z) and (x−y−z) are represented internally as (x+y)+z and (x−y)−z. This affects the values returned for the first and second argument. There are technical reasons why **part**(x+y+z,1) returns y+x instead of x+y.

```
part(x+y+z) ENTER                    2
part(x+y+z,2) ENTER                  z
part(x+y+z,1) ENTER                y+x
```

Similarly, x∗y∗z is represented internally as (x∗y)∗z. Again, there are technical reasons why the first argument is returned as y · x instead of x · y.

```
part(x*y*z) ENTER                    2
part(x*y*z,2) ENTER                  z
part(x*y*z,1) ENTER                y·x
```

When you extract sub-expressions from a matrix, remember that matrices are stored as lists of lists, as illustrated in the example to the right.

```
part([a,b,c;x,y,z],0) ENTER        "{"
part([a,b,c;x,y,z]) ENTER            2
part([a,b,c;x,y,z],2)→temp ENTER
                               {x  y  z}
part(temp,0) ENTER                 "{"
part(temp) ENTER                     3
part(temp,3) ENTER                   z
delVar temp ENTER                 Done
```

The example Program Editor function to the right uses **getType()** and **part()** to partially implement symbolic differentiation. Studying and completing this function can help teach you how to differentiate manually. You could even include functions that the TI-92 Plus cannot differentiate, such as Bessel functions.

```
:d(y,x)
:Func
:Local f
:If getType(y)="VAR"
:  Return when(y=x,1,0,0)
:If part(y)=0
:  Return 0 © y=π,∞,i,numbers
:part(y,0)→f
:If f="-" © if negate
:  Return ⁻d(part(y,1),x)
:If f="−" © if minus
:  Return d(part(y,1),x)
      -d(part(y,2),x)
:If f="+"
:  Return d(part(y,1),x)
      +d(part(y,2),x)
:If f="*"
:  Return part(y,1)*d(part(y,2),x)
      +part(y,2)*d(part(y,1),x)
:If f="{"
:  Return seq(d(part(y,k),x),
      k,1,part(y))
:Return undef
:EndFunc
```

PassErr   CATALOG

PassErr

Passes an error to the next level.

If "errornum" is zero, **PassErr** does not do anything.

The **Else** clause in the program should use **ClrErr** or **PassErr**. If the error is to be processed or ignored, use **ClrErr**. If what to do with the error is not known, use **PassErr** to send it to the next error handler. (See also **ClrErr**.)

Program listing:
(See **ClrErr** on page 106.)

Pause CATALOG

Pause [*expression*]

Suspends program execution. If you include *expression*, displays *expression* on the Program I/O screen.

expression can include conversion operations such as ▸**DD** and ▸**Rect**. You can also use the ▸ operator (page 221) to perform unit and number base conversions.

If the result of *expression* is too big to fit on a single screen, you can use the cursor pad to scroll the display.

Program execution resumes when you press ENTER.

Program segment:

```
   ⋮
:ClrIO
:DelVar temp
:1→temp[1]
:1→temp[2]
:Disp temp[2]
:© Guess the Pattern
:For i,3,20
:  temp[i-2]+temp[i-1]→temp[i]
:  Disp temp[i]
:  Disp temp,"Can you guess the
     next number?"
:  Pause
:EndFor
   ⋮
```

PlotsOff CATALOG

PlotsOff [**1**] [**, 2**] [**, 3**] ... [**, 9**]

Turns off the specified plots for graphing. When in 2-graph mode, only affects the active graph.

If no parameters, then turns off all plots.

PlotsOff 1,2,5 ENTER   Done

PlotsOff ENTER   Done

PlotsOn CATALOG

PlotsOn [**1**] [**, 2**] [**, 3**] ... [**, 9**]

Turns on the specified plots for graphing. When in 2-graph mode, only affects the active graph.

If you do not include any arguments, turns on all plots.

PlotsOn 2,4,5 ENTER   Done

PlotsOn ENTER   Done

vector▶**Polar**

Displays *vector* in polar form [r ∠θ]. The vector must be of dimension 2 and can be a row or a column.

Note: ▶**Polar** is a display-format instruction, not a conversion function. You can use it only at the end of an entry line, and it does not update ans.

Note: See also ▶**Rect** (page 173).

```
[1,3.]▶Polar ENTER
[x,y]▶Polar ENTER
```

■[1 3.]▶Polar   [3.16228 ∠ 1.24905]
■[x y]▶Polar
$$\left[\sqrt{x^2+y^2} \angle -\tan^{-1}\left(\frac{x}{y}\right) + \frac{\pi \cdot \text{sign}(y)}{2}\right]$$

---

complexValue▶**Polar**

Displays *complexVector* in polar form.

- Degree angle mode returns (r∠θ).

- Radian angle mode returns $re^{i\theta}$.

complexValue can have any complex form. However, an $re^{i\theta}$ entry causes an error in Degree angle mode.

Note: You must use the parentheses for an (r∠θ) polar entry.

In Radian angle mode:

3+4**i**▶Polar ENTER $e^{i \cdot (\frac{\pi}{2} - \tan^{-1}(3/4))} \cdot 5$

(4∠π/3)▶Polar ENTER $e^{\frac{i \cdot \pi}{3}} \cdot 4$

In Degree angle mode:

3+4**i**▶Polar ENTER $(5 \angle 90 - \tan^{-1}(3/4))$

Note: To type ▶**Polar** from the keyboard, press 2nd Y for the ▶ operator. To type ∠, press 2nd F.

polyEval() MATH/List menu

polyEval(*list1*, *expression1*) ⇒ *expression*
polyEval(*list1*, *list2*) ⇒ *expression*

Interprets the first argument as the coefficients of a descending-degree polynomial, and returns the polynomial evaluated for the value of the second argument.

```
polyEval({a,b,c},x) ENTER    a·x²+b·x+c

polyEval({1,2,3,4},2) ENTER           26

polyEval({1,2,3,4},{2,-7})
ENTER                            {26  -262}
```

PopUp CATALOG

PopUp *itemList*, *var*

Displays a pop-up menu containing the character strings from *itemList*, waits for you to select an item, and stores the number of your selection in *var*.

The elements of *itemList* must be character strings: {*item1String*, *item2String*, *item3String*, ...}

If *var* already exists and has a valid item number, that item is displayed as the default choice.

itemList must contain at least one choice.

```
PopUp {"1990","1991","1992"},var1
ENTER
```

PowerReg   MATH/Statistics/Regressions menu

PowerReg *list1*, *list2*[, [*list3*] [, *list4*, *list5*]]

Calculates the power regression and updates all the system statistics variables.

All the lists must have equal dimensions except for *list5*.

list1 represents xlist.
list2 represents ylist.
list3 represents frequency.
list4 represents category codes.
list5 represents category include list.

Note: *list1* through *list4* must be a variable name or c1–c99 (columns in the last data variable shown in the Data/Matrix Editor). *list5* does not have to be a variable name and cannot be c1–c99.

In function graphing mode:

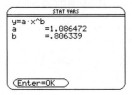
```
{1,2,3,4,5,6,7}→L1 ENTER    {1  2  3 ...}
{1,2,3,4,3,4,6}→L2 ENTER    {1  2  3 ...}
PowerReg L1,L2 ENTER             Done
ShowStat ENTER
```

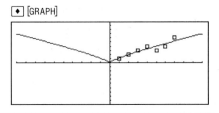

```
ENTER
Regeq(x)→y1(x) ENTER              Done
NewPlot 1,1,L1,L2 ENTER           Done
```

◆ [GRAPH]

Prgm   CATALOG

Prgm
⋮
EndPrgm

Required instruction that identifies the beginning of a program. Last line of program must be **EndPrgm**.

Program segment:

```
:prgmname()
:Prgm
 ⋮
:EndPrgm
```

---

product()   MATH/List menu

product(*list*) ⇒ *expression*

Returns the product of the elements contained in *list*.

```
product({1,2,3,4}) ENTER          24

product({2,x,y}) ENTER        2·x·y
```

---

product(*matrix1*) ⇒ *matrix*

Returns a row vector containing the products of the elements in the columns of *matrix1*.

```
product([1,2,3;4,5,6;7,8,9]) ENTER
                       [28  80  162]
```

Prompt   CATALOG

Prompt *var1*[, *var2*] [, *var3*] ...

Displays a prompt on the Program I/O screen for each variable in the argument list, using the prompt var1?. Stores the entered expression in the corresponding variable.

Prompt must have at least one argument.

Program segment:

```
 ⋮
Prompt A,B,C
 ⋮
EndPrgm
```

propFrac() MATH/Algebra menu

propFrac(*expression1*[, *var*]**)** ⇒ *expression*

    propFrac(*rational_number***)** returns
rational_number as the sum of an integer and
a fraction having the same sign and a greater
denominator magnitude than numerator
magnitude.

    propFrac(*rational_expression,var***)** returns the
sum of proper ratios and a polynomial with
respect to *var*. The degree of *var* in the
denominator exceeds the degree of *var* in the
numerator in each proper ratio. Similar
powers of *var* are collected. The terms and
their factors are sorted with *var* as the main
variable.

    If *var* is omitted, a proper fraction expansion
is done with respect to the most main
variable. The coefficients of the polynomial
part are then made proper with respect to
their most main variable first and so on.

    For rational expressions, **propFrac()** is a
faster but less extreme alternative to **expand()**
(page 130).

```
propFrac(4/3) ENTER              1 + 1/3
propFrac(-4/3) ENTER             -1-1/3
```

```
propFrac((x^2+x+1)/(x+1)+
 (y^2+y+1)/(y+1),x) ENTER
```

$$\blacksquare\ \text{propFrac}\left(\frac{x^2+x+1}{x+1}+\frac{y^2+y+1}{y+1},x\right)$$
$$\frac{1}{x+1}+x+\frac{y^2+y+1}{y+1}$$

```
propFrac(ans(1))
```

$$\blacksquare\ \text{propFrac}\left(\frac{1}{x+1}+x+\frac{y^2+y+1}{y+1}\right)$$
$$\frac{1}{x+1}+x+\frac{1}{y+1}+y$$

PtChg CATALOG

PtChg *x, y*
PtChg *xList, yList*

    Displays the Graph screen and reverses the
screen pixel nearest to window coordinates
(*x, y*).

Note: PtChg through **PtText** show
continuing similar examples.
```
PtChg 2,4 ENTER
```

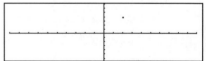

PtOff CATALOG

PtOff *x, y*
PtOff *xList, yList*

    Displays the Graph screen and turns off the
screen pixel nearest to window coordinates
(*x, y*).

```
PtOff 2,4 ENTER
```

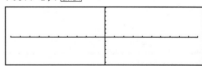

PtOn CATALOG

PtOn *x, y*
PtOn *xList, yList*

    Displays the Graph screen and turns on the
screen pixel nearest to window coordinates
(*x, y*).

```
PtOn 3,5 ENTER
```

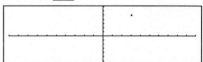

ptTest() CATALOG

ptTest (*x, y***)** ⇒ *Boolean constant expression*
ptTest (*xList, yList***)** ⇒ *Boolean constant expression*

    Returns true or false. Returns true only if the
screen pixel nearest to window coordinates
(*x, y*) is on.

```
ptTest(3,5) ENTER                true
```

PtText   CATALOG

PtText *string, x, y*

Displays the Graph screen and places the character string *string* on the screen at the pixel nearest the specified (*x, y*) window coordinates.

string is positioned with the upper-left corner of its first character at the coordinates.

PtText "sample",3,5 [ENTER]

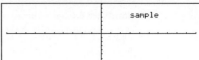

PxlChg   CATALOG

PxlChg *row, col*
PxlChg *rowList, colList*

Displays the Graph screen and reverses the pixel at pixel coordinates (*row, col*).

Note: Regraphing erases all drawn items.

PxlChg 2,4 [ENTER]

PxlCrcl   CATALOG

PxlCrcl *row, col, r* [, *drawMode*]

Displays the Graph screen and draws a circle centered at pixel coordinates (*row, col*) with a radius of *r* pixels.

If *drawMode* = 1, draws the circle (default).
If *drawMode* = 0, turns off the circle.
If *drawMode* = -1, inverts pixels along the circle.

Note: Regraphing erases all drawn items. See also **Circle** (page 106).

PxlCrcl 50,125,40,1 [ENTER]

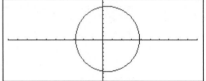

PxlHorz   CATALOG

PxlHorz *row* [, *drawMode*]

Displays the Graph screen and draws a horizontal line at pixel position *row*.

If *drawMode* = 1, draws the line (default).
If *drawMode* = 0, turns off the line.
If *drawMode* = -1, turns a line that is on to off or off to on (inverts pixels along the line).

Note: Regraphing erases all drawn items. See also **LineHorz** (page 146).

PxlHorz 25,1 [ENTER]

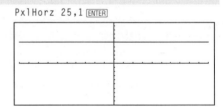

PxlLine   CATALOG

PxlLine *rowStart, colStart, rowEnd, colEnd* [, *drawMode*]

Displays the Graph screen and draws a line between pixel coordinates (*rowStart, colStart*) and (*rowEnd, colEnd*), including both endpoints.

If *drawMode* = 1, draws the line (default).
If *drawMode* = 0, turns off the line.
If *drawMode* = -1, turns a line that is on to off or off to on (inverts pixels along the line).

Note: Regraphing erases all drawn items. See also **Line** (page 146)

PxlLine 80,20,30,150,1 [ENTER]

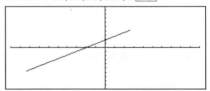

PxlOff   CATALOG

PxlOff *row, col*
PxlOff *rowList, colList*

Displays the Graph screen and turns off the
pixel at pixel coordinates (*row, col*).

Note: Regraphing erases all drawn items.

```
PxlHorz 25,1 [ENTER]
PxlOff 25,50 [ENTER]
```

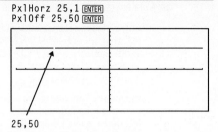

```
25,50
```

PxlOn   CATALOG

PxlOn *row, col*
PxlOn *rowList, colList*

Displays the Graph screen and turns on the
pixel at pixel coordinates (*row, col*).

Note: Regraphing erases all drawn items.

```
PxlOn 25,50 [ENTER]
```

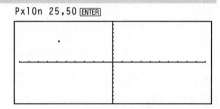

pxlTest()   CATALOG

pxlTest (*row, col*) ⇒ *Boolean expression*
pxlTest (*rowList, colList*) ⇒ *Boolean expression*

Returns true if the pixel at pixel coordinates
(*row, col*) is on. Returns false if the pixel is off.

Note: Regraphing erases all drawn items.

```
PxlOn 25,50 [ENTER]
[♦][HOME]
PxlTest(25,50) [ENTER]                    true

PxlOff 25,50 [ENTER]
[♦][HOME]
PxlTest(25,50) [ENTER]                    false
```

PxlText   CATALOG

PxlText *string, row, col*

Displays the Graph screen and places
character string *string* on the screen, starting
at pixel coordinates (*row, col*).

string is positioned with the upper-left corner
of its first character at the coordinates.

Note: Regraphing erases all drawn items.

```
PxlText "sample text",20,50 [ENTER]
```

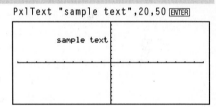

PxlVert   CATALOG

PxlVert *col* [, *drawMode*]

Draws a vertical line down the screen at pixel
position *col*.

If *drawMode* = 1, draws the line (default).
If *drawMode* = 0, turns off the line.
If *drawMode* = -1, turns a line that is on to off
or off to on (inverts pixels along the line).

Note: Regraphing erases all drawn items. See
also **LineVert** (page 146).

```
PxlVert 50,1 [ENTER]
```

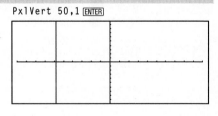

QR MATH/Matrix menu

QR *matrix*, *qMatName*, *rMatName*[, *tol*]

Calculates the Householder QR factorization of a real or complex *matrix*. The resulting Q and R matrices are stored to the specified *MatNames*. The Q matrix is unitary. The R matrix is upper triangular.

Optionally, any matrix element is treated as zero if its absolute value is less than *tol*. This tolerance is used only if the matrix has floating-point entries and does not contain any symbolic variables that have not been assigned a value. Otherwise, *tol* is ignored.

- If you use ◆ ENTER or set the mode to Exact/Approx=APPROXIMATE, computations are done using floating-point arithmetic.

- If *tol* is omitted or not used, the default tolerance is calculated as:

  $5\text{E}^-14 * $ **max(dim(**$matrix$**)) * rowNorm(**$matrix$**)**

The QR factorization is computed numerically using Householder transformations. The symbolic solution is computed using Gram-Schmidt. The columns in *qMatName* are the orthonormal basis vectors that span the space defined by *matrix*.

The floating-point number (9.) in m1 causes results to be calculated in floating-point form.

`[1,2,3;4,5,6;7,8,9.]→m1` ENTER

$$\begin{bmatrix} 1 & 2 & 3 \\ 4 & 5 & 6 \\ 7 & 8 & 9. \end{bmatrix}$$

`QR m1,qm,rm` ENTER   Done

`qm` ENTER
$$\begin{bmatrix} .123\dots & .904\dots & .408\dots \\ .492\dots & .301\dots & ^-.816\dots \\ .861\dots & ^-.301\dots & .408\dots \end{bmatrix}$$

`rm` ENTER
$$\begin{bmatrix} 8.124\dots & 9.601\dots & 11.078\dots \\ 0. & .904\dots & 1.809\dots \\ 0. & 0. & 0. \end{bmatrix}$$

`[m,n;o,p]→m1` ENTER $\begin{bmatrix} m & n \\ o & p \end{bmatrix}$

`QR m1,qm,rm` ENTER   Done

`qm` ENTER
$$\begin{bmatrix} \dfrac{m}{\sqrt{m^2+o^2}} & \dfrac{^-\text{sign}(m\cdot p-n\cdot o)\cdot o}{\sqrt{m^2+o^2}} \\ \dfrac{o}{\sqrt{m^2+o^2}} & \dfrac{m\cdot\text{sign}(m\cdot p-n\cdot o)}{\sqrt{m^2+o^2}} \end{bmatrix}$$

`rm` ENTER
$$\begin{bmatrix} \sqrt{m^2+o^2} & \dfrac{m\cdot n+o\cdot p}{\sqrt{m^2+o^2}} \\ 0 & \dfrac{|m\cdot p-n\cdot o|}{\sqrt{m^2+o^2}} \end{bmatrix}$$

QuadReg MATH/Statistics/Regressions menu

QuadReg *list1*, *list2*[, [*list3*] [, *list4*, *list5*]]

Calculates the quadratic polynomial regression and updates the system statistics variables.

All the lists must have equal dimensions except for *list5*.

list1 represents xlist.
list2 represents ylist.
list3 represents frequency.
list4 represents category codes.
list5 represents category include list.

Note: *list1* through *list4* must be a variable name or c1–c99 (columns in the last data variable shown in the Data/Matrix Editor). *list5* does not have to be a variable name and cannot be c1–c99.

In function graphing mode:

`{0,1,2,3,4,5,6,7}→L1` ENTER {1 2 3 ...}
`{4,3,1,1,2,2,3,3}→L2` ENTER {4 3 1 ...}
`QuadReg L1,L2` ENTER   Done
`ShowStat` ENTER

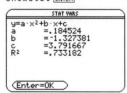

```
STAT VARS
y=a·x²+b·x+c
a     =.184524
b     =-1.327381
c     =3.791667
R²    =.733182

(Enter=OK)
```

ENTER
`Regeq(x)→y1(x)` ENTER   Done
`NewPlot 1,1,L1,L2` ENTER   Done

◆ [GRAPH]

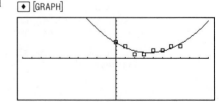

QuartReg   MATH/Statistics/Regressions menu

QuartReg *list1*, *list2*[, [*list3*] [, *list4*, *list5*]]

Calculates the quartic polynomial regression and updates the system statistics variables.

All the lists must have equal dimensions except for *list5*.

list1 represents xlist.
list2 represents ylist.
list3 represents frequency.
list4 represents category codes.
list5 represents category include list.

Note: *list1* through *list4* must be a variable name or c1–c99 (columns in the last data variable shown in the Data/Matrix Editor). *list5* does not have to be a variable name and cannot be c1–c99.

In function graphing mode:

```
{-2,-1,0,1,2,3,4,5,6}→L1 ENTER
                          {-2 -1 0 ...}
{4,3,1,2,4,2,1,4,6}→L2 ENTER
                          {4 3 1 ...}
QuartReg L1,L2 ENTER                  Done
ShowStat ENTER
```

```
            STAT VARS
y=a·x^4+b·x³+c·x²+d·x+e
a       =.023019
b       =-.166472
c       =.246795
d       =.24864
e       =1.998834
R²      =.700042

 Enter=OK
```

```
ENTER
Regeq(x)→y1(x) ENTER                  Done
NewPlot 1,1,L1,L2 ENTER               Done
```

[♦] [GRAPH]

R▶Pθ()   MATH/Angle menu

R▶Pθ (*xExpression*, *yExpression*) ⇒ *expression*
R▶Pθ (*xList*, *yList*) ⇒ *list*
R▶Pθ (*xMatrix*, *yMatrix*) ⇒ *matrix*

Returns the equivalent θ-coordinate of the (*x*,*y*) pair arguments.

Note: The result is returned as either a degree or radian angle, according to the current angle mode.

In Degree angle mode:

R▶Pθ(x,y) ENTER

$$\blacksquare\ R\blacktriangleright P\theta(x,y) \qquad\qquad 90\cdot sign(y) - tan^{-1}\left(\frac{x}{y}\right)$$

In Radian angle mode:

R▶Pθ(3,2) ENTER
R▶Pθ([3,-4,2],[0,π/4,1.5]) ENTER

$$\blacksquare\ R\blacktriangleright P\theta(3,2) \qquad\qquad\qquad tan^{-1}(2/3)$$
$$\blacksquare\ R\blacktriangleright P\theta\left(\begin{bmatrix}3 & -4 & 2\end{bmatrix},\begin{bmatrix}0 & \frac{\pi}{4} & 1.5\end{bmatrix}\right)$$
$$\left[0\quad tan^{-1}\left(\frac{16}{\pi}\right)+\frac{\pi}{2}\quad .643501\right]$$

R▶Pr()   MATH/Angle menu

R▶Pr (*xExpression*, *yExpression*) ⇒ *expression*
R▶Pr (*xList*, *yList*) ⇒ *list*
R▶Pr (*xMatrix*, *yMatrix*) ⇒ *matrix*

Returns the equivalent r-coordinate of the (*x*,*y*) pair arguments.

In Radian angle mode:

R▶Pr(3,2) ENTER
R▶Pr(x,y) ENTER
R▶Pr([3,-4,2],[0,π/4,1.5]) ENTER

$$\blacksquare\ R\blacktriangleright Pr(3,2) \qquad\qquad\qquad\qquad \sqrt{13}$$
$$\blacksquare\ R\blacktriangleright Pr(x,y) \qquad\qquad\qquad\qquad \sqrt{x^2+y^2}$$
$$\blacksquare\ R\blacktriangleright Pr\left(\begin{bmatrix}3 & -4 & 2\end{bmatrix},\begin{bmatrix}0 & \frac{\pi}{4} & 1.5\end{bmatrix}\right)$$
$$\left[3\quad \frac{\sqrt{\pi^2+256}}{4}\quad 2.5\right]$$

rand()   MATH/Probability menu

rand(n**)** ⇒ *expression*

n is an integer ≠ zero.

With no parameter, returns the next random number between 0 and 1 in the sequence. When an argument is positive, returns a random integer in the interval [1, n]. When an argument is negative, returns a random integer in the interval [⁻n, ⁻1].

```
RandSeed 1147 ENTER                Done
        └ (Sets the random-number seed.)
rand() ENTER                      0.158...
rand(6) ENTER                           5
rand(-100) ENTER                      -49
```

randMat()   MATH/Probability menu

randMat(numRows, numColumns**)** ⇒ *matrix*

Returns a matrix of integers between -9 and 9 of the specified dimension.

Both arguments must simplify to integers.

```
RandSeed 1147 ENTER                Done
                             ⎡ 8  -3   6⎤
randMat(3,3) ENTER           ⎢-2   3  -6⎥
                             ⎣ 0   4  -6⎦
```

Note: The values in this matrix will change each time you press ENTER.

randNorm()   MATH/Probability menu

randNorm(mean, sd**)** ⇒ *expression*

Returns a decimal number from the specific normal distribution. It could be any real number but will be heavily concentrated in the interval [mean-3*sd, mean+3*sd].

```
RandSeed 1147 ENTER                Done
randNorm(0,1) ENTER             0.492...
randNorm(3,4.5) ENTER          -3.543...
```

randPoly()   MATH/Probability menu

randPoly(var, order**)** ⇒ *expression*

Returns a polynomial in *var* of the specified order. The coefficients are random integers in the range ⁻9 through 9. The leading coefficient will not be zero.

order must be 0–99.

```
RandSeed 1147 ENTER                Done
randPoly(x,5) ENTER
          -2·x⁵+3·x⁴-6·x³+4·x-6
```

RandSeed   MATH/Probability menu

RandSeed number

If number = 0, sets the seeds to the factory defaults for the random-number generator. If number ≠ 0, it is used to generate two seeds, which are stored in system variables seed1 and seed2.

```
RandSeed 1147 ENTER                Done
rand() ENTER                      0.158...
```

RclGDB   CATALOG

RclGDB GDBvar

Restores all the settings stored in the Graph database variable GDBvar.

For a listing of the settings, see **StoGDB** on page 191.

```
RclGDB GDBvar ENTER                Done
```

RclPic   CATALOG

RclPic *picVar* [, *row*, *column*]

Displays the Graph screen and adds the picture stored in *picVar* at the upper left-hand corner pixel coordinates (*row*, *column*) using OR logic.

picVar must be a picture data type.

Default coordinates are (0, 0).

real()   MATH/Complex menu

real(*expression1***)** ⇒ *expression*

Returns the real part of the argument.

Note: All undefined variables are treated as real variables. See also **imag()** (page 142).

real(2+3*i*) [ENTER]	2
real(z) [ENTER]	z
real(x+*i*y) [ENTER]	x

real(*list1***)** ⇒ *list*

Returns the real parts of all elements.

real({a+*i*∗b,3,*i*}) [ENTER]   {a 3 0}

real(*matrix1***)** ⇒ *matrix*

Returns the real parts of all elements.

real([a+*i*∗b,3;c,*i*]) [ENTER] $\begin{bmatrix} a & 3 \\ c & 0 \end{bmatrix}$

▶Rect   MATH/Matrix/Vector ops menu

vector ▶**Rect**

Displays *vector* in rectangular form [x, y, z]. The vector must be of dimension 2 or 3 and can be a row or a column.

Note: ▶**Rect** is a display-format instruction, not a conversion function. You can use it only at the end of an entry line, and it does not update ans.

Note: See also ▶**Polar** (page 165).

[3,∠π/4,∠π/6]▶Rect [ENTER]

$$\left[\frac{3\cdot\sqrt{2}}{4} \quad \frac{3\cdot\sqrt{2}}{4} \quad \frac{3\cdot\sqrt{3}}{2}\right]$$

[a,∠b,∠c] [ENTER]   [a·cos(b)·sin(c)
                        a·sin(b)·sin(c) a·cos(c)]

complexValue ▶**Rect**

Displays *complexValue* in rectangular form a+b*i*. The *complexValue* can have any complex form. However, an re^{*i*θ} entry causes an error in Degree angle mode.

Note: You must use parentheses for an (r∠θ) polar entry.

In Radian angle mode:

4*e*^(π/3)▶Rect [ENTER] $4\cdot e^{\frac{\pi}{3}}$

(4∠π/3)▶Rect [ENTER] $2+2\cdot\sqrt{3}\cdot i$

In Degree angle mode:

(4∠60)▶Rect [ENTER] $2+2\cdot\sqrt{3}\cdot i$

Note: To type ▶**Rect** from the keyboard, press [2nd] Y for the ▶ operator. To type ∠, press [2nd] F.

ref()   MATH/Matrix menu

ref(*matrix1*[, *tol*]) ⇒ *matrix*

Returns the row echelon form of *matrix1*.

Optionally, any matrix element is treated as zero if its absolute value is less than *tol*. This tolerance is used only if the matrix has floating-point entries and does not contain any symbolic variables that have not been assigned a value. Otherwise, *tol* is ignored.

- If you use ● ENTER or set the mode to Exact/Approx=APPROXIMATE, computations are done using floating-point arithmetic.

- If *tol* is omitted or not used, the default tolerance is calculated as:

  5E⁻14 ∗ **max(dim(**matrix1**))** ∗ **rowNorm(**matrix1**)**

Note: See also **rref()** on page 177.

ref([⁻2,⁻2,0,⁻6;1,⁻1,9,⁻9;⁻5, 2,4,⁻4]) ENTER

$$\begin{bmatrix} 1 & -2/5 & -4/5 & 4/5 \\ 0 & 1 & 4/7 & 11/7 \\ 0 & 0 & 1 & -62/71 \end{bmatrix}$$

[a,b,c;e,f,g]→m1 ENTER $\begin{bmatrix} a & b & c \\ e & f & g \end{bmatrix}$

ref(m1) ENTER

$$\begin{bmatrix} 1 & \frac{f}{e} & \frac{g}{e} \\ 0 & 1 & \frac{a \cdot g - c \cdot e}{a \cdot f - b \cdot e} \end{bmatrix}$$

remain()   MATH/Number menu

remain(*expression1*, *expression2*) ⇒ *expression*
remain(*list1*, *list2*) ⇒ *list*
remain(*matrix1*, *matrix2*) ⇒ *matrix*

Returns the remainder of the first argument with respect to the second argument as defined by the identities:

remain(x,0) ≡ x
remain(x,y) ≡ x−y∗iPart(x/y)

As a consequence, note that **remain**(−x,y) ≡ −**remain**(x,y). The result is either zero or it has the same sign as the first argument.

Note: See also **mod()** (page 154).

remain(7,0) ENTER   7

remain(7,3) ENTER   1

remain(⁻7,3) ENTER   ⁻1

remain(7,⁻3) ENTER   1

remain(⁻7,⁻3) ENTER   ⁻1

remain({12,⁻14,16},{9,7,⁻5}) ENTER
{3   0   1}

remain([9,⁻7;6,4],[4,3;4,⁻3]) ENTER
$\begin{bmatrix} 1 & -1 \\ 2 & 1 \end{bmatrix}$

Rename   CATALOG

Rename *oldVarName*, *newVarName*

Renames the variable *oldVarName* as *newVarName*.

{1,2,3,4}→L1 ENTER   {1,2,3,4}
Rename L1, list1 ENTER   Done
list1 ENTER   {1,2,3,4}

Request   CATALOG

Request *promptString*, *var*

If **Request** is inside a **Dialog...EndDlog** construct, it creates an input box for the user to type in data. If it is a stand-alone instruction, it creates a dialog box for this input. In either case, if *var* contains a string, it is displayed and highlighted in the input box as a default choice. *promptString* must be ≤ 20 characters.

This instruction can be stand-alone or part of a dialog construct.

Request "Enter Your Name",str1 ENTER

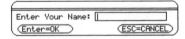

Return   CATALOG

Return [*expression*]

> Returns *expression* as the result of the function. Use within a **Func**...**EndFunc** block, or **Prgm**...**EndPrgm** block.
>
> **Note**: Use **Return** without an argument to exit a program.

```
Define factoral(nn)=Func
:local answer,count:1→answer
:For count,1,nn
:answer*count→answer:EndFor
:Return answer:EndFunc ENTER    Done
```
```
factoral(3) ENTER                      6
```

right()   MATH/List menu

right(*list1*[, *num*]) ⇒ *list*

> Returns the rightmost *num* elements contained in *list1*.
>
> If you omit *num*, returns all of *list1*.

```
right({1,3,-2,4},3) ENTER    {3 -2 4}
```

right(*sourceString*[, *num*]) ⇒ *string*

> Returns the rightmost *num* characters contained in character string *sourceString*.
>
> If you omit *num*, returns all of *sourceString*.

```
right("Hello",2) ENTER            "lo"
```

right(*comparison*) ⇒ *expression*

> Returns the right side of an equation or inequality.

```
right(x<3) ENTER                     3
```

rotate()   MATH/Base menu

rotate(*integer1*[,*#ofRotations*]) ⇒ *integer*

> Rotates the bits in a binary integer. You can enter *integer1* in any number base; it is converted automatically to a signed, 32-bit binary form. If the magnitude of *integer1* is too large for this form, a symmetric modulo operation brings it within the range.
>
> If *#of Rotations* is positive, the rotation is to the left. If *#of Rotations* is negative, the rotation is to the right. The default is ⁻1 (rotate right one bit).
>
> For example, in a right rotation:
>
> ┌► Each bit rotates right.
> 0b00000000000001111010110000110101
> ▲_____|
>   Rightmost bit rotates to leftmost.
>
> produces:
>
> 0b10000000000000111101011000011010
>
> The result is displayed according to the Base mode.

In Bin base mode:

```
rotate(0b1111010110000110101) ENTER
    0b10000000000000111101011000011010
```
```
rotate(256,1) ENTER     0b1000000000
```

In Hex base mode:

```
rotate(0h78E) ENTER            0h3C7
```
```
rotate(0h78E,-2) ENTER    0h800001E3
```
```
rotate(0h78E,2) ENTER         0h1E38
```

Important: To enter a binary or hexadecimal number, always use the 0b or 0h prefix (zero, not the letter O).

rotate(*list1*[,*#ofRotations*]**)** ⇒ *list*	In Dec base mode:

Returns a copy of *list1* rotated right or left by *#of Rotations* elements. Does not alter *list1*.

If *#of Rotations* is positive, the rotation is to the left. If *#of Rotations* is negative, the rotation is to the right. The default is ¯1 (rotate right one element).

```
rotate({1,2,3,4}) ENTER
                        {4 1 2 3}

rotate({1,2,3,4},-2) ENTER
                        {3 4 1 2}

rotate({1,2,3,4},1) ENTER
                        {2 3 4 1}
```

rotate(*string1*[,*#ofRotations*]**)** ⇒ *string*

Returns a copy of *string1* rotated right or left by *#of Rotations* characters. Does not alter *string1*.

If *#of Rotations* is positive, the rotation is to the left. If *#of Rotations* is negative, the rotation is to the right. The default is ¯1 (rotate right one character).

```
rotate("abcd") ENTER      "dabc"

rotate("abcd",-2) ENTER   "cdab"

rotate("abcd",1) ENTER    "bcda"
```

round()   MATH/Number menu

round(*expression1*[, *digits*]**)** ⇒ *expression*

Returns the argument rounded to the specified number of digits after the decimal point.

digits must be an integer in the range 0–12. If *digits* is not included, returns the argument rounded to 12 significant digits.

Note: Display digits mode may still affect how this is displayed.

```
round(1.234567,3) ENTER        1.235
```

round(*list1*[, *digits*]**)** ⇒ *list*

Returns a list of the elements rounded to the specified number of digits.

```
round({π,√(2),ln(2)},4) ENTER
                {3.1416 1.4142 .6931}
```

round(*matrix1*[, *digits*]**)** ⇒ *matrix*

Returns a matrix of the elements rounded to the specified number of digits.

```
round([ln(5),ln(3);π,e^(1)],1) ENTER
                [ 1.6   1.1 ]
                [ 3.1   2.7 ]
```

rowAdd()   MATH/Matrix/Row ops menu

rowAdd(*matrix1, rIndex1, rIndex2***)** ⇒ *matrix*

Returns a copy of *matrix1* with row *rIndex2* replaced by the sum of rows *rIndex1* and *rIndex2*.

```
rowAdd([3,4;-3,-2],1,2) ENTER
                [ 3   4 ]
                [ 0   2 ]

rowAdd([a,b;c,d],1,2) ENTER
                [ a     b   ]
                [ a+c   b+d ]
```

rowDim()   MATH/Matrix/Dimensions menu

rowDim(*matrix***)** ⇒ *expression*

Returns the number of rows in *matrix*.

Note: See also **colDim()** (page 107).

```
[1,2;3,4;5,6]→M1 ENTER
                [ 1   2 ]
                [ 3   4 ]
                [ 5   6 ]

rowdim(M1) ENTER               3
```

rowNorm() MATH/Matrix/Norms menu

rowNorm(*matrix***)** ⇒ *expression*

Returns the maximum of the sums of the absolute values of the elements in the rows in *matrix*.

Note: All matrix elements must simplify to numbers. See also **colNorm()** (page 107).

```
rowNorm([-5,6,-7;3,4,9;9,-9,-7])
ENTER                            25
```

rowSwap() MATH/Matrix/Row ops menu

rowSwap(*matrix1, rIndex1, rIndex2***)** ⇒ *matrix*

Returns *matrix1* with rows *rIndex1* and *rIndex2* exchanged.

```
[1,2;3,4;5,6]→Mat ENTER
```
$$\begin{bmatrix} 1 & 2 \\ 3 & 4 \\ 5 & 6 \end{bmatrix}$$

```
rowSwap(Mat,1,3) ENTER
```
$$\begin{bmatrix} 5 & 6 \\ 3 & 4 \\ 1 & 2 \end{bmatrix}$$

RplcPic CATALOG

RplcPic *picVar*[, *row*][, *column*]

Clears the Graph screen and places picture *picVar* at pixel coordinates (*row, column*). If you do not want to clear the screen, use **RclPic**.

picVar must be a picture data type variable. *row* and *column*, if included, specify the pixel coordinates of the upper left corner of the picture. Default coordinates are (0, 0).

Note: For less than full-screen pictures, only the area affected by the new picture is cleared.

rref() MATH/Matrix menu

rref(*matrix1*[, *tol*]**)** ⇒ *matrix*

Returns the reduced row echelon form of *matrix1*.

Optionally, any matrix element is treated as zero if its absolute value is less than *tol*. This tolerance is used only if the matrix has floating-point entries and does not contain any symbolic variables that have not been assigned a value. Otherwise, *tol* is ignored.

- If you use ◆ ENTER or set the mode to Exact/Approx=APPROXIMATE, computations are done using floating-point arithmetic.

- If *tol* is omitted or not used, the default tolerance is calculated as:

  5E⁻14 ∗ **max(dim(***matrix1***))** ∗ **rowNorm(***matrix1***)**

Note: See also **ref()** on page 174.

```
rref([-2,-2,0,-6;1,-1,9,-9;
-5,2,4,-4]) ENTER
```
$$\begin{bmatrix} 1 & 0 & 0 & 66/71 \\ 0 & 1 & 0 & \frac{147}{71} \\ 0 & 0 & 1 & -62/71 \end{bmatrix}$$

```
rref([a,b,x;c,d,y]) ENTER
```
$$\begin{bmatrix} 1 & 0 & \frac{d \cdot x - b \cdot y}{a \cdot d - b \cdot c} \\ 0 & 1 & \frac{-(c \cdot x - a \cdot y)}{a \cdot d - b \cdot c} \end{bmatrix}$$

Send   CATALOG

Send *list*

CBL (Calculator-Based Laboratory) instruction. Sends *list* to the link port.

Program segment:

```
     :
     :
:Send {1,0}
:Send {1,2,1}
     :
     :
```

SendCalc   CATALOG

SendCalc *var*

Sends variable *var* to the link port. This is for unit-to-unit linking.

Program segment:

```
     :
     :
:a+b→x
:SendCalc x
     :
     :
```

seq()   MATH/List menu

seq(*expression, var, low, high*[, *step*]**)** ⇒ *list*

Increments *var* from *low* through *high* by an increment of *step*, evaluates *expression*, and returns the results as a list. The original contents of *var* are still there after **seq()** is completed.

var cannot be a system variable.

The default value for *step* = 1.

```
seq(n^2,n,1,6) ENTER   {1 4 9 16 25 36}

seq(1/n,n,1,10,2) ENTER
                 {1 1/3 1/5 1/7 1/9}

sum(seq(1/n^2,n,1,10,1)) ENTER    196…
                                  ――――
                                  127…

or press • ENTER to get:          1.549…
```

setFold()   CATALOG

setFold(*newfolderName***)** ⇒ *oldfolderString*

Returns the name of the current folder as a string and sets *newfolderName* as the current folder.

The folder *newfolderName* must exist.

```
newFold chris ENTER              Done
setFold(main) ENTER           "chris"
setFold(chris)→oldfoldr ENTER  "main"
1→a ENTER                          1
setFold(#oldfoldr) ENTER      "chris"
a ENTER                            a
chris\a ENTER                      1
```

setGraph(*modeNameString***,** *settingString***)** ⇒ *string*

Sets the Graph mode *modeNameString* to *settingString*, and returns the previous setting of the mode. Storing the previous setting lets you restore it later.

modeNameString is a character string that specifies which mode you want to set. It must be one of the mode names from the table below.

settingString is a character string that specifies the new setting for the mode. It must be one of the settings listed below for the specific mode you are setting.

```
setGraph("Graph Order","Seq")
ENTER                           "SEQ"

setGraph("Coordinates","Off")
ENTER                           "RECT"
```

Note: Capitalization and blank spaces are optional when entering mode names.

Mode Name	Settings	
"Coordinates"	"Rect", "Polar", "Off"	
"Graph Order"	"Seq", "Simul" [1]	
"Grid"	"Off", "On" [2]	
"Axes"	"Off", "On"	(not 3D graph mode)
	"Off", "Axes", "Box"	(3D graph mode)
"Leading Cursor"	"Off", "On" [2]	
"Labels"	"Off", "On"	
"Style"	"Wire Frame", "Hidden Surface", "Contour Levels", "Wire and Contour", "Implicit Plot" [3]	
"Seq Axes"	"Time", "Web", "U1-vs-U2" [4]	
"DE Axes"	"Time", "t-vs-y' ", "y-vs-y' ", "y1-vs-y2", "y1-vs-y2' ", "y1'-vs-y2' " [5]	
	Tip: To type a prime symbol ('), press 2nd B.	
"Solution Method"	"RK", "Euler" [5]	
"Fields"	"SlpFld", "DirFld", "FldOff" [5]	

[1] Not available in Sequence, 3D, or Diff Equations graph mode.
[2] Not available in 3D graph mode.
[3] Applies only to 3D graph mode.
[4] Applies only to Sequence graph mode.
[5] Applies only to Diff Equations graph mode.

setMode(*modeNameString*, *settingString*) ⇒ *string*
setMode(*list*) ⇒ *stringList*

Sets mode *modeNameString* to the new setting *settingString*, and returns the current setting of that mode.

modeNameString is a character string that specifies which mode you want to set. It must be one of the mode names from the table below.

settingString is a character string that specifies the new setting for the mode. It must be one of the settings listed below for the specific mode you are setting.

list contains pairs of keyword strings and will set them all at once. This is recommended for multiple-mode changes. The example shown may not work if each of the pairs is entered with a separate **setMode()** in the order shown.

Use **setMode(***var***)** to restore settings saved with **getMode("ALL")→***var* on page 138.

Note: To set or return information about the Unit System mode, use **setUnits()** on page 181 or **getUnits()** on page 139 instead of **setMode()** or **getMode()**.

```
setMode("Angle","Degree")
ENTER                                "RADIAN"
sin(45) ENTER                           √2
                                        ──
                                        2

setMode("Angle","Radian")
ENTER                                "DEGREE"
sin(π/4) ENTER                          √2
                                        ──
                                        2

setMode("Display Digits",
"Fix 2") ENTER                       "FLOAT"

π ◆ ENTER                               3.14

setMode ("Display Digits",
"Float") ENTER                       "FIX 2"

π ◆ ENTER                               3.141…

setMode ({"Split Screen",
"Left-Right","Split 1 App",
"Graph","Split 2 App","Table"})
ENTER
                     {"Split 2 App" "Graph"
                          "Split 1 App" "Home"
                      "Split Screen" "FULL"}
```

Note: Capitalization and blank spaces are optional when entering mode names. Also, the results in these examples may be different on your unit.

Mode Name	Settings
"Graph"	"Function", "Parametric", "Polar", "Sequence", "3D", "Diff Equations"
"Display Digits"	"Fix 0", "Fix 1", ..., "Fix 12", "Float", "Float 1", ..., "Float 12"
"Angle"	"Radian", "Degree"
"Exponential Format"	"Normal", "Scientific", "Engineering"
"Complex Format"	"Real", "Rectangular", "Polar"
"Vector Format"	"Rectangular", "Cylindrical", "Spherical"
"Pretty Print"	"Off", "On"
"Split Screen"	"Full", "Top-Bottom", "Left-Right"
"Split 1 App"	"Home", "Y= Editor", "Window Editor", "Graph", "Table", "Data/Matrix Editor", "Program Editor", "Geometry", "Text Editor", "Numeric Solver"
"Split 2 App"	"Home", "Y= Editor", "Window Editor", "Graph", "Table", "Data/Matrix Editor", "Program Editor", "Geometry", "Text Editor", "Numeric Solver"
"Number of Graphs"	"1", "2"
"Graph2"	"Function", "Parametric", "Polar", "Sequence", "3D", "Diff Equations"
"Split Screen Ratio"	"1:1", "1:2", "2:1"
"Exact/Approx"	"Auto", "Exact", "Approximate"
"Base"	"Dec", "Hex", "Bin"

setTable() CATALOG

setTable(*modeNameString, settingString*) ⇒ *string*

Sets the table parameter *modeNameString* to *settingString*, and returns the previous setting of the parameter. Storing the previous setting lets you restore it later.

modeNameString is a character string that specifies which parameter you want to set. It must be one of the parameters from the table below.

settingString is a character string that specifies the new setting for the parameter. It must be one of the settings listed below for the specific parameter you are setting.

```
setTable("Graph <-> Table","ON")
ENTER                            "OFF"

setTable("Independent","AUTO")
ENTER                            "ASK"
```

● [TblSet]

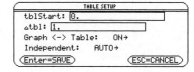

Note: Capitalization and blank spaces are optional when entering parameters.

Parameter Name	Settings
"Graph <-> Table"	"Off", "On"
"Independent"	"Auto", "Ask"

setUnits() CATALOG

setUnits(*list1*) ⇒ *list*

Sets the default units to the values specified in *list1*, and returns a list of the previous defaults.

- To specify the built-in SI (metric) or ENG/US system, *list1* uses the form:

  {"SI"} or {"ENG/US"}

- To specify a custom set of default units, *list1* uses the form:

  {"CUSTOM", "*cat1*", "*unit1*" [, "*cat2*", "*unit2*", ...]}

  where each *cat* and *unit* pair specifies a category and its default unit. (You can specify built-in units only, not user-defined units.) Any category not specified will use its previous custom unit.

- To return to the previous custom default units, *list1* uses the form:

  {"CUSTOM"}

If you want different defaults depending on the situation, create separate lists and save them to unique list names. To use a set of defaults, specify that list name in **setUnits()**.

You can use **setUnits()** to restore settings previously saved with **setUnits()** → *var* or with **getUnits()** → *var* on page 139.

All unit names must begin with an underscore _ ([2nd] P). You can also select units from a menu by pressing ● P.

```
setUnits({"SI"}) ENTER
                {"ENG/US"  "Length"  "_ft"
                           "Mass"    "_lb"  ...}
```

```
setUnits({"CUSTOM","Length","_cm",
"Mass","_gm"}) ENTER
                {"SI"  "Length"  "_m"
                       "Mass"    "_kg"  ...}
```

Note: Your screen may display different units.

Shade *expr1*, *expr2*, [*xlow*], [*xhigh*], [*pattern*], [*patRes*]

Displays the Graph screen, graphs *expr1* and *expr2*, and shades areas in which *expr1* is less than *expr2*. (*expr1* and *expr2* must be expressions that use x as the independent variable.)

xlow and *xhigh*, if included, specify left and right boundaries for the shading. Valid inputs are between xmin and xmax. Defaults are xmin and xmax.

pattern specifies one of four shading patterns:
1 = vertical (default)
2 = horizontal
3 = negative-slope 45°
4 = positive-slope 45°

patRes specifies the resolution of the shading patterns:
1= solid shading
2= 1 pixel spacing (default)
3= 2 pixels spacing
⋮
10= 9 pixels spacing

Note: Interactive shading is available on the Graph screen through the **Shade** instruction. Automatic shading of a specific function is available through the **Style** instruction (page 192). **Shade** is not valid in 3D graphing mode.

In the ZoomTrig viewing window:

Shade cos(x),sin(x) [ENTER]

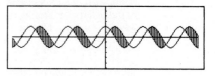

◆[HOME]
ClrDraw [ENTER]   Done
Shade cos(x),sin(x),0,5 [ENTER]

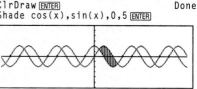

◆[HOME]
ClrDraw [ENTER]   Done
Shade cos(x),sin(x),0,5,2 [ENTER]

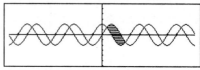

◆[HOME]
ClrDraw [ENTER]   Done
Shade cos(x),sin(x),0,5,2,1 [ENTER]

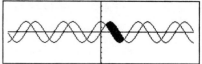

shift(_integer1_[,_#ofShifts_]**)** ⇒ _integer_

Shifts the bits in a binary integer. You can enter _integer1_ in any number base; it is converted automatically to a signed, 32-bit binary form. If the magnitude of _integer1_ is too large for this form, a symmetric modulo operation brings it within the range.

If _#ofShifts_ is positive, the shift is to the left. If _#ofShifts_ is negative, the shift is to the right. The default is ‾1 (shift right one bit).

In a right shift, the rightmost bit is dropped and 0 or 1 is inserted to match the leftmost bit. In a left shift, the leftmost bit is dropped and 0 is inserted as the rightmost bit.

For example, in a right shift:

┌► Each bit shifts right.
0b0000000000000001111010110000110101
↑   ↓
Inserts 0 if leftmost bit is 0,   Dropped
or 1 if leftmost bit is 1.

produces:

0b0000000000000000111101011000011010

The result is displayed according to the Base mode. Leading zeros are not shown.

In Bin base mode:

shift(0b1111010110000110101) [ENTER]
    0b111101011000011010

shift(256,1) [ENTER]   0b1000000000

In Hex base mode:

shift(0h78E) [ENTER]   0h3C7

shift(0h78E,‾2) [ENTER]   0h1E3

shift(0h78E,2) [ENTER]   0h1E38

Important: To enter a binary or hexadecimal number, always use the 0b or 0h prefix (zero, not the letter O).

---

shift(_list1_ [,_#ofShifts_]**)** ⇒ _list_

Returns a copy of _list1_ shifted right or left by _#ofShifts_ elements. Does not alter _list1_.

If _#ofShifts_ is positive, the shift is to the left. If _#ofShifts_ is negative, the shift is to the right. The default is ‾1 (shift right one element).

Elements introduced at the beginning or end of _list_ by the shift are set to the symbol "undef".

In Dec base mode:

shift({1,2,3,4}) [ENTER]
                    {undef 1 2 3}

shift({1,2,3,4},‾2) [ENTER]
                    {undef undef 1 2}

shift({1,2,3,4},1) [ENTER]
                    {2 3 4 undef}

---

shift(_string1_ [,_#ofShifts_]**)** ⇒ _string_

Returns a copy of _string1_ shifted right or left by _#ofShifts_ characters. Does not alter _string1_.

If _#ofShifts_ is positive, the shift is to the left. If _#ofShifts_ is negative, the shift is to the right. The default is ‾1 (shift right one character).

Characters introduced at the beginning or end of _string_ by the shift are set to a space.

shift("abcd") [ENTER]   " abc"

shift("abcd",‾2) [ENTER]   " ab"

shift("abcd",1) [ENTER]   "bcd "

ShowStat CATALOG

ShowStat

Displays a dialog box containing the last computed statistics results if they are still valid. Statistics results are cleared automatically if the data to compute them has changed.

Use this instruction after a statistics calculation, such as **LinReg**.

```
{1,2,3,4,5}→L1 ENTER      {1 2 3 4 5}
{0,2,6,10,25}→L2 ENTER   {0 2 6 10 25}
TwoVar L1,L2 ENTER
ShowStat ENTER
```

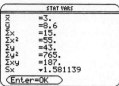

sign() MATH/Number menu

sign(*expression1*) $\Rightarrow$ *expression*
sign(*list1*) $\Rightarrow$ *list*
sign(*matrix1*) $\Rightarrow$ *matrix*

For real and complex *expression1*, returns *expression1*/**abs**(*expression1*) when *expression1*$\neq$ 0.

Returns 1 if *expression1* is positive.
Returns $^-$1 if *expression1* is negative.
sign(0) returns $\pm$1 if the complex format mode is REAL; otherwise, it returns itself.
sign(0) represents the unit circle in the complex domain.

For a list or matrix, returns the signs of all the elements.

```
sign(-3.2) ENTER                        -1.

sign({2,3,4,-5}) ENTER      {1   1   1  -1}

sign(1+abs(x)) ENTER                       1
```

If complex format mode is REAL:

```
sign([-3,0,3]) ENTER            [-1 ±1 1]
```

simult() MATH/Matrix menu

simult(*coeffMatrix*, *constVector*[, *tol*]) $\Rightarrow$ *matrix*

Returns a column vector that contains the solutions to a system of linear equations.

coeffMatrix must be a square matrix that contains the coefficients of the equations.

constVector must have the same number of rows (same dimension) as *coeffMatrix* and contain the constants.

Optionally, any matrix element is treated as zero if its absolute value is less than *tol*. This tolerance is used only if the matrix has floating-point entries and does not contain any symbolic variables that have not been assigned a value. Otherwise, *tol* is ignored.

- If you use ♦ ENTER or set the mode to Exact/Approx=APPROXIMATE, computations are done using floating-point arithmetic.

- If *tol* is omitted or not used, the default tolerance is calculated as:

  5E$^-$14 ∗ **max**(**dim**(*coeffMatrix*)) ∗ **rowNorm**(*coeffMatrix*)

Solve for x and y: $x + 2y = 1$
$3x + 4y = {}^-1$

```
simult([1,2;3,4],[1;-1]) ENTER
```

$$\begin{bmatrix} -3 \\ 2 \end{bmatrix}$$

The solution is x= $^-$3 and y=2.

Solve: $ax + by = 1$
$cx + dy = 2$

```
[a,b;c,d]→matx1 ENTER          [a b; c d]
simult(matx1,[1;2]) ENTER
```

$$\begin{bmatrix} \dfrac{-(2\cdot b-d)}{a\cdot d-b\cdot c} \\ \dfrac{2\cdot a-c}{a\cdot d-b\cdot c} \end{bmatrix}$$

simult(*coeffMatrix*, *constMatrix*[, *tol*]**)** ⇒ *matrix*

Solves multiple systems of linear equations, where each system has the same equation coefficients but different constants.

Each column in *constMatrix* must contain the constants for a system of equations. Each column in the resulting matrix contains the solution for the corresponding system.

Solve: x + 2y = 1   x + 2y = 2
        3x + 4y = ‾1   3x + 4y = ‾3

simult([1,2;3,4],[1,2;‾1,‾3]) ENTER

$$\begin{bmatrix} ‾3 & ‾7 \\ 2 & 9/2 \end{bmatrix}$$

For the first system, x= ‾3 and y=2. For the second system, x= ‾7 and y=9/2.

sin()   SIN key

sin(*expression1***)** ⇒ *expression*
sin(*list1***)** ⇒ *list*

sin(*expression1***)** returns the sine of the argument as an expression.

sin(*list1***)** returns a list of the sines of all elements in *list1*.

Note: The argument is interpreted as either a degree or radian angle, according to the current angle mode. You can use ° (page 219) or ʳ (page 219) to override the angle mode setting temporarily.

In Degree angle mode:

sin((π/4)ʳ) ENTER $\dfrac{\sqrt{2}}{2}$

sin(45) ENTER $\dfrac{\sqrt{2}}{2}$

sin({0,60,90}) ENTER   {0 $\dfrac{\sqrt{3}}{2}$ 1}

In Radian angle mode:

sin(π/4) ENTER $\dfrac{\sqrt{2}}{2}$

sin(45°) ENTER $\dfrac{\sqrt{2}}{2}$

---

sin(*squareMatrix1***)** ⇒ *squareMatrix*

Returns the matrix sine of *squareMatrix1*. This is *not* the same as calculating the sine of each element. For information about the calculation method, refer to **cos()** on page 109.

squareMatrix1 must be diagonalizable. The result always contains floating-point numbers.

In Radian angle mode:

sin([1,5,3;4,2,1;6,‾2,1]) ENTER

$$\begin{bmatrix} .942… & ‾.045… & ‾.031… \\ ‾.045… & .949… & ‾.020… \\ ‾.048… & ‾.005… & .961… \end{bmatrix}$$

sin⁻¹()   2nd [SIN⁻¹] key

sin⁻¹(*expression1***)** ⇒ *expression*
sin⁻¹(*list1***)** ⇒ *list*

sin⁻¹ (*expression1***)** returns the angle whose sine is *expression1* as an expression.

sin⁻¹ (*list1***)** returns a list of the inverse sines of each element of *list1*.

Note: The result is returned as either a degree or radian angle, according to the current angle mode setting.

In Degree angle mode:

sin⁻¹(1) ENTER   90

In Radian angle mode:

sin⁻¹({0,.2,.5}) ENTER
                        {0   .201…   .523…}

---

sin⁻¹(*squareMatrix1***)** ⇒ *squareMatrix*

Returns the matrix inverse sine of *squareMatrix1*. This is *not* the same as calculating the inverse sine of each element. For information about the calculation method, refer to **cos()** on page 109.

squareMatrix1 must be diagonalizable. The result always contains floating-point numbers.

In Radian angle mode and Rectangular complex format mode:

sin⁻¹([1,5,3;4,2,1;6,‾2,1]) ENTER

$$\begin{bmatrix} ‾.164…‾.064…·i & 1.490…‾2.105…·i & … \\ .725…‾1.515…·i & .947…‾.778…·i & … \\ 2.083…‾2.632…·i & ‾1.790…+1.271…·i & … \end{bmatrix}$$

sinh()   MATH/Hyperbolic menu

sinh(*expression1***)** ⇒ *expression*
sinh(*list1***)** ⇒ *list*

    sinh (*expression1*) returns the hyperbolic sine of the argument as an expression.

    sinh (*list*) returns a list of the hyperbolic sines of each element of *list1*.

```
sinh(1.2) ENTER                    1.509...
sinh({0,1.2,3.}) ENTER
                  {0   1.509...   10.017...}
```

---

sinh(*squareMatrix1***)** ⇒ *squareMatrix*

    Returns the matrix hyperbolic sine of *squareMatrix1*. This is *not* the same as calculating the hyperbolic sine of each element. For information about the calculation method, refer to **cos()** on page 109.

    squareMatrix1 must be diagonalizable. The result always contains floating-point numbers.

In Radian angle mode:

```
sinh([1,5,3;4,2,1;6,-2,1])  ENTER
        ┌360.954  305.708  239.604┐
        │352.912  233.495  193.564│
        └298.632  154.599  140.251┘
```

sinh⁻¹()   MATH/Hyperbolic menu

sinh⁻¹(*expression1***)** ⇒ *expression*
sinh⁻¹(*list1***)** ⇒ *list*

    sinh⁻¹ (*expression1*) returns the inverse hyperbolic sine of the argument as an expression.

    sinh⁻¹ (*list1*) returns a list of the inverse hyperbolic sines of each element of *list1*.

```
sinh⁻¹(0) ENTER                         0
sinh⁻¹({0,2.1,3}) ENTER
              {0   1.487...   sinh⁻¹(3)}
```

---

sinh⁻¹(*squareMatrix1***)** ⇒ *squareMatrix*

    Returns the matrix inverse hyperbolic sine of *squareMatrix1*. This is *not* the same as calculating the inverse hyperbolic sine of each element. For information about the calculation method, refer to **cos()** on page 109.

    squareMatrix1 must be diagonalizable. The result always contains floating-point numbers.

In Radian angle mode:

```
sinh⁻¹([1,5,3;4,2,1;6,-2,1])  ENTER
        ┌ .041...   2.155...   1.158... ┐
        │1.463...   .926...     .112... │
        └2.750...  -1.528...    .572... ┘
```

SinReg *list1*, *list2* [, [*iterations*], [*period*] [, *list3*, *list4*]]

Calculates the sinusoidal regression and updates all the system statistics variables.

All the lists must have equal dimensions except for *list4*.

list1 represents xlist.
list2 represents ylist.
list3 represents category codes.
list4 represents category include list.

iterations specifies the maximum number of times (1 through 16) a solution will be attempted. If omitted, 8 is used. Typically, larger values result in better accuracy but longer execution times, and vice versa.

period specifies an estimated period. If omitted, the difference between values in *list1* should be equal and in sequential order. If you specify *period*, the differences between x values can be unequal.

Note: *list1* through *list3* must be a variable name or c1–c99 (columns in the last data variable shown in the Data/Matrix Editor). *list4* does not have to be a variable name and cannot be c1–c99.

The output of **SinReg** is always in radians, regardless of the angle mode setting.

In function graphing mode:

```
seq(x,x,1,361,30)→L1 ENTER
                         {1 31 61 …}
{5.5,8,11,13.5,16.5,19,19.5,17,
14.5,12.5,8.5,6.5,5.5}→L2 ENTER
                         {5.5 8 11 …}
SinReg L1,L2 ENTER                Done
ShowStat ENTER
```

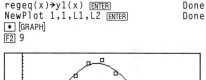

```
ENTER
regeq(x)→y1(x) ENTER             Done
NewPlot 1,1,L1,L2 ENTER          Done
♦ [GRAPH]
F2 9
```

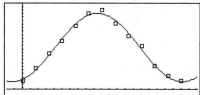

solve() MATH/Algebra menu

solve(*equation, var*) ⇒ *Boolean expression*
solve(*inequality, var*) ⇒ *Boolean expression*

Returns candidate real solutions of an equation or an inequality for *var*. The goal is to return candidates for all solutions. However, there might be equations or inequalities for which the number of solutions is infinite.

Solution candidates might not be real finite solutions for some combinations of values for undefined variables.

For the AUTO setting of the Exact/Approx mode, the goal is to produce exact solutions when they are concise, and supplemented by iterative searches with approximate arithmetic when exact solutions are impractical.

Due to default cancellation of the greatest common divisor from the numerator and denominator of ratios, solutions might be solutions only in the limit from one or both sides.

For inequalities of types ≥, ≤, <, or >, explicit solutions are unlikely unless the inequality is linear and contains only *var*.

For the EXACT setting of the Exact/Approx mode, portions that cannot be solved are returned as an implicit equation or inequality.

Use the "|" operator to restrict the solution interval and/or other variables that occur in the equation or inequality. When you find a solution in one interval, you can use the inequality operators to exclude that interval from subsequent searches.

false is returned when no real solutions are found. true is returned if **solve()** can determine that any finite real value of *var* satisfies the equation or inequality.

Since **solve()** always returns a Boolean result, you can use "and," "or," and "not" to combine results from **solve()** with each other or with other Boolean expressions.

Solutions might contain a unique new undefined variable of the form @n*j* with *j* being an integer in the interval 1–255. Such variables designate an arbitrary integer.

In real mode, fractional powers having odd denominators denote only the real branch. Otherwise, multiple branched expressions such as fractional powers, logarithms, and inverse trigonometric functions denote only the principal branch. Consequently, **solve()** produces only solutions corresponding to that one real or principal branch.

Note: See also **cSolve()** (page 112), **cZeros()** (page 116), **nSolve()** (page 159), and **zeros()** (page 204).

`solve(a*x^2+b*x+c=0,x)` ENTER

$$x = \frac{\sqrt{-(4 \cdot a \cdot c - b^2)} - b}{2 \cdot a}$$

$$\text{or } x = \frac{-(\sqrt{-(4 \cdot a \cdot c - b^2)} + b)}{2 \cdot a}$$

`ans(1)| a=1 and b=1 and c=1` ENTER
      Error: Non-real result

`solve((x-a)e^(x)=⁻x*(x-a),x)` ENTER
            x = a or x = ⁻.567...

`(x+1)(x-1)/(x-1)+x-3` ENTER   2·x-2
`solve(entry(1)=0,x)` ENTER   x = 1
`entry(2)|ans(1)` ENTER   undef
`limit(entry(3),x,1)` ENTER   0

`solve(5x-2 ≥ 2x,x)` ENTER   x ≥ 2/3

`exact(solve((x-a)e^(x)=⁻x*`
`(x-a),x))` ENTER
                    $e^x + x = 0$ or x = a

In Radian angle mode:

`solve(tan(x)=1/x,x)|x>0 and x<1`
ENTER   x = .860...

`solve(x=x+1,x)` ENTER   false

`solve(x=x,x)` ENTER   true

`2x-1≤1 and solve(x^2≠9,x)` ENTER
                    x ≤ 1 and x ≠ ⁻3

In Radian angle mode:

`solve(sin(x)=0,x)` ENTER   x = @n1·π

`solve(x^(1/3)=⁻1,x)` ENTER   x = ⁻1
`solve(√(x)=⁻2,x)` ENTER   false
`solve(⁻√(x)=⁻2,x)` ENTER   x = 4

solve(*equation1* **and** *equation2* [**and** ...], {*varOrGuess1,*
varOrGuess2 [, ...]}) ⇒ *Boolean expression*

Returns candidate real solutions to the
simultaneous algebraic equations, where
each *varOrGuess* specifies a variable that you
want to solve for.

Optionally, you can specify an initial guess
for a variable. Each *varOrGuess* must have the
form:

variable
– or –
variable = real or non-real number

For example, x is valid and so is x=3.

<u>If all of the equations are polynomials and if
you do NOT specify any initial guesses,</u>
solve() uses the lexical Gröbner/Buchberger
elimination method to attempt to determine
all real solutions.

For example, suppose you have a circle of
radius r at the origin and another circle of
radius r centered where the first circle
crosses the positive x-axis. Use **solve()** to find
the intersections.

As illustrated by r in the example to the right,
simultaneous *polynomial* equations can have
<u>extra variables that have no values</u>, but
represent given numeric values that could be
substituted later.

You can omit solution variables whose values
are not of interest, as in the example to the
right.

<u>You can also or instead include solution
variables that do not appear in the equations.</u>
For example, you can include z as a solution
variable to extend the previous example to
two parallel intersecting cylinders of radius r.

The cylinder solutions illustrate how families
of solutions might contain arbitrary constants
of the form @k, where *k* is an integer suffix
from 1 through 255. The suffix resets to 1
when you use **ClrHome** or F1 8:Clear Home.

For polynomial systems, computation time or
memory exhaustion may depend strongly on
the order in which you list solution variables.
If your initial choice exhausts memory or
your patience, try rearranging the variables in
the equations and/or *varOrGuess* list.

<u>If you do not include any guesses and if any
equation is non-polynomial in any variable
but all equations are linear in the solution
variables,</u> **solve()** uses Gaussian elimination
to attempt to determine all real solutions.

`solve(y=x^2-2 and`
`x+2y=-1,{x,y})` ENTER
$$x=1 \text{ and } y=-1$$
$$\text{or } x=-3/2 \text{ and } y=1/4$$

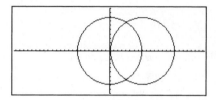

`solve(x^2+y^2=r^2 and`
`(x-r)^2+y^2=r^2,{x,y})` ENTER
$$x= \frac{r}{2} \text{ and } y= \frac{\sqrt{3} \cdot r}{2}$$
$$\text{or } x= \frac{r}{2} \text{ and } y= \frac{-\sqrt{3} \cdot r}{2}$$

`solve(x^2+y^2=r^2 and`
`(x-r)^2+y^2=r^2,{x})` ENTER
$$x= \frac{r}{2}$$

`solve(x^2+y^2=r^2 and`
`(x-r)^2+y^2=r^2,{x,y,z})` ENTER
$$x= \frac{r}{2} \text{ and } y= \frac{\sqrt{3} \cdot r}{2} \text{ and } z=@1$$
$$\text{or } x= \frac{r}{2} \text{ and } y= \frac{-\sqrt{3} \cdot r}{2} \text{ and } z=@1$$

`solve(x+e^(z)*y=1 and`
`x-y=sin(z),{x,y})` ENTER
$$x= \frac{e^z \cdot \sin(z)+1}{e^z+1} \text{ and } y= \frac{-(\sin(z)-1)}{e^z+1}$$

If a system is neither polynomial in all of its variables nor linear in its solution variables, **solve()** determines at most one solution using an approximate iterative method. To do so, the number of solution variables must equal the number of equations, and all other variables in the equations must simplify to numbers.

```
solve(e^(z)*y=1 and
⁻y=sin(z),{y,z}) ENTER
                y=.041… and z=3.183…
```

Each solution variable starts at its guessed value if there is one; otherwise, it starts at 0.0.

Use guesses to seek additional solutions one by one. For convergence, a guess may have to be rather close to a solution.

```
solve(e^(z)*y=1 and
⁻y=sin(z),{y,z=2π}) ENTER
                y=.001… and z=6.281…
```

SortA   MATH/List menu

SortA *listName1*[, *listName2*] [, *listName3*] …
SortA *vectorName1*[, *vectorName2*] [, *vectorName3*] …

Sorts the elements of the first argument in ascending order.

If you include additional arguments, sorts the elements of each so that their new positions match the new positions of the elements in the first argument.

All arguments must be names of lists or vectors. All arguments must have equal dimensions.

```
{2,1,4,3}→list1 ENTER          {2,1,4,3}
SortA list1 ENTER                   Done

list1 ENTER                       {1 2 3 4}
{4,3,2,1}→list2 ENTER             {4 3 2 1}
SortA list2,list1 ENTER              Done

list2 ENTER                       {1 2 3 4}
list1 ENTER                       {4 3 2 1}
```

SortD   MATH/List menu

SortD *listName1*[, *listName2*] [, *listName3*] …
SortD *vectorName1*[,*vectorName 2*] [,*vectorName 3*] …

Identical to **SortA**, except **SortD** sorts the elements in descending order.

```
{2,1,4,3}→list1 ENTER          {2 1 4 3}
{1,2,3,4}→list2 ENTER          {1 2 3 4}
SortD list1,list2 ENTER              Done
list1 ENTER                       {4 3 2 1}
list2 ENTER                       {3 4 1 2}
```

▶Sphere   MATH/Matrix/Vector ops menu

vector ▶**Sphere**

Displays the row or column vector in spherical form [ρ ∠θ ∠φ].

vector must be of dimension 3 and can be either a row or a column vector.

Note: ▶**Sphere** is a display-format instruction, not a conversion function. You can use it only at the end of an entry line.

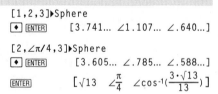

```
[1,2,3]▶Sphere
♦ ENTER      [3.741… ∠1.107… ∠.640…]

[2,∠π/4,3]▶Sphere
♦ ENTER      [3.605… ∠.785… ∠.588…]
```

$$\text{ENTER} \qquad \left[\sqrt{13} \quad \angle\frac{\pi}{4} \quad \angle\cos^{-1}\!\left(\frac{3\cdot\sqrt{13}}{13}\right)\right]$$

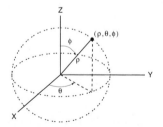

stdDev()   MATH/Statistics menu

stdDev(*list*) ⇒ *expression*

Returns the standard deviation of the elements in *list*.

Note: *list* must have at least two elements.

stdDev({a,b,c}) [ENTER]
stdDev({1,2,5,⁻6,3,⁻2}) [ENTER]

■ stdDev({a b c})
$$\frac{\sqrt{3 \cdot \left(a^2 - a \cdot (b+c) + b^2 - b \cdot c + c^2\right)}}{3}$$

■ stdDev({1 2 5 ⁻6 3 ⁻2})
$$\frac{\sqrt{62}}{2}$$

stdDev(*matrix1*) ⇒ *matrix*

Returns a row vector of the standard deviations of the columns in *matrix1*.

Note: *matrix1* must have at least two rows.

stdDev([1,2,5;⁻3,0,1;.5,.7,3]) [ENTER]
[2.179... 1.014... 2]

StoGDB   CATALOG

StoGDB *GDBvar*

Creates a Graph database (GDB) variable that contains the current:

* Graphing mode
* Y= functions
* Window variables
* Graph format settings
  1- or 2-Graph setting (split screen and ratio settings if 2-Graph mode)
  Angle mode
  Real/complex mode
* Initial conditions if Sequence or Diff Equations mode
* Table flags
* tblStart, Δtbl, tblInput

You can use **RclGDB** *GDBvar* to restore the graph environment.

*****Note:** These items are saved for both graphs in 2-Graph mode.

Stop   CATALOG

Stop

Used as a program instruction to stop program execution.

Program segment:

```
   :
For i,1,10,1
  If i=5
  Stop
EndFor
   :
```

StoPic   CATALOG

StoPic *picVar* [, *pxlRow, pxlCol*] [, *width, height*]

Displays the graph screen and copies a rectangular area of the display to the variable *picVar*.

pxlRow and *pxlCol*, if included, specify the upper-left corner of the area to copy (defaults are 0, 0).

width and *height*, if included, specify the dimensions, in pixels, of the area. Defaults are the width and height, in pixels, of the current graph screen.

Store   See →, page 222.

string()   MATH/String menu

string(*expression*) ⇒ *string*

Simplifies *expression* and returns the result as a character string.

```
string(1.2345) ENTER            "1.2345"
string(1+2) ENTER                    "3"
string(cos(x)+√(3)) ENTER
                          "cos(x) + √(3)"
```

Style   CATALOG

Style *equanum, stylePropertyString*

Sets the system graphing function *equanum* in the current graph mode to use the graphing property *stylePropertyString*.

equanum must be an integer from 1–99 and the function must already exist.

stylePropertyString must be one of: "Line", "Dot", "Square", "Thick", "Animate", "Path", "Above", or "Below".

Note that in parametric graphing, only the *xt* half of the pair contains the style information.

Valid style names vs. graphing mode:

Function:	all styles
Parametric/Polar:	line, dot, square, thick, animate, path
Sequence:	line, dot, square, thick
3D:	none
Diff Equations:	line, dot, square, thick, animate, path

Note: Capitalization and blank spaces are optional when entering *stylePropertyString* names.

```
Style 1,"thick" ENTER               Done
Style 10,"path" ENTER               Done
```

Note: In function graphing mode, these examples set the style of y1(x) to "Thick" and y10(x) to "Path".

subMat() CATALOG

subMat(*matrix1*[, *startRow*] [, *startCol*] [, *endRow*]
[, *endCol*]) ⇒ *matrix*

Returns the specified submatrix of *matrix1*.

Defaults: *startRow*=1, *startCol*=1, *endRow*=last
row, *endCol*=last column.

[1,2,3;4,5,6;7,8,9]→m1 ENTER

$$\begin{bmatrix} 1 & 2 & 3 \\ 4 & 5 & 6 \\ 7 & 8 & 9 \end{bmatrix}$$

subMat(m1,2,1,3,2) ENTER

$$\begin{bmatrix} 4 & 5 \\ 7 & 8 \end{bmatrix}$$

subMat(m1,2,2) ENTER

$$\begin{bmatrix} 5 & 6 \\ 8 & 9 \end{bmatrix}$$

sum() MATH/List menu

sum(*list***) ⇒ *expression*

Returns the sum of the elements in *list*.

sum({1,2,3,4,5}) ENTER   15

sum({a,2a,3a}) ENTER   6·a

sum(seq(n,n,1,10)) ENTER   55

---

sum(*matrix1***) ⇒ *matrix*

Returns a row vector containing the sums of
the elements in the columns in *matrix1*.

sum([1,2,3;4,5,6]) ENTER   [5 7 9]

sum([1,2,3;4,5,6;7,8,9]) ENTER
[12 15 18]

switch() CATALOG

switch([*integer1*]**) ⇒ *integer*

Returns the number of the active window.
Also can set the active window.

Note: Window 1 is left or top; Window 2 is
right or bottom.

If *integer1* = 0, returns the active window
number.

If *integer1* = 1, activates window 1 and
returns the previously active window
number.

If *integer1* = 2, activates window 2 and
returns the previously active window
number.

If *integer1* is omitted, switches windows and
returns the previously active window
number.

integer1 is ignored if the TI-92 Plus is not
displaying a split screen.

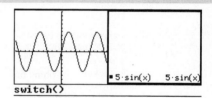

switch ENTER

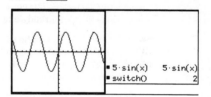

T (transpose)   **MATH/Matrix menu**

$matrix1^T \Rightarrow matrix$

Returns the complex conjugate transpose of *matrix1*.

`[1,2,3;4,5,6;7,8,9]→mat1` [ENTER]

$$\begin{bmatrix} 1 & 2 & 3 \\ 4 & 5 & 6 \\ 7 & 8 & 9 \end{bmatrix}$$

`mat1`^{T} [ENTER]

$$\begin{bmatrix} 1 & 4 & 7 \\ 2 & 5 & 8 \\ 3 & 6 & 9 \end{bmatrix}$$

`[a,b;c,d]→mat2` [ENTER]

$$\begin{bmatrix} a & b \\ c & d \end{bmatrix}$$

`mat2`^{T} [ENTER]

$$\begin{bmatrix} a & c \\ b & d \end{bmatrix}$$

`[1+`i`,2+`i`;3+`i`,4+`i`]→mat3` [ENTER]

$$\begin{bmatrix} 1+i & 2+i \\ 3+i & 4+i \end{bmatrix}$$

`mat3`^{T} [ENTER]

$$\begin{bmatrix} 1-i & 3-i \\ 2-i & 4-i \end{bmatrix}$$

Table   **CATALOG**

Table *expression1*[, *expression2*] [, *var1*]

Builds a table of the specified expressions or functions.

The expressions in the table can also be graphed. Expressions entered using the **Table** or **Graph** (page 140) commands are assigned increasing function numbers starting with 1. The expressions can be modified or individually deleted using the edit functions available when the table is displayed by pressing [F4] Header. The currently selected functions in the Y= Editor are temporarily ignored.

To clear the functions created by **Table** or **Graph**, execute the **ClrGraph** command or display the Y= Editor.

If the *var* parameter is omitted, the current graph-mode independent variable is assumed. Some valid variations of this instruction are:

Function graphing: **Table** *expr*, *x*

Parametric graphing: **Table** *xExpr*, *yExpr*, *t*

Polar graphing: **Table** *expr*, θ

Note: The **Table** command is not valid for 3D, sequence, or diff equations graphing. As an alternative, you may want to use **BldData** (page 104).

In function graphing mode.

`Table 1.25x*cos(x)` [ENTER]

x	1				
0.	0.				
1.	.67538				
2.	-1.04				
3.	-3.712				
4.	-3.268				
5.	1.7729				
6.	7.2013				
7.	6.5966				

`Table cos(time),time` [ENTER]

x	1	2			
0.	0.	1.			
1.	.67538	.5403			
2.	-1.04	-.4161			
3.	-3.712	-.99			
4.	-3.268	-.6536			
5.	1.7729	.28366			
6.	7.2013	.96017			
7.	6.5966	.7539			

tan()   [TAN] **key**

tan(*expression1*) ⇒ *expression*
tan(*list1*) ⇒ *list*

> **tan**(*expression1*) returns the tangent of the argument as an expression.
>
> **tan**(*list1*) returns a list of the tangents of all elements in *list1*.
>
> **Note:** The argument is interpreted as either a degree or radian angle, according to the current angle mode. You can use ° (page 219) or ʳ (page 219) to override the angle mode temporarily.

In Degree angle mode:

```
tan((π/4)ʳ) [ENTER]                    1
tan(45) [ENTER]                         1
tan({0,60,90}) [ENTER]    {0  √3  undef}
```

In Radian angle mode:

```
tan(π/4) [ENTER]                        1
tan(45°) [ENTER]                        1
tan({π,π/3,‑π,π/4}) [ENTER]   {0 √3 0 1}
```

---

tan(*squareMatrix1*) ⇒ *squareMatrix*

> Returns the matrix tangent of *squareMatrix1*. This is *not* the same as calculating the tangent of each element. For information about the calculation method, refer to **cos()** on page 109.
>
> *squareMatrix1* must be diagonalizable. The result always contains floating-point numbers.

In Radian angle mode:

```
tan([1,5,3;4,2,1;6,‑2,1]) [ENTER]
```

$$\begin{bmatrix} -28.291\dots & 26.088\dots & 11.114\dots \\ 12.117\dots & -7.835\dots & -5.481\dots \\ 36.818\dots & -32.806\dots & -10.459\dots \end{bmatrix}$$

tan⁻¹()   [2nd] [TAN⁻¹] **key**

tan⁻¹(*expression1*) ⇒ *expression*
tan⁻¹(*list1*) ⇒ *list*

> **tan⁻¹** (*expression1*) returns the angle whose tangent is *expression1* as an expression.
>
> **tan⁻¹** (*list1*) returns a list of the inverse tangents of each element of *list1*.
>
> **Note:** The result is returned as either a degree or radian angle, according to the current angle mode setting.

In Degree angle mode:

```
tan⁻¹(1) [ENTER]                       45
```

In Radian angle mode:

```
tan⁻¹({0,.2,.5}) [ENTER]
                     {0  .197...  .463...}
```

---

tan⁻¹(*squareMatrix1*) ⇒ *squareMatrix*

> Returns the matrix inverse tangent of *squareMatrix1*. This is *not* the same as calculating the inverse tangent of each element. For information about the calculation method, refer to **cos()** on page 109.
>
> *squareMatrix1* must be diagonalizable. The result always contains floating-point numbers.

In Radian angle mode:

```
tan⁻¹([1,5,3;4,2,1;6,‑2,1]) [ENTER]
```

$$\begin{bmatrix} -.083\dots & 1.266\dots & .622\dots \\ .748\dots & .630\dots & -.070\dots \\ 1.686\dots & -1.182\dots & .455\dots \end{bmatrix}$$

tanh()   MATH/Hyperbolic menu

tanh(*expression1*) ⇒ *expression*
tanh(*list1*) ⇒ *list*

> **tanh**(*expression1*) returns the hyperbolic tangent of the argument as an expression.
>
> **tanh**(*list*) returns a list of the hyperbolic tangents of each element of *list1*.

tanh(1.2) [ENTER]   .833...

tanh({0,1}) [ENTER]   {0   tanh(1)}

---

tanh(*squareMatrix1*) ⇒ *squareMatrix*

> Returns the matrix hyperbolic tangent of *squareMatrix1*. This is *not* the same as calculating the hyperbolic tangent of each element. For information about the calculation method, refer to **cos()** on page 109.
>
> *squareMatrix1* must be diagonalizable. The result always contains floating-point numbers.

In Radian angle mode:

tanh([1,5,3;4,2,1;6,-2,1]) [ENTER]

$$\begin{bmatrix} -.097... & .933... & .425... \\ .488... & .538... & -.129... \\ 1.282... & -1.034... & .428... \end{bmatrix}$$

tanh⁻¹()   MATH/Hyperbolic menu

tanh⁻¹(*expression1*) ⇒ *expression*
tanh⁻¹(*list1*) ⇒ *list*

> **tanh⁻¹**(*expression1*) returns the inverse hyperbolic tangent of the argument as an expression.
>
> **tanh⁻¹**(*list1*) returns a list of the inverse hyperbolic tangents of each element of *list1*.

In rectangular complex format mode:

tanh⁻¹(0) [ENTER]   0

tanh⁻¹({1,2.1,3}) [ENTER]
       {∞   .518... −1.570...·*i*   tanh⁻¹(3)}

---

tanh⁻¹(*squareMatrix1*) ⇒ *squareMatrix*

> Returns the matrix inverse hyperbolic tangent of *squareMatrix1*. This is *not* the same as calculating the inverse hyperbolic tangent of each element. For information about the calculation method, refer to **cos()** on page 109.
>
> *squareMatrix1* must be diagonalizable. The result always contains floating-point numbers.

In Radian angle mode and Rectangular complex format mode:

tanh⁻¹([1,5,3;4,2,1;6,-2,1]) [ENTER]

$$\begin{bmatrix} -.099...+.164...·i & .267...-1.490...·i & ... \\ -.087...-.725...·i & .479...-.947...·i & ... \\ .511...-2.083...·i & -.878...+1.790...·i & ... \end{bmatrix}$$

taylor()   MATH/Calculus menu

taylor(*expression1, var, order*[, *point*]**)** $\Rightarrow$ *expression*

Returns the requested Taylor polynomial. The polynomial includes non-zero terms of integer degrees from zero through *order* in (*var* minus *point*). **taylor()** returns itself if there is no truncated power series of this order, or if it would require negative or fractional exponents. Use substitution and/or temporary multiplication by a power of (*var* minus *point*) to determine more general power series.

point defaults to zero and is the expansion point.

taylor(e^($\sqrt{}$(x)),x,2) [ENTER]
taylor(e^(t),t,4)|t=$\sqrt{}$(x) [ENTER]

- taylor$\left(e^{\sqrt{x}}, x, 2\right)$ taylor$\left(e^{\sqrt{x}}, x, 2, \theta\right)$
- taylor$\left(e^{t}, t, 4\right)|t = \sqrt{x}$
$$\frac{x^2}{24} + \frac{x^{3/2}}{6} + \frac{x}{2} + \sqrt{x} + 1$$

taylor(1/(x*(x-1)),x,3) [ENTER]

- taylor$\left(\dfrac{1}{x \cdot (x - 1)}, x, 3\right)$
$$\text{taylor}\left(\frac{1}{x \cdot (x - 1)}, x, 3, \theta\right)$$

expand(taylor(x/(x*(x-1)),x,4)/x,x)
[ENTER]

- expand$\left(\dfrac{\text{taylor}\left(\dfrac{x}{x \cdot (x - 1)}, x, 4\right)}{x}, x\right)$
$$-x^3 - x^2 - x - \frac{1}{x} - 1$$

tCollect()   MATH\Algebra\Trig menu

tCollect(*expression1***)** $\Rightarrow$ *expression*

Returns an expression in which products and integer powers of sines and cosines are converted to a linear combination of sines and cosines of multiple angles, angle sums, and angle differences. The transformation converts trigonometric polynomials into a linear combination of their harmonics.

Sometimes **tCollect()** will accomplish your goals when the default trigonometric simplification does not. **tCollect()** tends to reverse transformations done by **tExpand()**. Sometimes applying **tExpand()** to a result from **tCollect()**, or vice versa, in two separate steps simplifies an expression.

tCollect((cos(α))^2) [ENTER]
$$\frac{\cos(2 \cdot \alpha) + 1}{2}$$

tCollect(sin(α)cos(β)) [ENTER]
$$\frac{\sin(\alpha-\beta)+\sin(\alpha+\beta)}{2}$$

tExpand()   MATH\Algebra\Trig menu

tExpand(*expression1***)** ⇒ *expression*

Returns an expression in which sines and cosines of integer-multiple angles, angle sums, and angle differences are expanded. Because of the identity $(\sin(x))^2+(\cos(x))^2=1$, there are many possible equivalent results. Consequently, a result might differ from a result shown in other publications.

Sometimes **tExpand()** will accomplish your goals when the default trigonometric simplification does not. **tExpand()** tends to reverse transformations done by **tCollect()**. Sometimes applying **tCollect()** to a result from **tExpand()**, or vice versa, in two separate steps simplifies an expression.

Note: Degree-mode scaling by $\pi/180$ interferes with the ability of **tExpand()** to recognize expandable forms. For best results, **tExpand()** should be used in Radian mode.

```
tExpand(sin(3φ)) ENTER
            4·sin(φ)·(cos(φ))²-sin(φ)
tExpand(cos(α-β)) ENTER
            cos(α)·cos(β)+sin(α)·sin(β)
```

Text   CATALOG

Text *promptString*

Displays the character string *promptString* dialog box.

If used as part of a **Dialog...EndDlog block**, *promptString* is displayed inside that dialog box. If used as a standalone instruction, **Text** creates a dialog box to display the string.

```
Text "Have a nice day." ENTER    Done
```

```
Have a nice day.
 Enter=OK
```

Then   See If, page 141.

Title   CATALOG

Title *titleString*, [*Lbl*]

Creates the title of a pull-down menu or dialog box when used inside a **Toolbar** or **Custom** construct, or a **Dialog...EndDlog** block.

Note: *Lbl* is only valid in the **Toolbar** construct. When present, it allows the menu choice to branch to a specified label inside the program.

Program segment:

```
   :
:Dialog
:Title      "This is a dialog box"
:Request    "Your name",Str1
:Dropdown   "Month you were born",
    seq(string(i),i,1,12),Var1
:EndDlog
   :
```

tmpCnv() CATALOG

tmpCnv(_expression1__°_tempUnit1_, _°_tempUnit2_**)**
  ⇒ _expression_ _°_tempUnit2_

Converts a temperature value specified by
expression1 from one unit to another. Valid
temperature units are:

_°C	Celsius
_°F	Fahrenheit
_°K	Kelvin
_°R	Rankine

  └─For _, press [2nd] P.
    For °, press [2nd] D.

For example, 100_°C converts to 212_°F:

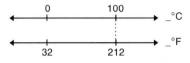

To convert a temperature range, use
∆tmpCnv() instead.

```
tmpCnv(100_°c,_°f) [ENTER]        212.·_°F

tmpCnv(32_°f,_°c) [ENTER]           0.·_°C

tmpCnv(0_°c,_°k) [ENTER]        273.15·_°K

tmpCnv(0_°f,_°r) [ENTER]        459.67·_°R
```

Note: To select temperature units from a
menu, press [♦] P.

∆tmpCnv() CATALOG

∆tmpCnv(_expression1__°_tempUnit1_, _°_tempUnit2_**)**
  ⇒ _expression_ _°_tempUnit2_

Converts a temperature range (the difference
between two temperature values) specified
by _expression1_ from one unit to another. Valid
temperature units are:

_°C	Celsius
_°F	Fahrenheit
_°K	Kelvin
_°R	Rankine

  └─For _, press [2nd] P.
    For °, press [2nd] D.

1_°C and 1_°K have the same magnitude, as
do 1_°F and 1_°R. However, 1_°C is 9/5 as
large as 1_°F.

For example, a 100_°C range (from 0_°C to
100_°C) is equivalent to a 180_°F range:

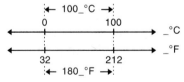

To convert a particular temperature value
instead of a range, use **tmpCnv()**.

To get ∆, you can press [2nd] G and then
[↑] D (or [2nd] [CHAR] 1 5).

```
∆tmpCnv(100_°c,_°f) [ENTER]       180.·_°F

∆tmpCnv(180_°f,_°c) [ENTER]       100.·_°C

∆tmpCnv(100_°c,_°k) [ENTER]       100.·_°K

∆tmpCnv(100_°f,_°r) [ENTER]       100.·_°R

∆tmpCnv(1_°c,_°f) [ENTER]           1.8·_°F
```

Note: To select temperature units from a
menu, press [♦] P.

Toolbar   CATALOG

Toolbar
 block
EndTBar

    Creates a toolbar menu.

    block can be either a single statement or a sequence of statements separated with the ":" character. The statements can be either Title or Item.

    Items must have labels. A Title must also have a label if it does not have an item.

Program segment:

```
       :
       :
:Toolbar
:   Title "Examples"
:   Item "Trig", t
:   Item "Calc", c
:   Item "Stop", Pexit
:EndTbar
       :
```

Note: When run in a program, this segment creates a menu with three choices that branch to three places in the program.

Trace   CATALOG

Trace

    Draws a Smart Graph and places the trace cursor on the first defined Y= function at the previously defined cursor position, or at the reset position if regraphing was necessary.

    Allows operation of the cursor and most keys when editing coordinate values. Several keys, such as the function keys, APPS, and MODE, are not activated during trace.

    Note: Press ENTER to resume operation.

Try   CATALOG

Try
 block1
Else
 block2
EndTry

    Executes *block1* unless an error occurs. Program execution transfers to *block2* if an error occurs in *block1*. Variable errornum contains the error number to allow the program to perform error recovery.

    block1 and *block2* can be either a single statement or a series of statements separated with the ":" character.

Program segment:

```
       :
       :
:Try
:   NewFold(temp)
:   Else
:
:   ©Already exists
:   ClrErr
:EndTry
       :
```

Note: See **ClrErr** (page 106) and **PassErr** (page 163).

TwoVar   MATH/Statistics menu

TwoVar *list1*, *list2*[, [*list3*] [, *list4*, *list5*]]

Calculates the **TwoVar** statistics and updates all the system statistics variables.

All the lists must have equal dimensions except for *list5*.

list1 represents xlist.
list2 represents ylist.
list3 represents frequency.
list4 represents category codes.
list5 represents category include list.

Note: *list1* through *list4* must be a variable name or c1–c99 (columns in the last data variable shown in the Data/Matrix Editor). *list5* does not have to be a variable name and cannot be c1–c99.

```
{0,1,2,3,4,5,6}→L1 [ENTER]     {0 1 2 …}
{0,2,3,4,3,4,6}→L2 [ENTER]     {0 2 3 …}
TwoVar L1,L2 [ENTER]              Done
ShowStat [ENTER]
```

```
           STAT VARS
 x̄      =3.
 ȳ      =3.142857
 Σx     =21.
 Σx²    =91.
 Σy     =22.
 Σy²    =90.
 Σxy    =88.
 Sx     ▾2.160247
 Sy     =1.864454
 nStat  =7.
 minX   =0.
 minY   =0.
 maxX   =6.
 maxY   =6.
  Enter=OK
```

Unarchiv   CATALOG

Unarchiv *var1* [, *var2*] [, *var3*] …

Moves the specified variables from the user data archive memory to RAM.

You can access an archived variable the same as you would a variable in RAM. However, you cannot delete, rename, or store to an archived variable because it is locked automatically.

To archive variables, use **Archive** (page 102).

```
10→arctest [ENTER]                 10
Archive arctest [ENTER]          Done
5*arctest [ENTER]                  50
15→arctest [ENTER]
```

```
                 ERROR
  Variable is locked, protected, or
  archived
  ESC=CANCEL
```

```
[ESC]
Unarchiv arctest [ENTER]         Done
15→arctest [ENTER]                 15
```

unitV()   MATH/Matrix/Vector ops menu

unitV(*vector1***)** ⇒ *vector*

Returns either a row- or column-unit vector, depending on the form of *vector1*.

vector1 must be either a single-row matrix or a single-column matrix.

$$\text{unitV}([a,b,c])\ [ENTER]$$
$$[\frac{a}{\sqrt{a^2+b^2+c^2}}\ \frac{b}{\sqrt{a^2+b^2+c^2}}\ \frac{c}{\sqrt{a^2+b^2+c^2}}]$$

$$\text{unitV}([1,2,1])\ [ENTER]$$
$$[\frac{\sqrt{6}}{6}\ \frac{\sqrt{6}}{3}\ \frac{\sqrt{6}}{6}]$$

$$\text{unitV}([1;2;3])\ [ENTER]$$
$$\begin{bmatrix}\frac{\sqrt{14}}{14}\\ \frac{\sqrt{14}}{7}\\ \frac{3\cdot\sqrt{14}}{14}\end{bmatrix}$$

Unlock   CATALOG

Unlock *var1*[, *var2*][, *var3*]...

Unlocks the specified variables.

Note: The variables can be locked using the **Lock** command (page 149).

variance() MATH/Statistics menu

variance(*list*) ⇒ *expression*

Returns the variance of *list*.

Note: *list* must contain at least two elements.

```
variance({a,b,c}) ENTER
```
$$\frac{a^2-a\cdot(b+c)+b^2-b\cdot c+c^2}{3}$$

```
variance({1,2,5,-6,3,-2}) ENTER    31/2
```

variance(*matrix1*) ⇒ *matrix*

Returns a row vector containing the variance of each column in *matrix1*.

Note: *matrix1* must contain at least two rows.

```
variance([1,2,5;-3,0,1;.5,.7,3])
ENTER                [4.75   1.03   4]
```

when() CATALOG

when(*condition*, *trueResult* [, *falseResult*]
　　[, *unknownResult*]) ⇒ *expression*

Returns *trueResult*, *falseResult*, or *unknownResult*, depending on whether *condition* is true, false, or unknown. Returns the input if there are too few arguments to specify the appropriate result.

Omit both *falseResult* and *unknownResult* to make an expression defined only in the region where *condition* is true.

```
when(x<0,x+3)|x=5 ENTER
                        when(x<0,3+x)
```

Use an undef *falseResult* to define an expression that graphs only on an interval.

```
ClrGraph ENTER
Graph when(x≥-π and x<0,x+3,undef)
ENTER
```

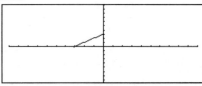

Omit only the *unknownResult* to define a two-piece expression.

```
Graph when(x<0,x+3,5-x^2) ENTER
```

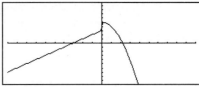

Nest **when()** to define expressions that have more than two pieces.

```
[♦] [HOME]
ClrGraph ENTER                        Done
Graph when(x<0,when(x<-π,
4*sin(x),2x+3),5-x^2) ENTER
```

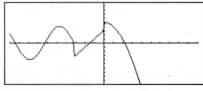

when() is helpful for defining recursive functions.

```
when(n>0,n*factoral(n-1),1)
→factoral(n) ENTER                    Done
factoral(3) ENTER                        6
3! ENTER                                  6
```

While   CATALOG

While *condition*
    block
EndWhile

Executes the statements in *block* as long as *condition* is true.

block can be either a single statement or a sequence of statements separated with the ":" character.

Program segment:

```
   :
:1→i
:0→temp
:While i<=20
:  temp+1/i→temp
:  i+1→i
:EndWhile
:Disp "sum of reciprocals up to
20",temp
   :
```

"With"   See I, page 222.

xor   MATH/Test menu

Boolean expression1 **xor** *Boolean expression2* ⇒
  Boolean expression

Returns true if *Boolean expression1* is **true** and *Boolean expression2* is false, or vice versa. Returns false if *Boolean expression1* and *Boolean expression2* are both true or both false. Returns a simplified Boolean expression if either of the original Boolean expressions cannot be resolved to true or false.

Note: See **or** (page 160).

```
true xor true ENTER           false

(5>3) xor (3>5) ENTER           true
```

---

integer1 **xor** *integer2* ⇒ *integer*

Compares two real integers bit-by-bit using an **xor** operation. Internally, both integers are converted to signed, 32-bit binary numbers. When corresponding bits are compared, the result is 1 if either bit (but not both) is 1; the result is 0 if both bits are 0 or both bits are 1. The returned value represents the bit results, and is displayed according to the Base mode.

You can enter the integers in any number base. For a binary or hexadecimal entry, you must use the 0b or 0h prefix, respectively. Without a prefix, integers are treated as decimal (base 10).

If you enter a decimal integer that is too large for a signed, 32-bit binary form, a symmetric modulo operation is used to bring the value into the appropriate range.

Note: See **or** (page 160).

In Hex base mode:

```
0h7AC36 xor 0h3D5F ENTER      0h79169
```
└ **Important:** Zero, not the letter O.

In Bin base mode:

```
0b100101 xor 0b100 ENTER      0b100001
```

Note: A binary entry can have up to 32 digits (not counting the 0b prefix). A hexadecimal entry can have up to 8 digits.

XorPic CATALOG

XorPic *picVar*[, *row*] [, *column*]

Displays the picture stored in *picVar* on the current Graph screen.

Uses XOR logic for each pixel. Only those pixel positions that are exclusive to either the screen or the picture are turned on. This instruction turns off pixels that are turned on in both images.

picVar must contain a pic data type.

row and *column*, if included, specify the pixel coordinates for the upper left corner of the picture. Defaults are (0, 0).

zeros() MATH/Algebra menu

zeros(*expression*, *var***)** $\Rightarrow$ *list*

Returns a list of candidate real values of *var* that make *expression*=0. **zeros()** does this by computing **exp▶list(solve(***expression*=0,*var***))**.

For some purposes, the result form for **zeros()** is more convenient than that of **solve()**. However, the result form of **zeros()** cannot express implicit solutions, solutions that require inequalities, or solutions that do not involve *var*.

Note: See also **cSolve()** (page 112), **cZeros()** (page 116), and **solve()** (page 188).

```
zeros(a*x^2+b*x+c,x) ENTER
```
$$\left\{\frac{^-(\sqrt{^-(4\cdot a\cdot c-b^2)}+b)}{2\cdot a} \quad \frac{\sqrt{^-(4\cdot a\cdot c-b^2)}-b}{2\cdot a}\right\}$$

```
a*x^2+b*x+c|x=ans(1)[2] ENTER        0
```

```
exact(zeros(a*(e^(x)+x)(sign
  (x)-1),x)) ENTER                    {}
```
```
exact(solve(a*(e^(x)+x)(sign
  (x)-1)=0,x)) ENTER
        e^x + x = 0 or x>0 or a = 0
```

---

zeros({*expression1*, *expression2*}, {*varOrGuess1*, *varOrGuess2* [, ...]}**)** $\Rightarrow$ *matrix*

Returns candidate real zeros of the simultaneous algebraic *expressions*, where each *varOrGuess* specifies an unknown whose value you seek.

Optionally, you can specify an initial guess for a variable. Each *varOrGuess* must have the form:

variable
– or –
variable = real or non-real number

For example, x is valid and so is x=3.

If all of the expressions are polynomials and if you do NOT specify any initial guesses, **zeros()** uses the lexical Gröbner/Buchberger elimination method to attempt to determine **all** real zeros.

For example, suppose you have a circle of radius r at the origin and another circle of radius r centered where the first circle crosses the positive x-axis. Use **zeros()** to find the intersections.

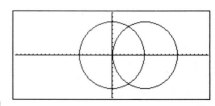

As illustrated by r in the example to the right, simultaneous *polynomial* expressions can have extra variables that have no values, but represent given numeric values that could be substituted later.

```
zeros({x^2+y^2-r^2,
(x-r)^2+y^2-r^2},{x,y}) [ENTER]
```

$$\begin{bmatrix} \dfrac{r}{2} & \dfrac{\sqrt{3}\cdot r}{2} \\ \dfrac{r}{2} & \dfrac{-\sqrt{3}\cdot r}{2} \end{bmatrix}$$

Each row of the resulting matrix represents an alternate zero, with the components ordered the same as the *varOrGuess* list. To extract a row, index the matrix by [*row*].

Extract row 2:

```
ans(1)[2] [ENTER]
```

$$\begin{bmatrix} \dfrac{r}{2} & \dfrac{-\sqrt{3}\cdot r}{2} \end{bmatrix}$$

You can omit unknowns whose values are not of interest, as in the example to the right.

```
zeros({x^2+y^2-r^2,
(x-r)^2+y^2-r^2},{x}) [ENTER]
```

$$\begin{bmatrix} \dfrac{r}{2} \\ \dfrac{r}{2} \end{bmatrix}$$

You can also or instead include unknowns that do not appear in the expressions. For example, you can include z as an unknown to extend the previous example to two parallel intersecting cylinders of radius r. The cylinder zeros illustrate how families of zeros might contain arbitrary constants in the form @*k*, where *k* is an integer suffix from 1 through 255. The suffix resets to 1 when you use **ClrHome** or [F1] 8:Clear Home.

```
zeros({x^2+y^2-r^2,
(x-r)^2+y^2-r^2},{x,y,z}) [ENTER]
```

$$\begin{bmatrix} \dfrac{r}{2} & \dfrac{\sqrt{3}\cdot r}{2} & @1 \\ \dfrac{r}{2} & \dfrac{-\sqrt{3}\cdot r}{2} & @1 \end{bmatrix}$$

For polynomial systems, computation time or memory exhaustion may depend strongly on the order in which you list unknowns. If your initial choice exhausts memory or your patience, try rearranging the variables in the expressions and/or *varOrGuess* list.

If you do not include any guesses and if any expression is non-polynomial in any variable but all expressions are linear in the unknowns, **zeros()** uses Gaussian elimination to attempt to determine all real zeros.

```
zeros({x+e^(z)*y-1,x-y-sin(z)},
{x,y}) [ENTER]
```

$$\begin{bmatrix} \dfrac{e^z\cdot\sin(z)+1}{e^z+1} & \dfrac{-(\sin(z)-1)}{e^z+1} \end{bmatrix}$$

If a system is neither polynomial in all of its variables nor linear in its unknowns, **zeros()** determines at most one zero using an approximate iterative method. To do so, the number of unknowns must equal the number of expressions, and all other variables in the expressions must simplify to numbers.

```
zeros({e^(z)*y-1,-y-sin(z)},{y,z})
[ENTER]
```

$$\begin{bmatrix} .041\ldots & 3.183\ldots \end{bmatrix}$$

Each unknown starts at its guessed value if there is one; otherwise, it starts at 0.0.

Use guesses to seek additional zeros one by one. For convergence, a guess may have to be rather close to a zero.

```
zeros({e^(z)*y-1,-y-sin(z)},
{y,z=2π}) [ENTER]
```

$$\begin{bmatrix} .001\ldots & 6.281\ldots \end{bmatrix}$$

ZoomBox CATALOG

ZoomBox

Displays the Graph screen, lets you draw a box that defines a new viewing window, and updates the window.

In function graphing mode:

```
1.25x*cos(x)→y1(x) ENTER          Done
ZoomStd:ZoomBox ENTER
```

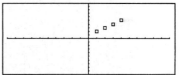

1st corner
2nd corner

2nd Corner?
xc:2.10084   yc: -2.15688

The display after defining ZoomBox by pressing ENTER the second time.

ZoomData CATALOG

ZoomData

Adjusts the window settings based on the currently defined plots (and data) so that all statistical data points will be sampled, and displays the Graph screen.

Note: Does not adjust ymin and ymax for histograms.

In function graphing mode:

```
{1,2,3,4}→L1 ENTER               {1 2 3 4}
{2,3,4,5}→L2 ENTER               {2 3 4 5}
newPlot 1,1,L1,L2 ENTER              Done
ZoomStd ENTER
```

```
◆ [HOME]
ZoomData ENTER
```

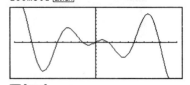

ZoomDec CATALOG

ZoomDec

Adjusts the viewing window so that Δx and Δy = 0.1 displays the Graph screen with the origin centered on the screen.

In function graphing mode:

```
1.25x*cos(x)→y1(x) ENTER          Done
ZoomStd ENTER
```

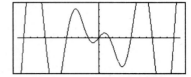

```
◆ [HOME]
ZoomDec ENTER
```

ZoomFit CATALOG

ZoomFit

Displays the Graph screen, and calculates the necessary window dimensions for the dependent variables to view all the picture for the current independent variable settings.

In function graphing mode:

```
1.25x*cos(x)→y1(x) ENTER          Done
ZoomStd ENTER
```

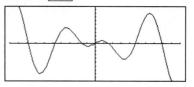

```
♦ [HOME]
ZoomFit ENTER
```

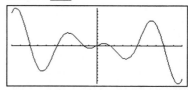

ZoomIn CATALOG

ZoomIn

Displays the Graph screen, lets you set a center point for a zoom in, and updates the viewing window.

The magnitude of the zoom is dependent on the Zoom factors xFact and yFact. In 3D Graph mode, the magnitude is dependent on xFact, yFact, and zFact.

In function graphing mode:

```
1.25x*cos(x)→y1(x) ENTER          Done
ZoomStd:ZoomIn ENTER
```

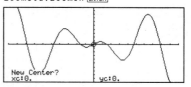

```
ENTER
```

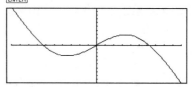

ZoomInt CATALOG

ZoomInt

Displays the Graph screen, lets you set a center point for the zoom, and adjusts the window settings so that each pixel is an integer in all directions.

In function graphing mode:

```
1.25x*cos(x)→y1(x) ENTER          Done
ZoomStd:ZoomInt ENTER
```

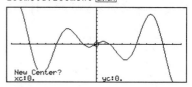

```
ENTER
```

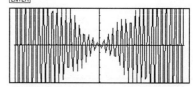

ZoomOut CATALOG

ZoomOut

Displays the Graph screen, lets you set a center point for a zoom out, and updates the viewing window.

The magnitude of the zoom is dependent on the Zoom factors xFact and yFact. In 3D Graph mode, the magnitude is dependent on xFact, yFact, and zFact.

In function graphing mode:

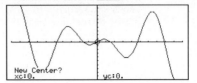

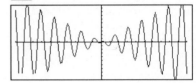

ZoomPrev CATALOG

ZoomPrev

Displays the Graph screen, and updates the viewing window with the settings in use before the last zoom.

ZoomRcl CATALOG

ZoomRcl

Displays the Graph screen, and updates the viewing window using the settings stored with the **ZoomSto** instruction.

ZoomSqr CATALOG

ZoomSqr

Displays the Graph screen, adjusts the x or y window settings so that each pixel represents an equal width and height in the coordinate system, and updates the viewing window.

In 3D Graph mode, **ZoomSqr** lengthens the shortest two axes to be the same as the longest axis.

In function graphing mode:

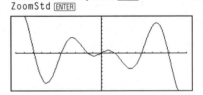

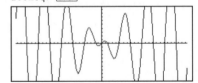

ZoomStd CATALOG

ZoomStd

Sets the window variables to the following standard values, and then updates the viewing window.

Function graphing:
x: [⁻10, 10, 1], y: [⁻10, 10, 1] and xres=2

Parametric graphing:
t: [0, 2π, π/24], x: [⁻10, 10, 1], y:[⁻10, 10, 1]

Polar graphing:
θ: [0, 2π, π/24], x: [⁻10, 10, 1], y: [⁻10, 10, 1]

Sequence graphing:
nmin=1, nmax=10, plotStrt=1, plotStep=1,
x: [⁻10, 10, 1], y: [⁻10, 10, 1]

3D graphing:
eyeθ°=20, eyeφ°=70, eyeψ°=0
x: [⁻10, 10, 14], y: [⁻10, 10, 14],
z: [⁻10, 10], ncontour=5

Differential equations graphing:
t: [0, 10, .1, 0], x: [⁻1, 10, 1], y: [⁻10, 10, 1],
ncurves=0, Estep=1, diftol=.001, fldres=20,
dtime=0

In function graphing mode:

1.25x*cos(x)→y1(x) [ENTER]   Done
ZoomStd [ENTER]

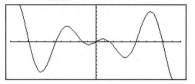

ZoomSto CATALOG

ZoomSto

Stores the current Window settings in the Zoom memory. You can use **ZoomRcl** to restore the settings.

ZoomTrig CATALOG

ZoomTrig

Displays the Graph screen, sets Δx to π/24, and xscl to π/2, centers the origin, sets the y settings to [⁻4, 4, .5], and updates the viewing window.

In function graphing mode:

1.25x*cos(x)→y1(x) [ENTER]   Done
ZoomStd [ENTER]

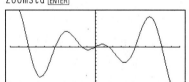

[♦] [HOME]
ZoomTrig [ENTER]

+ (add)   ⊞ key

expression1 + *expression2* ⇒ *expression*	56 [ENTER] 56
	ans(1)+4 [ENTER] 60
Returns the sum of *expression1* and	ans(1)+4 [ENTER] 64
expression2.	ans(1)+4 [ENTER] 68
	ans(1)+4 [ENTER] 72

list1 + *list2* ⇒ *list*	{22,π,π/2}→L1 [ENTER] {22 π π/2}
matrix1 + *matrix2* ⇒ *matrix*	{10,5,π/2}→L2 [ENTER] {10 5 π/2}
	L1+L2 [ENTER] {32 π+5 π}
Returns a list (or matrix) containing the sums of corresponding elements in *list1* and *list2* (or *matrix1* and *matrix2*).	ans(1)+{π, ⁻5, ⁻π} [ENTER] {π+32 π 0}
Dimensions of the arguments must be equal.	[a,b;c,d]+[1,0;0,1] [ENTER] $\begin{bmatrix} a+1 & b \\ c & d+1 \end{bmatrix}$

expression + *list1* ⇒ *list*	15+{10,15,20} [ENTER] {25 30 35}
list1 + *expression* ⇒ *list*	
	{10,15,20}+15 [ENTER] {25 30 35}
Returns a list containing the sums of *expression* and each element in *list1*.	

expression + *matrix1* ⇒ *matrix*	20+[1,2;3,4] [ENTER]
matrix1 + *expression* ⇒ *matrix*	$\begin{bmatrix} 21 & 2 \\ 3 & 24 \end{bmatrix}$
Returns a matrix with *expression* added to each element on the diagonal of *matrix1*. *matrix1* must be square.	
Note: Use .+ (dot plus) to add an expression to each element.	

− (subtract)   ⊟ key

expression1 - *expression2* ⇒ *expression*	6−2 [ENTER] 4
Returns *expression1* minus *expression2*.	π−π/6 [ENTER] $\dfrac{5 \cdot \pi}{6}$

list1 - *list2* ⇒ *list*	{22,π,π/2}−{10,5,π/2} [ENTER] {12 π−5 0}
matrix1 - *matrix2* ⇒ *matrix*	[3,4]−[1,2] [ENTER] [2 2]
Subtracts each element in *list2* (or *matrix2*) from the corresponding element in *list1* (or *matrix1*), and returns the results.	
Dimensions of the arguments must be equal.	

expression - *list1* ⇒ *list*	15−{10,15,20} [ENTER] {5 0 ⁻5}
list1 - *expression* ⇒ *list*	
	{10,15,20}−15 [ENTER] {⁻5 0 5}
Subtracts each *list1* element from *expression* or subtracts *expression* from each *list1* element, and returns a list of the results.	

expression - *matrix1* ⇒ *matrix*	20−[1,2;3,4] [ENTER]
matrix1 - *expression* ⇒ *matrix*	$\begin{bmatrix} 19 & ⁻2 \\ ⁻3 & 16 \end{bmatrix}$
expression − *matrix1* returns a matrix of *expression* times the identity matrix minus *matrix1*. *matrix1* must be square.	
matrix1 − *expression* returns a matrix of *expression* times the identity matrix subtracted from *matrix1*. *matrix1* must be square.	
Note: Use .- (dot minus) to subtract an expression from each element.	

* (multiply)   ⊠ key

expression1 * *expression2* ⇒ *expression*	2*3.45 [ENTER]	6.9
Returns the product of *expression1* and *expression2*.	x*y*x [ENTER]	$x^2 \cdot y$

list1 * *list2* ⇒ *list*	{1.0,2,3}*{4,5,6} [ENTER]	{4. 10 18}
Returns a list containing the products of the corresponding elements in *list1* and *list2*.	{2/a,3/2}*{a²,b/3} [ENTER]	$\{2 \cdot a \quad \frac{b}{2}\}$
Dimensions of the lists must be equal.		

matrix1 * *matrix2* ⇒ *matrix*	[1,2,3;4,5,6]*[a,d;b,e;c,f] [ENTER]
Returns the matrix product of *matrix1* and *matrix2*. The number of rows in *matrix1* must equal the number of columns in *matrix2*.	$\blacksquare \begin{bmatrix} 1 & 2 & 3 \\ 4 & 5 & 6 \end{bmatrix} \cdot \begin{bmatrix} a & d \\ b & e \\ c & f \end{bmatrix}$ $\begin{bmatrix} a+2 \cdot b+3 \cdot c & d+2 \cdot e+3 \cdot f \\ 4 \cdot a+5 \cdot b+6 \cdot c & 4 \cdot d+5 \cdot e+6 \cdot f \end{bmatrix}$

expression * *list1* ⇒ *list* *list1* * *expression* ⇒ *list*	π*{4,5,6} [ENTER]	$\{4 \cdot \pi \quad 5 \cdot \pi \quad 6 \cdot \pi\}$
Returns a list containing the products of *expression* and each element in *list1*.		

expression * *matrix1* ⇒ *matrix* *matrix1* * *expression* ⇒ *matrix*	[1,2;3,4]*.01 [ENTER]	$\begin{bmatrix} .01 & .02 \\ .03 & .04 \end{bmatrix}$
Returns a matrix containing the products of *expression* and each element in *matrix1*.	λ*identity(3) [ENTER]	$\begin{bmatrix} \lambda & 0 & 0 \\ 0 & \lambda & 0 \\ 0 & 0 & \lambda \end{bmatrix}$
Note: Use **.*** (dot multiply) to multiply an expression by each element.		

/ (divide)   ÷ key

expression1 / *expression2* ⇒ *expression*	2/3.45 [ENTER]	.57971
Returns the quotient of *expression1* divided by *expression2*.	x^3/x [ENTER]	x^2

list1 / *list2* ⇒ *list*	{1.0,2,3}/{4,5,6} [ENTER]
Returns a list containing the quotients of *list1* divided by *list2*.	{.25 2/5 1/2}
Dimensions of the lists must be equal.	

expression / *list1* ⇒ *list* *list1* / *expression* ⇒ *list*	a/{3,a,√(a)} [ENTER]
	$\{ \frac{a}{3} \quad 1 \quad \sqrt{a}\}$
Returns a list containing the quotients of *expression* divided by *list1* or *list1* divided by *expression*.	{a,b,c}/(a*b*c) [ENTER]
	$\{\frac{1}{b \cdot c} \quad \frac{1}{a \cdot c} \quad \frac{1}{a \cdot b}\}$

matrix1 / *expression* ⇒ *matrix*	[a,b,c]/(a*b*c) [ENTER]
Returns a matrix containing the quotients of *matrix1/expression*.	$\begin{bmatrix} \frac{1}{b \cdot c} & \frac{1}{a \cdot c} & \frac{1}{a \cdot b} \end{bmatrix}$
Note: Use **./** (dot divide) to divide an expression by each element.	

¯ (negate)   [(-)] key and MATH/Base menu

¯expression1 ⇒ *expression*
¯list1 ⇒ *list*
¯matrix1 ⇒ *matrix*

Returns the negation of the argument.

For a list or matrix, returns all the elements negated.

If *expression1* is a binary or hexadecimal integer, the negation gives the two's complement.

```
¯2.43 ENTER                                        ¯2.43
¯{¯1,0.4,1.2E19} ENTER
                                          {1 ¯.4 ¯1.2E19}
¯a* ¯b ENTER                                          a·b
```

In Bin base mode:

```
0b100101▶dec ENTER                                     37
```
└─ **Important:** Zero, not the letter O.
```
¯0b100101 ENTER
   0b111111111111111111111111111011011
ans(1)▶dec ENTER                                      ¯37
```

Note: To type ▶, press [2nd] Y.

%   CHAR/Punctuation menu

expression1 **%** ⇒ *expression*
list1 **%** ⇒ *list*
matrix1 **%** ⇒ *matrix*

Returns $\dfrac{argument}{100}$.

For a list or matrix, returns a list or matrix with each element divided by 100.

```
13% ◆ ENTER                                          .13
{1, 10, 100}% ◆ ENTER          {.01 .1  1.}
```

=   [=] key

expression1 = *expression2* ⇒ *Boolean expression*
list1 = *list2* ⇒ *Boolean list*
matrix1 = *matrix2* ⇒ *Boolean matrix*

Returns true if *expression1* is determined to be equal to *expression2*.

Returns false if *expression1* is determined to not be equal to *expression2*.

Anything else returns a simplified form of the equation.

For lists and matrices, returns comparisons element by element.

Example function listing using math test symbols: =, ≠, <, ≤, >, ≥

```
:g(x)
:Func
:If x≤¯5 Then
:   Return 5
:   ElseIf x>¯5 and x<0 Then
:   Return ¯x
:   ElseIf x≥0 and x≠10 Then
:   Return x
:   ElseIf x=10 Then
:   Return 3
:EndIf
:EndFunc
```

Graph g(x) ENTER

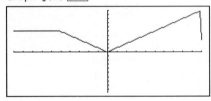

/= (not equal)   [2nd] [V] **key** or [÷] [=] **keys**

expression1 **/=** *expression2* ⇒ *Boolean expression*
list1 **/=** *list2* ⇒ *Boolean list*
matrix1 **/=** *matrix2* ⇒ *Boolean matrix*

    Returns true if *expression1* is determined to be
    not equal to *expression2*.

    Returns false if *expression1* is determined to
    be equal to *expression2*.

    Anything else returns a simplified form of the
    equation.

    For lists and matrices, returns comparisons
    element by element.

See "=" example on previous page.

<   [2nd] [<] **key**

expression1 < *expression2* ⇒ *Boolean expression*
list1 < *list2* ⇒ *Boolean list*
matrix1 < *matrix2* ⇒ *Boolean matrix*

    Returns true if *expression1* is determined to be
    less than *expression2*.

    Returns false if *expression1* is determined to
    be greater than or equal to *expression2*.

    Anything else returns a simplified form of the
    equation.

    For lists and matrices, returns comparisons
    element by element.

See "=" example on previous page.

<=   [2nd] [<] [=] **keys**

expression1 <= *expression2* ⇒ *Boolean expression*
list1 <= *list2* ⇒ *Boolean list*
matrix1 <= *matrix2* ⇒ *Boolean matrix*

    Returns true if *expression1* is determined to be
    less than or equal to *expression2*.

    Returns false if *expression1* is determined to
    be greater than *expression2*.

    Anything else returns a simplified form of the
    equation.

    For lists and matrices, returns comparisons
    element by element.

See "=" example on previous page.

>   2nd [>] key

expression1 > expression2 ⇒   *Boolean expression*
list1 > list2 ⇒   *Boolean list*
matrix1 > matrix2 ⇒   *Boolean matrix*

See "=" example on page 212.

Returns true if *expression1* is determined to be greater than *expression2*.

Returns false if *expression1* is determined to be less than or equal to *expression2*.

Anything else returns a simplified form of the equation.

For lists and matrices, returns comparisons element by element.

>=   2nd [>] [=] keys

expression1 >= expression2 ⇒   *Boolean expression*
list1 >= list2 ⇒   *Boolean list*
matrix1 >= matrix2 ⇒   *Boolean matrix*

See "=" example on page 212.

Returns true if *expression1* is determined to be greater than or equal to *expression2*.

Returns false if *expression1* is determined to be less than *expression2*.

Anything else returns a simplified form of the equation.

For lists and matrices, returns comparisons element by element.

.+ (dot add)   [.] [+] keys

matrix1 .+ matrix2 ⇒   *matrix*
expression .+ matrix1 ⇒   *matrix*

matrix1 .+ matrix2 returns a matrix that is the sum of each pair of corresponding elements in *matrix1* and *matrix2*.

expression .+ matrix1 returns a matrix that is the sum of *expression* and each element in *matrix1*.

```
[a,2;b,3].+[c,4;5,d] ENTER
x.+[c,4;5,d] ENTER
```

$$\begin{bmatrix} a & 2 \\ b & 3 \end{bmatrix} .+ \begin{bmatrix} c & 4 \\ 5 & d \end{bmatrix} \qquad \begin{bmatrix} a+c & 6 \\ b+5 & d+3 \end{bmatrix}$$

$$x .+ \begin{bmatrix} c & 4 \\ 5 & d \end{bmatrix} \qquad \begin{bmatrix} x+c & x+4 \\ x+5 & x+d \end{bmatrix}$$

.- (dot subt.)   [.] [-] keys

matrix1 .- matrix2 ⇒   *matrix*
expression .- matrix1 ⇒   *matrix*

matrix1 .- matrix2 returns a matrix that is the difference between each pair of corresponding elements in *matrix1* and *matrix2*.

expression .- matrix1 returns a matrix that is the difference of *expression* and each element in *matrix1*.

```
[a,2;b,3].-[c,4;d,5] ENTER
x.-[c,4;d,5] ENTER
```

$$\begin{bmatrix} a & 2 \\ b & 3 \end{bmatrix} .- \begin{bmatrix} c & 4 \\ d & 5 \end{bmatrix} \qquad \begin{bmatrix} a-c & -2 \\ b-d & -2 \end{bmatrix}$$

$$x .- \begin{bmatrix} c & 4 \\ d & 5 \end{bmatrix} \qquad \begin{bmatrix} x-c & x-4 \\ x-d & x-5 \end{bmatrix}$$

.* (dot mult.) [.] [×] keys

$matrix1 .* matrix2 \Rightarrow matrix$
$expression .* matrix1 \Rightarrow matrix$

$matrix1 .* matrix2$ returns a matrix that is the product of each pair of corresponding elements in $matrix1$ and $matrix2$.

$expression .* matrix1$ returns a matrix containing the products of $expression$ and each element in $matrix1$.

[a,2;b,3].*[c,4;5,d] ENTER
x.*[a,b;c,d] ENTER

$$\blacksquare \begin{bmatrix} a & 2 \\ b & 3 \end{bmatrix} .* \begin{bmatrix} c & 4 \\ 5 & d \end{bmatrix} \qquad \begin{bmatrix} a \cdot c & 8 \\ 5 \cdot b & 3 \cdot d \end{bmatrix}$$

$$\blacksquare x .* \begin{bmatrix} a & b \\ c & d \end{bmatrix} \qquad \begin{bmatrix} a \cdot x & b \cdot x \\ c \cdot x & d \cdot x \end{bmatrix}$$

./ (dot divide) [.] [÷] keys

$matrix1 ./ matrix2 \Rightarrow matrix$
$expression ./ matrix1 \Rightarrow matrix$

$matrix1 ./ matrix2$ returns a matrix that is the quotient of each pair of corresponding elements in $matrix1$ and $matrix2$.

$expression ./ matrix1$ returns a matrix that is the quotient of $expression$ and each element in $matrix1$.

[a,2;b,3]./[c,4;5,d] ENTER
x./[c,4;5,d] ENTER

$$\blacksquare \begin{bmatrix} a & 2 \\ b & 3 \end{bmatrix} ./ \begin{bmatrix} c & 4 \\ 5 & d \end{bmatrix} \qquad \begin{bmatrix} \frac{a}{c} & 1/2 \\ \frac{b}{5} & \frac{3}{d} \end{bmatrix}$$

$$\blacksquare x ./ \begin{bmatrix} c & 4 \\ 5 & d \end{bmatrix} \qquad \begin{bmatrix} \frac{x}{c} & \frac{x}{4} \\ \frac{x}{5} & \frac{x}{d} \end{bmatrix}$$

.^ (dot power) [.] [^] keys

$matrix1 .^ matrix2 \Rightarrow matrix$
$expression .^ matrix1 \Rightarrow matrix$

$matrix1 .^ matrix2$ returns a matrix where each element in $matrix2$ is the exponent for the corresponding element in $matrix1$.

$expression .^ matrix1$ returns a matrix where each element in $matrix1$ is the exponent for $expression$.

[a,2;b,3].^[c,4;5,d] ENTER
x.^[c,4;5,d] ENTER

$$\blacksquare \begin{bmatrix} a & 2 \\ b & 3 \end{bmatrix} .^ \begin{bmatrix} c & 4 \\ 5 & d \end{bmatrix} \qquad \begin{bmatrix} a^c & 16 \\ b^5 & 3^d \end{bmatrix}$$

$$\blacksquare x .^ \begin{bmatrix} c & 4 \\ 5 & d \end{bmatrix} \qquad \begin{bmatrix} x^c & x^4 \\ x^5 & x^d \end{bmatrix}$$

! (factorial) [2nd] [W] key

$expression1! \Rightarrow expression$
$list1! \Rightarrow list$
$matrix1! \Rightarrow matrix$

Returns the factorial of the argument.

For a list or matrix, returns a list or matrix of factorials of the elements.

The TI-92 Plus computes a numeric value for only non-negative whole-number values.

5! ENTER   120

{5,4,3}! ENTER   {120   24   6}

[1,2;3,4]! ENTER $\begin{bmatrix} 1 & 2 \\ 6 & 24 \end{bmatrix}$

& (append) [2nd] [H] key

$string1 \& string2 \Rightarrow string$

Returns a text string that is $string2$ appended to $string1$.

"Hello " & "Nick" ENTER   "Hello Nick"

∫(*expression1*, *var*[, *lower*] [,*upper*]) ⇒ *expression*

Returns the integral of *expression1* with respect to the variable *var* from *lower* to *upper*.

∫(x^2,x,a,b) [ENTER] $\dfrac{^-a^3}{3} + \dfrac{b^3}{3}$

Returns an anti-derivative if *lower* and *upper* are omitted. A symbolic constant of integration such as C is omitted.

∫(x^2,x) [ENTER] $\dfrac{x^3}{3}$

However, *lower* is added as a constant of integration if only *upper* is omitted.

∫(a*x^2,x,c) [ENTER] $\dfrac{a \cdot x^3}{3} + c$

Equally valid anti-derivatives might differ by a numeric constant. Such a constant might be disguised—particularly when an anti-derivative contains logarithms or inverse trigonometric functions. Moreover, piecewise constant expressions are sometimes added to make an anti-derivative valid over a larger interval than the usual formula.

∫(1/(2-cos(x)),x)→tmp(x) [ENTER]
ClrGraph:Graph tmp(x):Graph
1/(2-cos(x)):Graph √(3)
(2tan⁻¹(√(3)(tan(x/2)))/3) [ENTER]

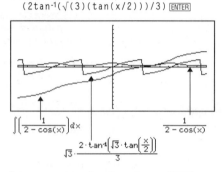

$$\int \left(\frac{1}{2 - \cos(x)} \right) dx \qquad\qquad \frac{1}{2 - \cos(x)}$$

$$\sqrt{3} \cdot \frac{2 \cdot \tan^{-1}\left(\sqrt{3} \cdot \tan\left(\frac{x}{2} \right) \right)}{3}$$

∫() returns itself for pieces of *expression1* that it cannot determine as an explicit finite combination of its built-in functions and operators.

∫(b*e^(-x^2)+a/(x^2+a^2),x) [ENTER]

$$\blacksquare \int \left(b \cdot e^{-x^2} + \frac{a}{x^2 + a^2} \right) dx$$
$$b \cdot \int \left(e^{-x^2} \right) dx + \tan^{-1}\left(\frac{x}{a} \right)$$

When *lower* and *upper* are both present, an attempt is made to locate any discontinuities or discontinuous derivatives in the interval *lower* < *var* < *upper* and to subdivide the interval at those places.

For the AUTO setting of the Exact/Approx mode, numerical integration is used where applicable when an anti-derivative or a limit cannot be determined.

For the APPROX setting, numerical integration is tried first, if applicable. Anti-derivatives are sought only where such numerical integration is inapplicable or fails.

∫(e^(-x^2),x,-1,1)[♦] [ENTER]   1.493...

∫() can be nested to do multiple integrals. Integration limits can depend on integration variables outside them.

Note: See also **nInt()** (page 158).

∫(∫(ln(x+y),y,0,x),x,0,a) [ENTER]

$$\blacksquare \int_0^a \int_0^x \ln(x + y)\,dy\,dx$$
$$\frac{a^2 \cdot \ln(a)}{2} + a^2 \cdot (\ln(2) - 3/4)$$

√() (sqr. root) [2nd] [√] key

√ (*expression1*) ⇒ *expression*
√ (*list1*) ⇒ *list*

Returns the square root of the argument.

For a list, returns the square roots of all the elements in *list1*.

√(4) [ENTER]   2

√({9,a,4}) [ENTER]   {3 √a 2}

Π() (product) **MATH/Calculus menu**

Π(*expression1, var, low, high*) ⇒ *expression*

Evaluates *expression1* for each value of *var* from *low* to *high*, and returns the product of the results.

Π(*expression1, var, low, low*−1) ⇒ 1

Π(*expression1, var, low, high*) ⇒ 1/Π(*expression1, var, high*+1, *low*−1) if *high* < *low*−1

Π(1/n,n,1,5) [ENTER] $\frac{1}{120}$

Π(k^2,k,1,n) [ENTER]   (n!)²

Π({1/n,n,2},n,1,5) [ENTER]
$\{\frac{1}{120}$ 120 32$\}$

Π(k,k,4,3) [ENTER]   1

Π(1/k,k,4,1) [ENTER]   6

Π(1/k,k,4,1)*Π(1/k,k,2,4) [ENTER]   1/4

Σ() (sum) [2nd] [Σ] key

Σ(*expression1, var, low, high*) ⇒ *expression*

Evaluates *expression1* for each value of *var* from *low* to *high*, and returns the sum of the results.

Σ(*expression1, var, low, low*−1) ⇒ 0

Σ(*expression1, var, low, high*) ⇒ ⁻Σ(*expression1, var, high*+1, *low*−1) if *high* < *low*−1

Σ(1/n,n,1,5) [ENTER] $\frac{137}{60}$

Σ(k^2,k,1,n) [ENTER] $\frac{n\cdot(n+1)\cdot(2\cdot n+1)}{6}$

Σ(1/n^2,n,1,∞) [ENTER] $\frac{\pi^2}{6}$

Σ(k,k,4,3) [ENTER]   0

Σ(k,k,4,1) [ENTER]   ⁻5

Σ(k,k,4,1)+Σ(k,k,2,4) [ENTER]   4

∧ (power) ⌃ **key**

$expression1 \wedge expression2 \Rightarrow expression$

$list1 \wedge list2 \Rightarrow list$

Returns the first argument raised to the power of the second argument.

For a list, returns the elements in *list1* raised to the power of the corresponding elements in *list2*.

In the real domain, fractional powers that have reduced exponents with odd denominators use the real branch versus the principal branch for complex mode.

4^2 [ENTER]   16

{a,2,c}^{1,b,3} [ENTER]   {a 2^b c^3}

$expression \wedge list1 \Rightarrow list$

Returns *expression* raised to the power of the elements in *list1*.

p^{a,2,-3} [ENTER] $\{p^a \quad p^2 \quad \frac{1}{p^3}\}$

$list1 \wedge expression \Rightarrow list$

Returns the elements in *list1* raised to the power of *expression*.

{1,2,3,4}^-2 [ENTER]
$\{1 \quad 1/4 \quad 1/9 \quad 1/16\}$

$squareMatrix1 \wedge integer \Rightarrow matrix$

Returns *squareMatrix1* raised to the *integer* power.

squareMatrix1 must be a square matrix.

If *integer* = -1, computes the inverse matrix. If *integer* < -1, computes the inverse matrix to an appropriate positive power.

[1,2;3,4]^2 [ENTER]
[1,2;3,4]^-1 [ENTER]
[1,2;3,4]^-2 [ENTER]

(indirection) [2nd] [T] **key**

*varNameString*

Refers to the variable whose name is *varNameString*. This lets you create and modify variables from a program using strings.

Program segment:

```
   ⋮
:Request "Enter Your Name",str1
:NewFold #str1
   ⋮

   ⋮
:For i,1,5,1
:   ClrGraph
:   Graph i*x
:   StoPic #("pic" & string(i))
:EndFor
   ⋮
```

^r (radian)   MATH/Angle menu

expression1^r ⇒ *expression*
list1^r ⇒ *list*
matrix1^r ⇒ *matrix*

In Degree angle mode, multiplies *expression1* by $180/\pi$. In Radian angle mode, returns *expression1* unchanged.

This function gives you a way to use a radian angle while in Degree mode. (In Degree angle mode, **sin()**, **cos()**, **tan()**, and polar-to-rectangular conversions expect the angle argument to be in degrees.)

Hint: Use ^r if you want to force radians in a function or program definition regardless of the mode that prevails when the function or program is used.

In Degree or Radian angle mode:

cos((π/4)^r) [ENTER] $\dfrac{\sqrt{2}}{2}$

cos({0^r,(π/12)^r,⁻π^r}) [ENTER]

$\{1 \quad \dfrac{(\sqrt{3}+1)\cdot\sqrt{2}}{4} \quad -1\}$

° (degree)   [2nd] [D] key

expression° ⇒ *value*
list1° ⇒ *list*
matrix1° ⇒ *matrix*

In Radian angle mode, multiplies *expression* by $\pi/180$. In Degree angle mode, returns *expression* unchanged.

This function gives you a way to use a degree angle while in Radian mode. (In Radian angle mode, **sin()**, **cos()**, **tan()**, and polar-to-rectangular conversions expect the angle argument to be in radians.)

In Radian angle mode:

cos(45°) [ENTER] $\dfrac{\sqrt{2}}{2}$

cos({0,π/4,90°,30.12°}) [♦] [ENTER]
$\{1 \quad .707... \quad 0 \quad .864...\}$

∠ (angle)   [2nd] [F] key

[*radius*,∠θ_*angle*] ⇒ *vector* (polar input)
[*radius*,∠θ_*angle*,Z_*coordinate*] ⇒ *vector* (cylindrical input)
[*radius*,∠θ_*angle*,∠φ_*angle*] ⇒ *vector* (spherical input)

Returns coordinates as a vector depending on the Vector Format mode setting: rectangular, cylindrical, or spherical.

[5,∠60°,∠45°] [ENTER]

In Radian mode and vector format set to:

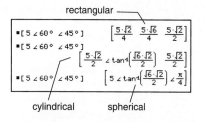

(*magnitude* ∠ *angle*) ⇒ *complexValue* (polar input)

Enters a complex value in (r∠θ) polar form. The *angle* is interpreted according to the current Angle mode setting.

In Radian angle mode and Rectangular complex format mode:

5+3*i*−(10∠π/4) [ENTER]
$5-5\cdot\sqrt{2}+(3-5\cdot\sqrt{2})\cdot i$

[♦] [ENTER]
$-2.071...-4.071...\cdot i$

2nd [D] key (°), 2nd [B] key ('), 2nd [L] key (")

$dd°mm'ss.ss"$ ⇒ *expression*

In Degree angle mode:

dd	A positive or negative number
mm	A non-negative number
$ss.ss$	A non-negative number

25°13'17.5" ENTER   25.221...

25°30' ENTER   51/2

Returns $dd+(mm/60)+(ss.ss/3600)$.

This base-60 entry format lets you:

- Enter an angle in degrees/minutes/seconds without regard to the current angle mode.

- Enter time as hours/minutes/seconds.

' (prime)   **2nd [B] key**

variable'
variable"

deSolve(y''=y^(-1/2) and y(0)=0
and y'(0)=0,t,y) ENTER

$$\frac{2 \cdot y^{3/4}}{3} = t$$

Enters a prime symbol in a differential equation. A single prime symbol denotes a 1st-order differential equation, two prime symbols denote a 2nd-order, etc.

_ (underscore)   **2nd [P] key**

*expression*_*unit*

3_m▶_ft ENTER   9.842...·_ft

Designates the units for an *expression*. All unit names must begin with an underscore.

Note: To type ▶, press 2nd Y.

You can use pre-defined units or create your own units. For a list of pre-defined units, refer to the chapter about constants and measurement units in this book. You can press ♦ P to select units from a menu, or you can type the unit names directly.

---

*variable*_

Assuming z is undefined:

When *variable* has no value, it is treated as though it represents a complex number. By default, without the _, the variable is treated as real.

real(z) ENTER   z
real(z_) ENTER   real(z_)

imag(z) ENTER   0
imag(z_) ENTER   imag(z_)

If *variable* has a value, the _ is ignored and *variable* retains its original data type.

Note: You can store a complex number to a variable without using _. However, for best results in calculations such as **cSolve()** and **cZeros()**, the _ is recommended.

     2nd [Y] **key**

$expression\_unit1 ▶ \_unit2 ⇒ expression\_unit2$ 3_m ▶ _ft ENTER   9.842… · _ft

Converts an expression from one unit to another. The units must be in the same category.

The _ underscore character designates the units. For a list of valid pre-defined units, refer to the chapter about constants and measurement units in this book. You can press ◆ P to select units from a menu, or you can type the unit names directly.

To get the _ underscore when typing units directly, press 2nd P.

Note: The ▶ conversion operator does not handle temperature units. Use **tmpCnv()** and **ΔtmpCnv()** instead.

10^()   CATALOG

$10\char94 (expression1) ⇒ expression$
$10\char94 (list1) ⇒ list$ 10^1.5 ENTER   31.622…

Returns 10 raised to the power of the argument.

10^{0,-2,2,a} ENTER $\{1 \ \frac{1}{100} \ 100 \ 10^a\}$

For a list, returns 10 raised to the power of the elements in *list1*.

$10\char94 (squareMatrix1) ⇒ squareMatrix$ 10^([1,2,3;4,5,6;7,8,9]) ENTER

Returns 10 raised to the power of *squareMatrix1*. This is *not* the same as calculating 10 raised to the power of each element. For information about the calculation method, refer to **cos()** on page 109.

$$\begin{bmatrix} 1.143\text{…}{\scriptstyle E7} & 8.171\text{…}{\scriptstyle E6} & 6.675\text{…}{\scriptstyle E6} \\ 9.956\text{…}{\scriptstyle E6} & 7.115\text{…}{\scriptstyle E6} & 5.813\text{…}{\scriptstyle E6} \\ 7.652\text{…}{\scriptstyle E6} & 5.469\text{…}{\scriptstyle E6} & 4.468\text{…}{\scriptstyle E6} \end{bmatrix}$$

squareMatrix1 must be diagonalizable. The result always contains floating-point numbers.

x⁻¹   2nd [x⁻¹] **key**

$expression1 \ \mathbf{x^{-1}} ⇒ expression$
$list1 \ \mathbf{x^{-1}} ⇒ list$ 3.1^-1 ENTER   .322581

Returns the reciprocal of the argument.

{a,4,-.1,x-2}^-1 ENTER

$$\{\frac{1}{a} \ \ \frac{1}{4} \ \ -10 \ \ \frac{1}{x-2}\}$$

For a list, returns the reciprocals of the elements in *list1*.

$squareMatrix1 \ \mathbf{x^{-1}} ⇒ squareMatrix$ [1,2;3,4]^-1 ENTER
[1,2;a,4]^-1 ENTER

Returns the inverse of *squareMatrix1*.

squareMatrix1 must be a non-singular square matrix.

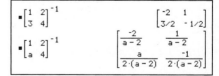

| ("with") | [2nd] [K] **key** |

expression | *Boolean expression1* [*and Boolean*
expression2]...[*and Boolean expressionN*]

> The "with" (|) symbol serves as a binary
> operator. The operand to the left of | is an
> expression. The operand to the right of |
> specifies one or more relations that are
> intended to affect the simplification of the
> expression. Multiple relations after | must be
> joined by a logical "and".

> The "with" operator provides three basic
> types of functionality: substitutions, interval
> constraints, and exclusions.

> Substitutions are in the form of an equality,
> such as x=3 or y=sin(x). To be most effective,
> the left side should be a simple variable.
> *expression* | *variable = value* will substitute
> *value* for every occurrence of *variable* in
> *expression*.

> Interval constraints take the form of one or
> more inequalities joined by logical "and"
> operators. Interval constraints also permit
> simplification that otherwise might be invalid
> or not computable.

> Exclusions use the "not equals" (/= or ≠)
> relational operator to exclude a specific
> value from consideration. They are used
> primarily to exclude an exact solution when
> using **cSolve()**, **cZeros()**, **fMax()**, **fMin()**, **solve()**,
> **zeros()**, etc.

x+1| x=3 [ENTER]   4

x+y| x=sin(y) [ENTER]   sin(y)+y

x+y| sin(y)=x [ENTER]   x+y

x^3−2x+7→f(x) [ENTER]   Done

f(x)| x=√(3) [ENTER]   √3+7

(sin(x))^2+2sin(x)−6| sin(x)=d [ENTER]
                                              d²+2d−6

solve(x^2−1=0,x)|x>0 and x<2 [ENTER]
                                               x = 1

√(x)*√(1/x)|x>0 [ENTER]   1

√(x)*√(1/x) [ENTER] $\sqrt{\frac{1}{x}} \cdot \sqrt{x}$

solve(x^2−1=0,x)| x≠1 [ENTER]   x = ⁻1

| → (store) | [STO►] **key** |

expression → *var*
list → *var*
matrix → *var*
expression → *fun_name(parameter1,...)*
list → *fun_name(parameter1,...)*
matrix → *fun_name(parameter1,...)*

> If variable *var* does not exist, creates *var* and
> initializes it to *expression*, *list*, or *matrix*.

> If *var* already exists and if it is not locked or
> protected, replaces its contents with
> *expression*, *list*, or *matrix*.

> **Hint:** If you plan to do symbolic computations
> using undefined variables, avoid storing
> anything into commonly used, one-letter
> variables such as a, b, c, x, y, z, etc.

π/4→myvar [ENTER] $\frac{\pi}{4}$

2cos(x)→Y1(x) [ENTER]   Done

{1,2,3,4}→Lst5 [ENTER]   {1 2 3 4}

[1,2,3;4,5,6]→MatG [ENTER] $\begin{bmatrix} 1 & 2 & 3 \\ 4 & 5 & 6 \end{bmatrix}$

"Hello"→str1 [ENTER]   "Hello"

© (comment)　　[2nd] [X] **key or Program Editor/Control menu**

© [*text*]

© processes *text* as a comment line, which can be used to annotate program instructions.

© can be at the beginning or anywhere in the line. Everything to the right of ©, to the end of the line, is the comment.

Program segment:

```
  ⋮
:© Get 10 points from the Graph
  screen
:For i,1,10 © This loops 10 times
  ⋮
```

0b, 0h　　　[0] [B] **keys,** [0] [H] **keys**

0b *binaryNumber*
0h *hexadecimalNumber*

└── A binary number can have up to 32 digits. A hexadecimal number can have up to 8.

└─ Zero, not the letter O, followed by b or h.

Denotes a binary or hexadecimal number, respectively. To enter a binary or hex number, you must enter the 0b or 0h prefix regardless of the Base mode. Without a prefix, a number is treated as decimal (base 10).

Results are displayed according to the Base mode.

In Dec base mode:

0b10+0hF+10 [ENTER]　　　　　　27

In Bin base mode:

0b10+0hF+10 [ENTER]　　　　0b11011

In Hex base mode:

0b10+0hF+10 [ENTER]　　　　　0h1B

Reference Information

This appendix contains a comprehensive list of TI-92 Plus error messages and character codes. It also includes information about how certain TI-92 Plus operations are calculated, compatibility issues when transferring data between the TI-92 Plus and TI-92, and service and warranty information.

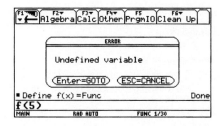

For additional information, refer to Appendix B and C in the *TI-92 Guidebook*. For example, if you have difficulty operating the TI-92 Plus, Appendix C in the *TI-92 Guidebook* contains an "In Case of Difficulty" section that gives suggestions that may help you correct the problem.

TI-92 Plus Error Messages

This section lists error messages that may be displayed when input or internal errors are encountered. The number to the left of each error message represents an internal error number that is not displayed. If the error occurs inside a Try...EndTry block, the error number is stored in system variable *errornum*. Many of the error messages are self-explanatory and do not require descriptive information. However, additional information has been added for some error messages.

Error Number	Description
10	**A function did not return a value**
20	**A test did not resolve to TRUE or FALSE** Generally, undefined variables cannot be compared. For example, the test If a<b will cause this error if either a or b is undefined when the If statement is executed.
30	**Argument cannot be a folder name**
40	**Argument error**
50	**Argument mismatch** Two or more arguments must be of the same type. For example, **PtOn** *expression1,expression2* and **PtOn** *list1,list2* are both valid, but **PtOn** *expression,list* is a mismatch.
60	**Argument must be a Boolean expression or integer**
70	**Argument must be a decimal number**
80	**Argument must be a label name**
90	**Argument must be a list**
100	**Argument must be a matrix**
110	**Argument must be a Pic**
120	**Argument must be a Pic or string**
130	**Argument must be a string**
140	**Argument must be a variable name** For example, DelVar 12 is invalid because a number cannot be a variable name.
150	**Argument must be an empty folder name**

Error Number	Description
160	**Argument must be an expression**
	For example, zeros(2x+3=0,x) is invalid because the first argument is an equation.
165	**Batteries too low for sending/receiving product code**
170	**Bound**
	For the interactive graph math functions like 2:Zero, the lower bound must be less than the upper bound to define the search interval.
180	**Break**
	The ON key was pressed during a long calculation or during program execution.
185	**Checksum error**
190	**Circular definition**
	This message is displayed to avoid running out of memory during infinite replacement of variable values during simplification. For example, a+1→a, where a is an undefined variable, will cause this error.
200	**Constraint expression invalid**
	For example, solve(3x^2−4=0, x)	x<0 or x>5 would produce this error message because the constraint is separated by "or" and not "and."
210	**Data type**
	An argument is of the wrong data type.
220	**Dependent Limit**
	A limit of integration is dependent on the integration variable. For example, $\int$(x^2,x,1,x) is not allowed.
225	**Diff Eq setup**
230	**Dimension**
	A list or matrix index is not valid. For example, if the list {1,2,3,4} is stored in L1, then L1[5] is a dimension error because L1 only contains four elements.
240	**Dimension mismatch**
	Two or more arguments must be of the same dimension. For example, [1,2]+[1,2,3] is a dimension mismatch because the matrices contain a different number of elements.
250	**Divide by zero**

Error Number	Description
260	**Domain error**
	An argument must be in a specified domain. For example, ans(100) is not valid because the argument for **ans()** must be in the range 1–99.
270	**Duplicate variable name**
280	**Else and ElseIf invalid outside of If..EndIf block**
290	**EndTry is missing the matching Else statement**
295	**Excessive iteration**
300	**Expected 2 or 3-element list or matrix**
310	**First argument of nSolve must be a univariate equation**
	The first argument must be an equation, and the equation cannot contain a non-valued variable other than the variable of interest. For example, nSolve(3x^2–4=0, x) is a valid equation; however, nSolve(3x^2–4, x) is not an equation, and nSolve(3x^2–y=0,x) is not a univariate equation because y has no value in this example.
320	**First argument of solve or cSolve must be an equation or inequality**
	For example, solve(3x^2–4, x) is invalid because the first argument is not an equation.
330	**Folder**
	An attempt was made in the VAR-LINK menu to store a variable in a folder that does not exist.
335	**Graph functions y1(x)...y99(x) not available in Diff Equations mode**
340	**Incomplete initial object list**
	There are too few initial objects chosen to define the macro's final object.
345	**Inconsistent units**
350	**Index out of range**
360	**Indirection string is not a valid variable name**
370	**Initial and final are same object**
	The initial and final objects chosen for the geometry macro are the same object.
380	**Invalid ans()**
390	**Invalid assignment**
400	**Invalid assignment value**

Error Number	Description

405   **Invalid axes**

410   **Invalid command**

420   **Invalid folder name**

430   **Invalid for the current mode settings**

440   **Invalid implied multiply**

For example, x(x+1) is invalid; whereas, x∗(x+1) is the correct syntax. This is to avoid confusion between implied multiplication and function calls.

450   **Invalid in a function or current expression**

Only certain commands are valid in a user-defined function. Entries that are made in the Window Editor, Table Editor, Data/Matrix Editor, and Geometry, as well as system prompts such as Lower Bound cannot contain any commands or a colon (:). See also "Creating and Evaluating User-Defined Functions" in Chapter 10 in the *TI-92 Guidebook*.

460   **Invalid in Custom..EndCustm block**

470   **Invalid in Dialog..EndDlog block**

480   **Invalid in Toolbar..EndTBar block**

490   **Invalid in Try..EndTry block**

500   **Invalid label**

Label names must follow the same rules used for naming variables.

510   **Invalid list or matrix**

For example, a list inside a list such as {2,{3,4}} is not valid.

520   **Invalid outside Custom..EndCustm or ToolBar..EndTbar blocks**

For example, an **Item** command is attempted outside a **Custom** or **ToolBar** structure.

530   **Invalid outside Dialog..EndDlog, Custom..EndCustm, or ToolBar..EndTBar blocks**

For example, a Title command is attempted outside a **Dialog**, **Custom**, or **ToolBar** structure.

540   **Invalid outside Dialog..EndDlog block**

For example, the **DropDown** command is attempted outside a **Dialog** structure.

550   **Invalid outside function or program**

A number of commands are not valid outside a program or a function. For example, Local cannot be used unless it is in a program or function.

Error Number	Description
560	**Invalid outside Loop..EndLoop, For..EndFor, or While..EndWhile blocks**
	For example, the **Exit** command is valid only inside these loop blocks.
570	**Invalid pathname**
	For example, \\var is invalid.
575	**Invalid polar complex**
580	**Invalid program reference**
	Programs cannot be referenced within functions or expressions such as 1+p(x) where p is a program.
590	**Invalid syntax block**
	A **Dialog..EndDlog** block is empty or has more than one title. A **Custom..EndCustm** block cannot contain PIC variables, and items must be preceded by a title. A **Toolbar..EndTBar** block must have a second argument if no items follow; or items must have a second argument and must be preceded by a title.
600	**Invalid table**
605	**Invalid use of units**
610	**Invalid variable name in a Local statement**
620	**Invalid variable or function name**
630	**Invalid variable reference**
640	**Invalid vector syntax**
650	**Link transmission**
	A transmission between two units was not completed. Verify that the connecting cable is connected firmly to both units.
660	**Macro objects cannot be redefined**
	An object in Geometry that was created by a macro cannot be redefined with Redefine Object.
665	**Matrix not diagonalizable**
670 673	**Memory**
	The calculation required more memory than was available at that time. If you get this error when you run a large program, you may need to break the program into separate, smaller programs or functions (where one program or function calls another).
680	**Missing (**

Error Number	Description
690	**Missing)**
700	**Missing "**
710	**Missing]**
720	**Missing }**
730	**Missing start or end of block syntax**
740	**Missing Then in the If..EndIf block**
750	**Name is not a function or program**
760	**No final object** No final objects were selected for a macro definition in Geometry.
765	**No functions selected**
770	**No initial object** No initial objects were selected for a macro definition in Geometry.
780	**No solution found** Using the interactive math features (F5:Math) in the Graph application can give this error. For example, if you attempt to find an inflection point of the parabola y1(x)=x^2, which does not exist, this error will be displayed.
790	**Non-algebraic variable in expression** If a is the name of a PIC, GDB, MAC, FIG, etc., a+1 is invalid. Use a different variable name in the expression or delete the variable.
800	**Non-real result** For example, if the unit is in the REAL setting of the Complex Format mode, ln(-2) is invalid.
810	**Not enough memory to save current variable. Please delete unneeded variables on the Var-Link screen and re-open editor as current OR re-open editor and use F1 8 to clear editor.** This error message is caused by very low memory conditions inside the Data/Matrix Editor.
820	**Objects are unrelated** A macro cannot be defined because the initial and final objects selected are geometrically unrelated.
830	**Overflow**
840	**Plot setup**

Error Number	Description
850	**Program not found** A program reference inside another program could not be found in the provided path during execution.
860	**Recursion is limited to 255 calls deep**
870	**Reserved name or system variable**
880	**Sequence setup**
885	**Signature error**
890	**Singular matrix**
895	**Slope fields need one selected function and are used for 1st-order equations only**
900	**Stat**
910	**Syntax** The structure of the entry is incorrect. For example, x+−y (x plus minus y) is invalid; whereas, x+ ⁻y (x plus negative y) is correct.
920	**The point does not lie on a path**
930	**Too few arguments** The expression or equation is missing one or more arguments. For example, d(f(x)) is invalid; whereas, d(f(x),x) is the correct syntax.
940	**Too many arguments** The expression or equation contains an excessive number of arguments and cannot be evaluated.
950	**Too many subscripts**
955	**Too many undefined variables**
960	**Undefined variable**
965	**Unlicensed product code**
970	**Variable in use so references or changes are not allowed**
980	**Variable is locked, protected, or archived**
990	**Variable name is limited to 8 characters**
1000	**Window variables domain**
1010	**Zoom**

Error Number	Description
	Warning: ♦1 - ♦9 must be executed from Home screen
	Warning: ∞^0 or undef^0 replaced by 1
	Warning: 0^0 replaced by 1
	Warning: 1^∞ or 1^undef replaced by 1
	Warning: cSolve might specify more zeros
	Warning: Differentiating an equation may produce a false equation
	Warning: Expected finite real integrand
	Warning: Memory full, simplification might be incomplete
	Warning: More solutions may exist
	Warning: Object already exists
	Warning: Operation might introduce false solutions
	Warning: Operation might lose solutions
	Warning: Operation requires and returns 32 bit value
	Warning: Overflow replaced by ∞ or ⁻∞
	Warning: Questionable accuracy
	Warning: Questionable solution
	Warning: Solve might specify more zeros
	Warning: Trig function argument too big for accurate reduction

TI–92 Plus Character Codes

The **char()** function lets you refer to any character by its numeric character code. For example, to display ◆ on the Program I/O screen, use `Disp char(127)`. You can use **ord()** to find the numeric code of a character. For example, `ord("A")` returns 65. Two TI-92 Plus character codes have changed from the TI-92: character 177 is now ± instead of a superscript + and character 184 is now a superscript + instead of ˣ.

1. SOH	41.)	81. Q	121. y	161. ¡	201. É
2. STX	42. *	82. R	122. z	162. ¢	202. Ê
3. ETX	43. +	83. S	123. {	163. £	203. Ë
4. EOT	44. ,	84. T	124. I	164. ¤	204. Ì
5. ENQ	45. –	85. U	125. }	165. ¥	205. Í
6. ACK	46. .	86. V	126. ~	166. ¦	206. Î
7. BELL	47. /	87. W	127. ◆	167. §	207. Ï
8. BS	48. 0	88. X	128. α	168. √	208. Ð
9. TAB	49. 1	89. Y	129. β	169. ©	209. Ñ
10. LF	50. 2	90. Z	130. Γ	170. ª	210. Ò
11. ✒	51. 3	91. [	131. γ	171. «	211. Ó
12. FF	52. 4	92. \	132. Δ	172. ¬	212. Ô
13. CR	53. 5	93.]	133. δ	173. -	213. Õ
14. 🔒	54. 6	94. ^	134. ε	174. ®	214. Ö
15. ✓	55. 7	95. _	135. ζ	175. ‾	215. ×
16. ▪	56. 8	96. `	136. θ	176. °	216. Ø
17. ◀	57. 9	97. a	137. λ	177. ±	217. Ù
18. ▶	58. :	98. b	138. ξ	178. ²	218. Ú
19. ▲	59. ;	99. c	139. Π	179. ³	219. Û
20. ▼	60. <	100. d	140. π	180. ⁻¹	220. Ü
21. ←	61. =	101. e	141. ρ	181. μ	221. Ý
22. →	62. >	102. f	142. Σ	182. ¶	222. Þ
23. ↑	63. ?	103. g	143. σ	183. ·	223. ß
24. ↓	64. @	104. h	144. τ	184. ⁺	224. à
25. ◀	65. A	105. i	145. φ	185. ¹	225. á
26. ▶	66. B	106. j	146. ψ	186. º	226. â
27. ↑	67. C	107. k	147. Ω	187. »	227. ã
28. ∪	68. D	108. l	148. ω	188. d	228. ä
29. ∩	69. E	109. m	149. ᴇ	189. ∫	229. å
30. ⊂	70. F	110. n	150. e	190. ∞	230. æ
31. ∈	71. G	111. o	151. i	191. ¿	231. ç
32. SPACE	72. H	112. p	152. ʳ	192. À	232. è
33. !	73. I	113. q	153. ᴛ	193. Á	233. é
34. "	74. J	114. r	154. x̄	194. Â	234. ê
35. #	75. K	115. s	155. ȳ	195. Ã	235. ë
36. $	76. L	116. t	156. ≤	196. Ä	236. ì
37. %	77. M	117. u	157. ≠	197. Å	237. í
38. &	78. N	118. v	158. ≥	198. Æ	238. î
39. '	79. O	119. w	159. ∠	199. Ç	239. ï
40. (	80. P	120. x	160. ..	200. È	240. ð

241. ñ	
242. ò	
243. ó	
244. ô	
245. õ	
246. ö	
247. ÷	
248. ø	
249. ù	
250. ú	
251. û	
252. ü	
253. ý	
254. þ	
255. ÿ	

Regression Formulas

This section describes how the statistical regressions are calculated.

Least-Squares Algorithm

Most of the regressions use non-linear recursive least-squares techniques to optimize the following cost function, which is the sum of the squares of the residual errors:

$$J = \sum_{i=1}^{N} \left[residualExpression \right]^2$$

where: $residualExpression$ is in terms of x_i and y_i
x_i is the independent variable list
y_i is the dependent variable list
N is the dimension of the lists

This technique attempts to recursively estimate the constants in the model expression to make J as small as possible.

For example, $y=a\ sin(bx+c)+d$ is the model equation for **SinReg**. So its residual expression is:

$a\ sin(bx_i+c)+d-y_i$

For **SinReg**, therefore, the least-squares algorithm finds the constants a, b, c, and d that minimize the function:

$$J = \sum_{i=1}^{N} \left[a\ sin(bx_i + c) + d - y_i \right]^2$$

Regressions

Regression	Description
CubicReg	Uses the least-squares algorithm to fit the third-order polynomial: $y=ax^3+bx^2+cx+d$ For four data points, the equation is a polynomial fit; for five or more, it is a polynomial regression. At least four data points are required.
ExpReg	Uses the least-squares algorithm and transformed values x and $\ln(y)$ to fit the model equation: $y=ab^x$
LinReg	Uses the least-squares algorithm to fit the model equation: $y=ax+b$ where a is the slope and b is the y-intercept.

Regression	Description
LnReg	Uses the least-squares algorithm and transformed values $\ln(x)$ and y to fit the model equation: $y=a+b \ln(x)$
Logistic	Uses the least-squares algorithm to fit the model equation: $y=c/(1+a\ e^{-bx})$
MedMed	Uses the median-median line (resistant line) technique to calculate summary points x1, y1, x2, y2, x3, and y3, and fits the model equation: $y=ax+b$ where a is the slope and b is the y-intercept.
PowerReg	Uses the least-squares algorithm and transformed values $\ln(x)$ and $\ln(y)$ to fit the model equation: $y=ax^{b}$
QuadReg	Uses the least-squares algorithm to fit the second-order polynomial: $y=ax^{2}+bx+c$ For three data points, the equation is a polynomial fit; for four or more, it is a polynomial regression. At least three data points are required.
QuartReg	Uses the least-squares algorithm to fit the fourth-order polynomial: $y=ax^{4}+bx^{3}+cx^{2}+dx+e$ For five data points, the equation is a polynomial fit; for six or more, it is a polynomial regression. At least five data points are required.
SinReg	Uses the least-squares algorithm to fit the model equation: $y=a\ sin(bx+c)+d$

Contour Levels and Implicit Plot Algorithm

Contours are calculated and plotted by the following method. An implicit plot is the same as a contour, except that an implicit plot is for the z=0 contour only.

Algorithm

Based on your x and y Window variables, the distance between xmin and xmax and between ymin and ymax is divided into a number of grid lines specified by xgrid and ygrid. These grid lines intersect to form a series of rectangles.

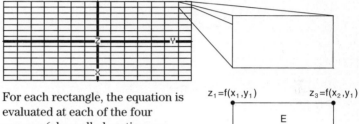

For each rectangle, the equation is evaluated at each of the four corners (also called vertices or grid points) and an average value (E) is calculated:

$z_1 = f(x_1, y_1)$ $z_3 = f(x_2, y_1)$

E

$z_2 = f(x_1, y_2)$ $z_4 = f(x_2, y_2)$

$$E = \frac{z_1 + z_2 + z_3 + z_4}{4}$$

The E value is treated as the value of the equation at the center of the rectangle.

For each specified contour value (C_i):

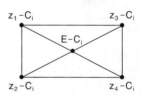

$z_1 - C_i$ $z_3 - C_i$

$E - C_i$

$z_2 - C_i$ $z_4 - C_i$

- At each of the five points shown to the right, the difference between the point's z value and the contour value is calculated.

- A sign change between any two adjacent points implies that a contour crosses the line that joins those two points. Linear interpolation is used to approximate where the zero crosses the line.

- Within the rectangle, any zero crossings are connected with straight lines.

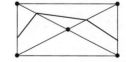

- This process is repeated for each contour value.

Each rectangle in the grid is treated similarly.

Runge-Kutta Method

For Runge-Kutta integrations of ordinary differential equations, the TI-92 Plus uses the Bogacki-Shampine 3(2) formula as found in the journal *Applied Math Letters*, 2 (1989), pp. 1–9.

Bogacki-Shampine 3(2) Formula

The Bogacki-Shampine 3(2) formula provides a result of 3rd-order accuracy and an error estimate based on an embedded 2nd-order formula. For a problem of the form:

$$y' = f(x, y)$$

and a given step size h, the Bogacki-Shampine formula can be written:

$$F_1 = f(x_n, y_n)$$

$$F_2 = f\left(x_n + h\frac{1}{2}, y_n + h\frac{1}{2}F_1\right)$$

$$F_3 = f\left(x_n + h\frac{3}{4}, y_n + h\frac{3}{4}F_2\right)$$

$$y_{n+1} = y_n + h\left(\frac{2}{9}F_1 + \frac{1}{3}F_2 + \frac{4}{9}F_3\right)$$

$$x_{n+1} = x_n + h$$

$$F_4 = f(x_{n+1}, y_{n+1})$$

$$errest = h\left(\frac{5}{72}F_1 - \frac{1}{12}F_2 - \frac{1}{9}F_3 + \frac{1}{8}F_4\right)$$

The error estimate *errest* is used to control the step size automatically. For a thorough discussion of how this can be done, refer to *Numerical Solution of Ordinary Differential Equations* by L. F. Shampine (New York: Chapman & Hall, 1994).

The TI-92 Plus software does not adjust the step size to land on particular output points. Rather, it takes the biggest steps that it can (based on the error tolerance diftol) and obtains results for $x_n \leq x \leq x_{n+1}$ using the cubic interpolating polynomial passing through the point (x_n, y_n) with slope F_1 and through (x_{n+1}, y_{n+1}) with slope F_4. The interpolant is efficient and provides results throughout the step that are just as accurate as the results at the ends of the step.

Compatibility between the TI-92 Plus and TI-92

> Because of functionality changes and enhancements to the TI-92 Plus, there are some incompatibilities with the TI-92. Where possible, data transfer is allowed between these two products; however, some functionality differences remain.

Main Types of Incompatibilities

The main types of functionality differences are:

- The TI-92 Plus has new functions, instructions, and system variables that do not exist on the TI-92.

- The TI-92 Plus changes the way you can use variables to define and evaluate a user-defined function or program. For example, you can now define a function in terms of a variable such as x and then evaluate that function using an expression containing the same variable. This caused a Circular definition error on the TI-92. Refer to page 241 for more information.

- The TI-92 Plus requires some changes to the way functions and programs manage local variables. Refer to page 242 for more information.

Text versus Tokenized

When you create a function or program, it exists in text form until you run it. Then it is converted automatically to a tokenized form.

- Data in text form can be shared between the TI-92 and TI-92 Plus. When transferring data in text form, you may not see an error even though the function or program may not give the same results when run on the other calculator.

Note: *If you edit a function or program that is in tokenized form, it returns to text form until the next time you run it.*

- Data in tokenized form contains information that describes included functionality. There are some differences in the tokenized forms of the TI-92 and TI-92 Plus.

  - If you attempt to send a tokenized function, program, or other data type from a TI-92 Plus to a TI-92, the TI-92 Plus automatically checks to be sure the functionality is acceptable for the TI-92. If not, the data is not sent. This is for your protection because the tokenized data could cause the TI-92 to lock up if the data is sent with invalid functionality.

  - Even if the tokenized data is sent, this does not guarantee that the data will give the same results on the other unit.

Compatibility between the TI-92 Plus and TI-92 (Continued)

**TI-92 to
TI-92 Plus**

All user-defined variables, including functions and programs, can be sent from a TI-92 to a TI-92 Plus. However, they may behave differently on the TI-92 Plus. Examples are:

- Conflicts between new TI-92 Plus system variable, function, and instruction names and TI-92 user-defined names.

- Programs or functions that use symbolic local variables. On the TI-92 Plus, a local variable must be initialized with a value before it can be referenced (meaning that a local variable cannot be used symbolically), or you must use a global variable instead. This includes programs that evaluate strings as local variables that are symbolic, such as **expr()**.

**TI-92 Plus to
TI-92**

Any functionality that exists on the TI-92 Plus and NOT on the TI-92 will NOT run as expected on a TI-92. In some cases (text form), the data will transfer but may give an error when run on the TI-92. In other cases (tokenized form), the data may not be sent to the TI-92.

If the data contains functionality available on a TI-92, it can probably be sent to and run on a TI-92 with the same results. Exceptions include:

- Graph databases (GDBs) will not be sent because the TI-92 Plus uses a new GDB structure that has more information than the TI-92 GDB.

- A function or program defined in terms of a variable such as x and then evaluated using some expression containing that same variable will run on the TI-92 Plus, but will give a Circular definition error on the TI-92.

- Some existing TI-92 functions and instructions have enhanced functionality on the TI-92 Plus (such as **NewData**, **setMode()**, and matrix functions that use the optional tolerance argument). These functions and instructions may not be sent at all or may cause an error on a TI-92.

- Archived variables will not be sent to a TI-92. Unarchive the variables first.

- Data variables that contain headers will not be sent. Those without headers will be sent only if the contents are TI-92 compatible.

Circular Definition Errors with Functions and Programs

Previously, a **Circular definition** error message was displayed if you evaluated a user-defined function or ran a program with the same variable used to define it. This is changed in the TI-92 Plus. For information about user-defined functions and programs, refer to the *TI-92 Guidebook*.

What Caused the Circular Definition Previously?

For example, when creating a user-defined function, you specify one or more variables in the argument list.

Define f(x) = sin(2x)

└─────────────────── Argument list

Note: *To avoid this error, a TI-92 user can define a function or program with argument names (usually two or more characters) not likely to be used to evaluate the function or run the program, such as:*

Define f(xx) = sin(2xx)

Previously, an error message was displayed if you evaluated the function with an expression containing the same variables that were in the argument list used to define the function. For example:

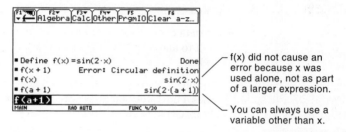

f(x) did not cause an error because x was used alone, not as part of a larger expression.

You can always use a variable other than x.

This Situation Does Not Display an Error Message with the TI-92 Plus

With the TI-92 Plus, this situation no longer displays an error message. For example:

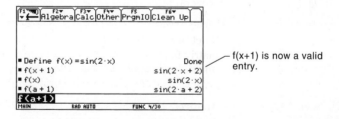

f(x+1) is now a valid entry.

Some Circular Definition Errors Still Exist

The changes to user-defined functions and programs as described previously do not eliminate all Circular definition errors. For example:

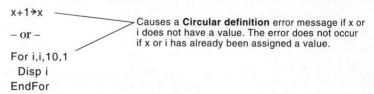

x+1→x

– or –

For i,i,10,1
 Disp i
EndFor

Causes a **Circular definition** error message if x or i does not have a value. The error does not occur if x or i has already been assigned a value.

Using Local Variables in Functions or Programs

If a user-defined function or program contains a local variable that is not initialized, the TI-92 Plus displays an **Undefined variable** error message when that variable is referenced.

What Causes the Error Message?

With the TI-92, a user-defined function or program can include local variables that have not been assigned a value. With the TI-92 Plus, however, an Undefined variable error message is displayed when you evaluate the function or run the program. For example:

```
Define fact(n)=Func:
Local m:  ─────────── Local variable m is not assigned an
While n>1:            initial value. This works on the TI-92
  n*m→m: n−1→n:       but not on the TI-92 Plus.
EndWhile:
Return m:
EndFunc
```

A local variable is a temporary variable that exists only while the function is being evaluated or the program is running. In the example above, the local variable m exists independently of any variable m that exists outside of the function.

With the TI-92 Plus, You Must Initialize Local Variables

With the TI-92 Plus, all local variables must be assigned an initial value before they are referenced.

```
Define fact(n)=Func:
Local m: 1→m:  ─────────── 1 is stored as the initial value for m.
While n>1:
  n*m→m: n−1→n:
EndWhile:
Return m:
EndFunc
```

A result of this change is that a function or program on a TI-92 Plus cannot use a local variable to perform symbolic calculations.

To Perform Symbolic Calculations

If you want a function or program to perform symbolic calculations, you must use a global variable instead of a local. However, you must be certain that the global variable does not already exist outside of the program. The following methods can help.

- Refer to a global variable name, typically with two or more characters, that is not likely to exist outside of the function or program.

- Include **DelVar** within the function or program to delete the global variable, if it exists, before referring to it. (**DelVar** does not delete locked or archived variables.)

Information about TI Products, Service, and Warranty

> For additional information about TI products, service, and warranty, please see below.

For U.S. Customers Only

General Questions

Call Texas Instruments Customer Support:

1-800-TI-CARES (1-800-842-2737)

Technical Questions

Call the Programming Assistance Group of Customer Support:

1-972-917-8324

Service Information

Always contact Texas Instruments Customer Support before returning a product for service.

Customer Support Hours

8:00AM – 4:30PM CST on Monday – Thursday and
9:30AM – 4:30PM CST on Friday

For more information about TI products and services, contact TI by e-mail or visit the TI calculator home page on the World Wide Web.

ti-cares@ti.com
http://www.ti.com/calc

One-Year Limited Warranty for Commercial Electronic Product (for U.S. only)

This Texas Instruments electronic product warranty extends only to the original purchaser and user of the product.

Warranty Duration. This Texas Instruments electronic product is warranted to the original purchaser for a period of one (1) year from the original purchase date.

Warranty Coverage. This Texas Instruments electronic product is warranted against defective materials and construction. **THIS WARRANTY IS VOID IF THE PRODUCT HAS BEEN DAMAGED BY ACCIDENT OR UNREASONABLE USE, NEGLECT, IMPROPER SERVICE, OR OTHER CAUSES NOT ARISING OUT OF DEFECTS IN MATERIALS OR CONSTRUCTION.**

Warranty Disclaimers. ANY IMPLIED WARRANTIES ARISING OUT OF THIS SALE, INCLUDING BUT NOT LIMITED TO THE IMPLIED WARRANTIES OF MERCHANTABILITY AND FITNESS FOR A PARTICULAR PURPOSE, ARE LIMITED IN DURATION TO THE ABOVE ONE-YEAR PERIOD. TEXAS INSTRUMENTS SHALL NOT BE LIABLE FOR LOSS OF USE OF THE PRODUCT OR OTHER INCIDENTAL OR CONSEQUENTIAL COSTS, EXPENSES, OR DAMAGES INCURRED BY THE CONSUMER OR ANY OTHER USER.

Some states/provinces do not allow the exclusion or limitation of implied warranties or consequential damages, so the above limitations or exclusions may not apply to you.

Legal Remedies. This warranty gives you specific legal rights, and you may also have other rights that vary from state to state or province to province.

Warranty Performance. During the above one (1) year warranty period, your defective product will be either repaired or replaced with a reconditioned model of an equivalent quality (at TI's option) when the product is returned, postage prepaid, to Texas Instruments Service Facility. The warranty of the repaired or replacement unit will continue for the warranty of the original unit or six (6) months, whichever is longer. Other than the postage requirement, no charge will be made for such repair and/or replacement. TI strongly recommends that you insure the product for value prior to mailing.

For Non-U.S. Customers Only

TI Products and Services Information

For more information about TI products and services, contact TI by e-mail or visit the TI calculator home page on the World Wide Web.

e-mail address:

ti-cares@ti.com

Internet address:

http://www.ti.com/calc

Service and Warranty Information

For information about the length and terms of the warranty or about product service, refer to the warranty statement enclosed with this product or contact your local Texas Instruments retailer/distributor.

Index

Locate commands and functions by the actions they perform. For example, abs( ) is listed as "absolute value function, abs( )." Mathematical operators and symbols are also listed by their actions. For example, + is listed as "addition operator (+)" and ' is listed as "prime symbol (')." Actions beginning with a number are listed as if the number were written in alphabetic characters. For example, "10-to-the-power function, 10^( )" is listed in the Ts as if it were "ten-to-the-power function, 10^( )."

Index (Continued)

Index (Continued)

Index (Continued)

temperature functions
  converting a range, ΔtmpCnv( ), *74, 199*
  converting a value, tmpCnv( ), *74, 199*
10-to-the-power function, 10^( ), *221*
3rd-order differential equations, *47*
3D graphing
  animating, *25*
  contour plots, *26*
  contour styles, *26*
  drawing contours command, DrwCtour, *28, 126*
  implicit plots, *30*
  rotating graph at line of sight, eyeψ, *24*
  switching between styles, *23*
  switching between views, *21*
  viewing angles, *24*
  Window variables, *24*
TI contact information, *243*
TI-Graph Link, *2*
TI-92 Plus module
  installing, *2*
  removing old, *3*
  serial number, *4*
  version number, *4*
time plots axes settings, *48*
tmax Window variable, *39*
toolbar commands. *See also* custom toolbar
  commands
  create a toolbar menu command, Toolbar, *200*
  end toolbar menu command, EndTBar. *See*
    Toolbar, *200*
toolbar in split screen mode, *66*
tools, geometry, *8, 9*
top-level function or operator, part( ), *162*
tplot Window variable, *39*
trace command, Trace, *200*
transmitting
  canceling from sending or receiving unit, *16, 20*
  incompatibilities, *239*
  product code, *17*
  variables or folders between two TI-92 units, *15, 16*
trig collect function, tCollect( ), *197*
trig expand function, tExpand( ), *198*
tstep Window variable, *39*
two's complement, negation operator (⁻), *212*
two-variable statistics command, TwoVar, *201*

U

unarchiving
  archive command, Archive, *102*
  unarchive command, Unarchiv, *201*
  variables, *90*
undefined variable error, *242*
underscore character (_), *220*
unit vector function, unitV( ), *201*

units
  combining multiple, *72*
  conversion operator (▶), *221*
  converting, *73*
  converting a temperature range function,
    ΔtmpCnv( ), *74, 199*
  converting a temperature value function,
    tmpCnv( ), *74, 199*
  creating user-defined, *76*
  defaults, *75, 77*
  entering, *71*
  get function, getUnits( ), *139*
  naming conventions, *71, 76*
  parentheses with, *72*
  pre-defined, *77*
  selecting from menu, *71*
  set function, setUnits( ), *181*
unknown variable, solving for, *65*
unlock variable command, Unlock, *201*
upgrades
  multiple units, *18*
  obtaining, *17*
  product code, *17*
  software certificate, *17*
using complex variables in symbolic
  calculations, *12*

V

variables
  archiving, *88, 90*
  backing up, *18*
  clearing from numeric solver, *67*
  clearing single-character, *6*
  common errors with numeric solver, *63*
  complex in symbolic calculations, *12*
  defining, *6, 63, 242*
  fldpic system, *41*
  global, *242*
  local, *242*
  opening saved equation, *62*
  solve for unknown, *60, 65*
  specifying bounds for unknown, *64*
  symbolic calculations, *242*
  transmitting between units, *15*
  unarchiving, *88, 90*
  Window, differential equations, *39, 40*
  Window, 3D graphing, *24*
variance function, variance( ), *202*
Var-Link screen
  changes to, *89*
  displaying, *88, 89*
  using for archiving, *90*
version number, *4*
vertical line command, LineVert, *146*
vertical line pixel command, PxlVert, *169*
viewing angles, measuring in 3D graphics, *24*